OXFORD

9C

Maths Links

Alf Ledsham

Contents

1 Algebra
Sequences and graphs 1
2 Number
Proportional reasoning 7
3 Geometry
Geometrical reasoning and construction 16
4 Algebra
Equations 24
5 Statistics
Surveys 30
6 Geometry
Measures 38
7 Number
Calculations 43
8 Algebra
Graphs 51
9 Statistics
Probability 58
10 Geometry
Transformations and scale 64
11 Algebra
Expressions and formulae 69
12 Statistics
Interpreting statistics 77
13 Geometry
3-D shapes and trigonometry 84
14 Number
Calculation plus 89

Glossary 93

Homework Book

OXFORD
UNIVERSITY PRESS

Great Clarendon Street, Oxford OX2 6DP

Oxford University Press is a department of the University of Oxford.
It furthers the University's objective of excellence in research, scholarship, and education by publishing worldwide in

Oxford New York

Auckland Cape Town Dar es Salaam Hong Kong Karachi
Kuala Lumpur Madrid Melbourne Mexico City Nairobi
New Delhi Shanghai Taipei Toronto

With offices in

Argentina Austria Brazil Chile Czech Republic France Greece
Guatemala Hungary Italy Japan South Korea Poland Portugal
Singapore Switzerland Thailand Turkey Ukraine Vietnam

First published 2009

British Library Cataloguing in Publication Data
Data available

ISBN 9780199153121

10 9 8 7 6 5 4 3 2 1

Printed in Great Britain by Ashford Colour Press Ltd, Gosport

Paper used in the production of this book is a natural, recyclable product made from wood grown in sustainable forests. The manufacturing process conforms to the environmental regulations of the country of origin.

1a Position-to-term rules

example

Find the nth term (or the 'position-to-term' rule) for the sequence 11, 16, 21, 26, 31, …

The terms all differ by 5, so the 'zeroth' term would be $11 - 5 = 6$. Therefore the nth term is $5n + 6$.

1 Generate the first five terms for these sequences.
[T(n) is the nth term.]

a $T(n) = n + 6$ **b** $T(n) = 5n$ **c** $T(n) = n - 3$
d $T(n) = 2n + 5$ **e** $T(n) = 2n - 7$ **f** $T(n) = 10 - n$
g $T(n) = 3 - n$ **h** $T(n) = 32 - 2n$ **i** $T(n) = 105 - 5n$
j $T(n) = \frac{1}{2}n + 4$

2 Find the nth term (or the 'position-to-term' rule) for these sequences.

a 4, 8, 12, 16, 20, … **b** 3, 5, 7, 9, 11, … **c** 5, 8, 11, 14, 17, …
d 2, 5, 8, 11, 14, … **e** 2, 7, 12, 17, 22, … **f** 1, 7, 13, 19, 25, …
g $2\frac{1}{2}, 3, 3\frac{1}{2}, 4, 4\frac{1}{2}, \ldots$ **h** -4, -1, 2, 5, 8, … **i** -7, -5, -3, -1, 1, …
j 10, 8, 6, 4, 2, … **k** 10, 7, 4, 1, -2, … **l** 9, 4, -1, -6, -11, …

3 For each of these two patterns, copy and complete the table and find the 'position-to-term' rule for the number of dots.

a **b**

Pattern number (or term number)	1	2	3	4
Number of dots				

4 Jake is climbing Mount Snowdon in Wales. The table shows his altitude at hourly intervals after starting off. Find the 'position-to-term' rule for his sequence. Find also his altitude at the start of his climb.

Time after starting (hours)	Start	1	2	3	4
Altitude (m)	?	540	720	900	1080

1b Quadratic sequences

example

Generate the first five terms of the quadratic sequence for which the nth term (or the 'position-to-term rule') is given by $T(n) = n^2 - 3n$.

1st term $= 1^2 - 3 \times 1 = 1 - 3 \quad = -2$
2nd term $= 2^2 - 3 \times 2 = 4 - 6 \quad = -2$
3rd term $= 3^2 - 3 \times 3 = 9 - 9 \quad = 0$
4th term $= 4^2 - 3 \times 4 = 16 - 12 = 4$
5th term $= 5^2 - 3 \times 5 = 25 - 15 = 10$
Therefore the first five terms are -2, -2, 0, 4 and 10.

1 Generate the first five terms of each quadratic sequence.
[$T(n)$ is the nth term.]

a $T(n) = n^2 + 2$ **b** $T(n) = 4n^2$ **c** $T(n) = 2n^2 + 1$
d $T(n) = 3n^2 - 1$ **e** $T(n) = n^2 + 2n$ **f** $T(n) = n^2 - n$
g $T(n) = n^2 + 3n + 2$ **h** $T(n) = n^2 + 4n - 5$ **i** $T(n) = n^2 - 2n - 3$

2 Match these sequences with the general term expressions.

a 4, 7, 12, 19, 28, ... **b** 0, 3, 8, 15, 24, ... **c** 2, 6, 12, 20, 30, ...
d 4, 10, 18, 28, 40, ... **e** -1, 0, 3, 8, 15, ... **f** 4, 9, 16, 25, 36, ...
g 8, 15, 24, 35, 48, ... **h** 0, 5, 12, 21, 32, ... **i** 1, 0, 1, 4, 9, ...

General term expressions, $T(n)$

i $n^2 + 3n$ **ii** $n^2 + 4n + 3$ **iii** $n^2 + 2n - 3$
iv $n^2 + 3$ **v** $n^2 - 2n$ **vi** $n^2 + n$
vii $n^2 - 4n + 4$ **viii** $n^2 + 2n + 1$ **ix** $n^2 - 1$

3 Bob is doing an experiment with a light bulb. He runs different currents through the filament and measures the corresponding voltage across the bulb terminals.

Current	0 amp	1 amp	2 amps	3 amps	4 amps
Voltage	0 volts	0.5 volts	2 volts	4.5 volts	8 volts

Find the general term of the quadratic sequence that the voltage figures follow.

1c Patterns and sequences

example

a Find the sum of the first five odd numbers. What do you notice about the answer?

b Find the sum of the first six even numbers. The answer is connected to a triangular number. Can you see how?

a $1 + 3 + 5 + 7 + 9 = 25$. The answer is the fifth square number.

b $2 + 4 + 6 + 8 + 10 + 12 = 42$. The answer is the sixth triangular number (21) multiplied by 2.

1 Copy and complete these tables and state what you notice.

a

Square numbers	1	4	9	16	25	36	49	64	81	100
Triangular numbers	1	3	6	10	15	21	28	36	45	55
Square number – triangular number	0									

b

Square numbers	1	4	9	16	25	36	49	64	81	100
Odd numbers	1	3	5							
Square number – odd numbers	0									

c

Triangular numbers	1									
Odd numbers	1									
Triangular number – odd number	0									

2 a The sum of the first n odd numbers is n^2. Find the sum of
i the first 50 odd numbers **ii** the odd numbers between 0 and 60.

b The sum of the first n even numbers is $n(n + 1)$. Find the sum of
i the first 50 even numbers
ii the even numbers between 1 and 41.

3 1 and 36 are two numbers that are both square and triangular. Can you find one more number like this?

1d Graphs of linear functions

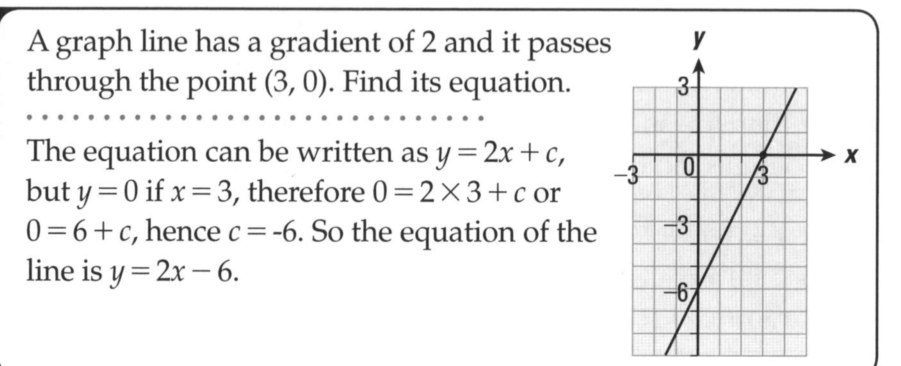

example

A graph line has a gradient of 2 and it passes through the point (3, 0). Find its equation.

The equation can be written as $y = 2x + c$, but $y = 0$ if $x = 3$, therefore $0 = 2 \times 3 + c$ or $0 = 6 + c$, hence $c = -6$. So the equation of the line is $y = 2x - 6$.

1 Look at the three graph lines which have been drawn. Match each one with one of these equations.

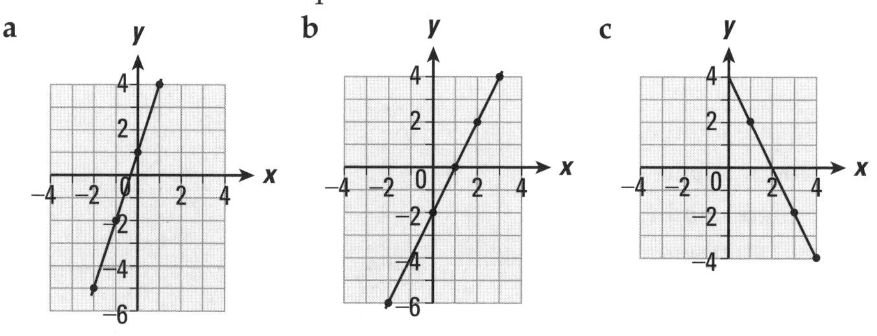

i $y = 4 - 2x$ (or $2x + y = 4$) **ii** $y = 3x + 1$ **iii** $y = 2x - 2$

2 Find the equation of each of these lines.

a The gradient is 2 and it passes through the point (3, 12).

b The gradient is 3 and it passes through the point (1, 10).

c The gradient is -4 and it passes through the point (1, 1).

d The gradient is -1 and it passes through the point (7, 0).

1e Inverse of a linear function

example

Find the inverse function for $y = 2x - 1$.

Interchanging x and y gives
$x = 2y - 1$,
so $x + 1 = 2y$
therefore $y = \frac{1}{2}x + \frac{1}{2}$

It can be seen that one graph line is a reflection of the other in the line $y = x$.

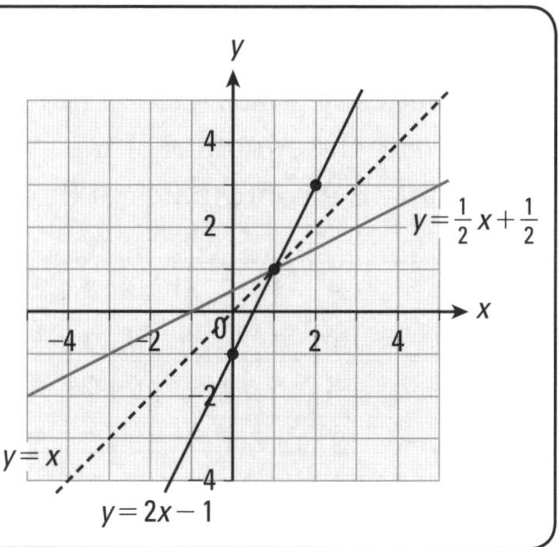

1 Draw for each of these three graph lines

i a copy of the grid illustrated

ii the line $y = x$ and the graph line for the inverse of the function given.

a $y = 2x + 4$ (Find y for x equal to -3, -2, -1, 0, 1, and 2.)

b $y = 2x - 2$ (Find y for x equal to -2, -1, 0, 1, 2, 3 and 4.)

c $y = x - 4$ (Find y for x equal to -2, 0, 2, 4, 6 and 8.)

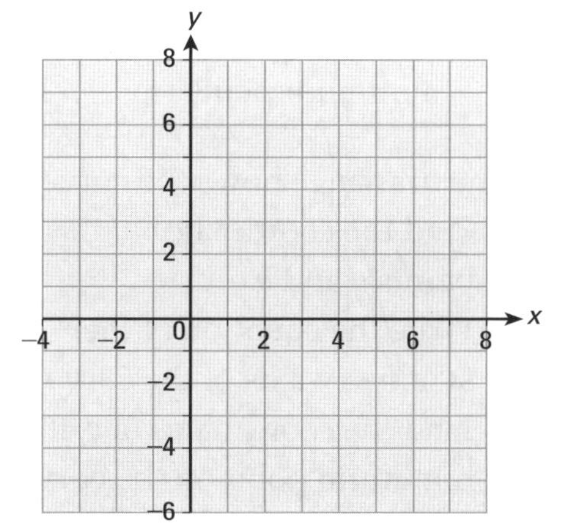

2 Find the inverse of each of these functions

a $y = 4x + 16$

b $y = 6x + 12$

c $y = 5x - 10$

d $y = 8x - 16$

e $y = \frac{1}{3}x - 2$

f $y = \frac{1}{5}x - 1$

g $y = \frac{1}{4}x + 2$

h $y = \frac{1}{2}x + 5$

i $y = 5 - x$

j $y = 0$

Quadratic functions

example

a Draw a graph of $y = x^2 + 2x$. Calculate y for whole number values of x between -4 and 2.

b Write the equation of the symmetry axis of the curve.

c State the coordinates of the minimum point on the curve.

a

$x =$	-4	-3	-2	-1	0	1	2
x^2	16	9	4	1	0	1	4
$+2x$	-8	-6	-4	-2	0	2	4
$y =$	8	3	0	-1	0	3	8

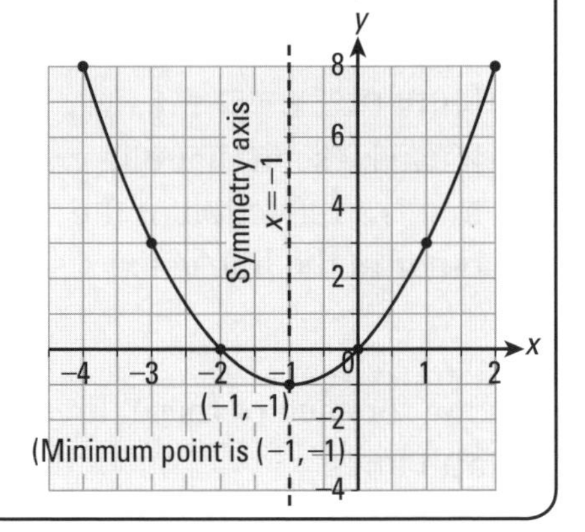

b The equation of the symmetry axis is $x = -1$.

c The coordinates of the minimum point are (-1, -1).

1 The drawing shows the curve $y = x^2 + x$.

a Find the coordinates of the points a and b.

b Write the equation of the symmetry axis of the curve.

c Find the coordinates of c, the minimum point on the curve.

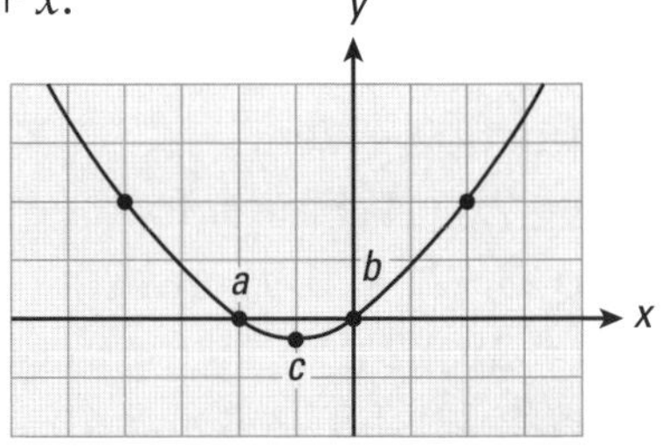

2 Copy the drawing.
Draw on your copy the line $y = x + 6$ and find the coordinates of the points where it cuts the curve.

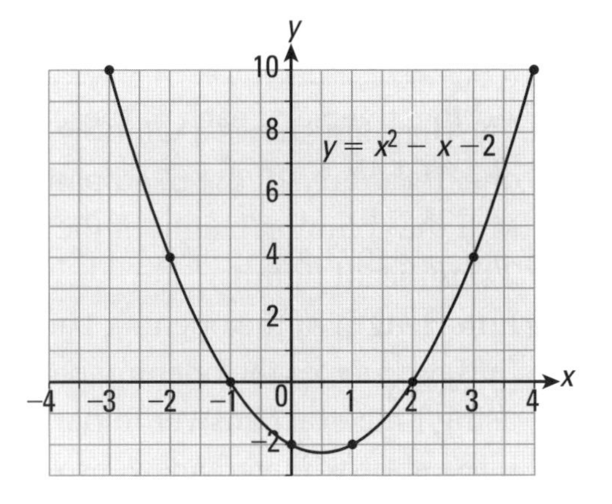

2a Significant figures

example

A tray measures 0.34 m by 0.225 m. Find its area and correct your answer to 2 significant figures.

Area = $0.34 \times 0.225 = 0.076\underline{5}\,\text{m}^2$, but to 2 significant figures this is $0.077\,\text{m}^2$. (The third significant figure is 5, therefore the second one is rounded up. This is always done for the 'test' figure being 5 or greater.) Note that the zero after the decimal point does not count as a significant figure.

1 Correct each of these to **i** 1 significant figure **ii** 2 significant figures **iii** 3 significant figures.

a 4867 **b** 3712 **c** 28 346 **d** 36 721

2 Correct each of these to **i** 1 significant figure **ii** 2 significant figures.

a 5.637 **b** 8.273 **c** 0.834 **d** 0.912
e 0.0763 **f** 0.0937 **g** 0.00815 **h** 0.00696

3 Copy and complete the table.

Calculation	**Exact answer**	**Answer correct to 1 sig. fig.**	**Answer correct to 2 sig. fig.**	**Answer correct to 3 sig. fig.**
121.5×6.4				
15.6×6.15				
$144.3 \div 25$				
$2.799 \div 1.8$				

4 a The diagram shows a window with a fixed pane and an opening one. If the area of the fixed pane is $1.5\,\text{m}^2$ and its length is 1.2 m, find the common height of the panes **i** exactly **ii** correct to 2 significant figures.

b If the length of the opening pane is 0.6 m, find the area of the opening pane by using **i** the exact answer to part **a** and **ii** the approximated answer to part **a**.

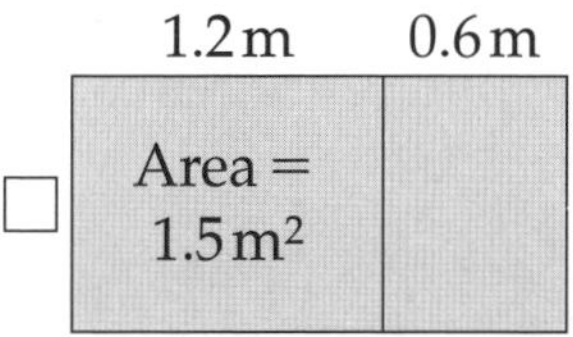

2b Calculating with fractions

example

Evaluate **a** $1\frac{3}{10}+\frac{13}{15}$ **b** $2\frac{1}{10}\times\frac{5}{14}$ **c** $\frac{5}{16}\div 2\frac{1}{12}$

a $1\frac{3}{10}+\frac{13}{15}=\frac{13}{10}+\frac{13}{15}=\frac{39}{30}+\frac{26}{30}=\frac{65}{30}=\frac{13}{6}=2\frac{1}{6}$

b $2\frac{1}{10}\times\frac{5}{14}=\frac{21}{10}\times\frac{5}{14}=\frac{105}{140}=\frac{21}{28}=\frac{3}{4}$

c $\frac{5}{16}\div 2\frac{1}{12}=\frac{5}{16}\div\frac{25}{12}=\frac{5}{16}\times\frac{12}{25}=\frac{60}{400}=\frac{3}{20}$

For questions **1**, **2** and **3** work out all parts and give each answer in its simplest form.

1 **a** $\frac{3}{10}+\frac{8}{15}$ **b** $\frac{1}{6}+\frac{11}{15}$ **c** $\frac{1}{4}+\frac{7}{20}$ **d** $\frac{4}{5}+\frac{9}{20}$
e $3\frac{1}{4}-2\frac{7}{20}$ **f** $1\frac{3}{5}+2\frac{3}{20}$ **g** $2\frac{5}{6}+1\frac{4}{15}$ **h** $3\frac{1}{10}+1\frac{1}{15}$

2 **a** $\frac{5}{9}\times\frac{6}{7}$ **b** $\frac{7}{12}\times\frac{9}{10}$ **c** $\frac{9}{16}\times\frac{4}{5}$ **d** $\frac{12}{35}\times\frac{14}{15}$
e $1\frac{5}{6}\times 2\frac{7}{10}$ **f** $8\times\frac{5}{12}$ **g** $9\times\frac{14}{15}$ **h** $12\times 1\frac{1}{8}$

3 **a** $\frac{5}{9}\div\frac{11}{12}$ **b** $\frac{7}{8}\div\frac{9}{10}$ **c** $\frac{5}{12}\div\frac{20}{21}$ **d** $\frac{8}{15}\div\frac{16}{21}$
e $1\frac{3}{10}\div 1\frac{1}{15}$ **f** $2\frac{1}{12}\div 1\frac{3}{4}$ **g** $8\div\frac{24}{25}$ **h** $6\div\frac{21}{25}$

4 **a** The diagram shows a table and its extension. If the area of the table, without the extension, is $\frac{9}{10}\text{m}^2$ and its length is $1\frac{1}{5}$m, find its width.

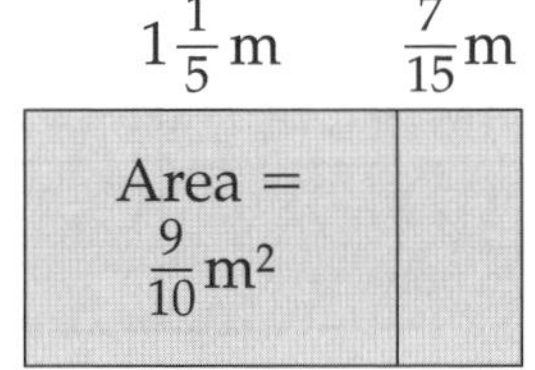

b If the length of the extension is $\frac{7}{15}$m, find
i the area of the extension
ii the area of the extended table.

c Find the length of the extended table.

5 Jean is $1\frac{7}{20}$m tall, her sister Janet is $1\frac{1}{5}$m tall. Find the difference between their heights, giving your answer **i** as a fraction in metres **ii** in centimetres.

2c Fractions and proportion

Find the proportion of the rectangle that is shaded.

The area of the shaded part is $\frac{1}{2} \times 3 \times 3$ squares $=$ $4\frac{1}{2}$ squares, therefore the proportion shaded is $4\frac{1}{2}$ out of 12 or 9 out of 24, and $\frac{9}{24} = \frac{3}{8}$.

1 Find the proportion of the rectangle which is shaded for each of these. Find which part **i, ii** or **iii** has a different answer from the other two.

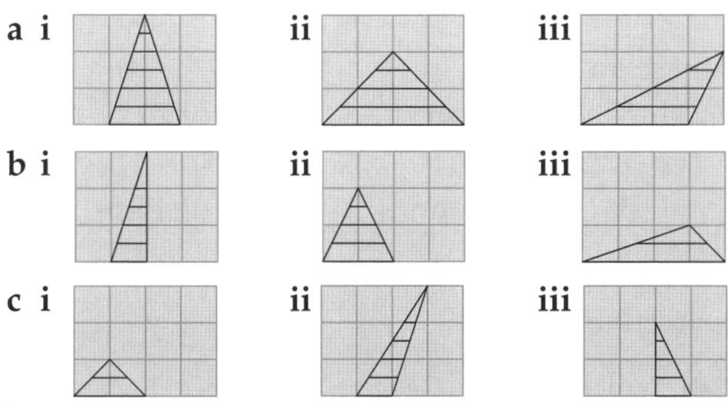

2 Calculate these proportions giving your answers as mixed numbers where appropriate.

a $\frac{5}{8}$ of 200 m **b** $\frac{5}{6}$ of £150 **c** $\frac{7}{12}$ of 108 kg **d** $\frac{4}{9}$ of 135 cm

e $\frac{3}{4}$ of 10 m **f** $\frac{3}{10}$ of 15 cm **g** $\frac{9}{10}$ of $1\frac{1}{4}$ kg **h** $\frac{2}{7}$ of $5\frac{1}{4}$ tonnes

3 Calculate these fractional changes.

a Increase £60 by $\frac{3}{5}$
b Increase 80 m by $\frac{3}{4}$
c Increase 24 kg by $\frac{5}{12}$
d Increase 30 cm by $\frac{1}{6}$
e Decrease 50 cm by $\frac{2}{5}$
f Decrease 40 m by $\frac{3}{8}$
g Decrease 36 kg by $\frac{4}{9}$
h Decrease £105 by $\frac{1}{7}$
i Decrease 112 mm by $\frac{1}{8}$

2d Percentage increase and decrease

example

a A television costs £180, but in a sale there is a price reduction of 15%. Find the sale price.

b Zeke has 20 marbles, but he plays a game and wins 7 more. Express his proportional increase as a percentage.

a The reduction is 15% of £180 which is $\frac{15}{100} \times £180 = £27$.
Therefore the sale price is $£180 - £27 = £153$.

b His proportional increase is $\frac{7}{20}$ which as a percentage is $\frac{7}{20} \times 100\%$ or 35%.

1 Work out each of these amounts.

a 25% of £172 **b** 85% of 120 cm **c** 35% of 70 kg
d 24% of 90 m **e** 12.5% of £56 **f** 62.5% of 112 cm
g 80% of 12.5 kg **h** 36% of 3.5 tonnes **i** 14% of 4.5 m

2 Here are Marcus's Year 9 exam results. Express each of the proportions as a percentage.

Mathematics	English	French	History	Geography	Science	Technology
57 out of 75	52 out of 80	33 out of 60	49 out of 70	36 out of 90	66 out of 110	54 out of 120

3 Work out the amounts of these percentage changes.

a Increase £96 by 25% **b** Increase 105 cm by 40%
c Increase 28 kg by 15% **d** Increase 4.5 m by 20%
e Decrease £60 by 15% **f** Decrease 140 cm by 35%
g Decrease 30 kg by 5% **h** Decrease 2.5 tonnes by 12%
i Decrease 7.2 m by 12.5%

4 At the start of 2008 Julian was 150 cm tall and his mass was 50 kg. By the end of the year he was 156 cm tall and his mass was 51.5 kg. Express both of these increases as **i** a proportion **ii** a percentage.

2e Percentage change

example

Jim is looking at a car that he would like to buy. The dealer says that he can have it for £13 200 because a reduction of 12% is on offer. What was the original price of the car?

£13 200 is 100% − 12% = 88% of the original price.

Therefore the original price was $\frac{100}{88} \times 13\,200 = £15\,000$

Copy and complete the table for each question.

1 The table summarizes the details of reduced prices in a sale.

Item	**Television**	**Cooker**	**Fridge**	**Sofa**	**Table**	**Laptop**	**DVD player**	**Sewing machine**
Original price								
Reduction (%)	15%	12%	16%	7.5%	8%	20%	12.5%	4.5%
Actual reduction					£12	£58	£7.50	£3.60
Sale price	£204	£308	£210	£296				

2 The table shows details about how six children grew during 2008.

	Aazi	**Roxie**	**Sharma**	**Wayne**	**Simo**	**Helena**
Height at the start of 2008						
Increase in height (%)	2%	5%	3%	2.5%	1.25%	4%
Actual increase in height				4 cm	1.5 cm	4.5 cm
Height at the end of 2008	127.5 cm	147 cm	154.5 cm			

2f Proportional change

example

Rosie invests £1200 in her bank and the interest rate is 5%.
Find the value of her savings after **a** 1 year **b** 2 years **c** 3 years.

a After 1 year the value = $1200 \times 1.05 = £1260$
b After 2 years the value = 1260×1.05 (or 1200×1.05^2) = £1323
c After 3 years the value = 1323×1.05 (or 1200×1.05^3) = £1389.15

1 Bob invests £8000 in his bank and the interest rate is 5%. Find the value of his savings after **a** 1 year **b** 2 years **c** 3 years **d** 4 years.

2 On his third birthday Jisanne was 100 cm tall and he grew at a rate of 10% a year until he was six. Find his height on
a his fourth birthday **b** his fifth birthday **c** his sixth birthday.

3 Peter bought a new car for £20 000, but its value depreciated by 10% each year. Find the value of the car after
a 1 year **b** 2 years **c** 3 years **d** 4 years.

4 Joanna bought a motor cycle for £2500, but its value depreciated by 20% each year. Find the value of the motor cycle after
a 1 year **b** 2 years **c** 3 years **d** 4 years.

5 A mains operated digital clock is disconnected but because of a time-delay circuit the voltage across it does not drop to zero straightaway. Instead it drops by 20% for every interval of 10 minutes. If the voltage was 250 volts when it was disconnected find the voltage after **a** 10 minutes **b** 20 minutes **c** 30 minutes **d** 40 minutes **e** 50 minutes

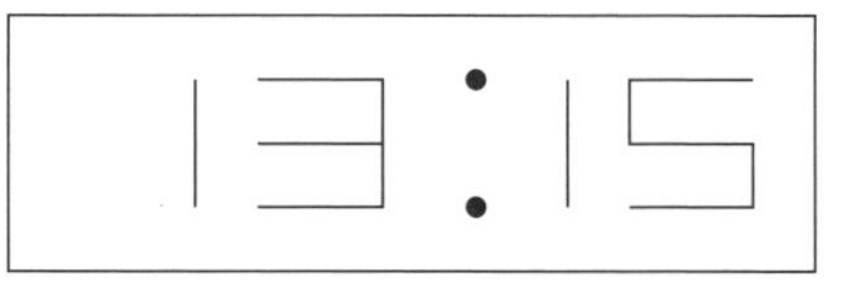

f If the clock figures are no longer illuminated after the voltage has dropped to 100 volts, after how many minutes (approximately) would you expect them to go out?

2g Ratio and proportion

example

There are 28 students in Class 9B and the ratio of boys to girls is 3 : 4. Find the proportion and number of **i** girls, and **ii** boys.

As $3 + 4 = 7$, the proportion of **i** boys is $\frac{3}{7}$ and of **ii** girls is $\frac{4}{7}$.
The number of **i** boys is therefore $\frac{3}{7} \times 28 = 12$ and the number of **ii** girls is $\frac{4}{7} \times 28 = 16$.

1 Write each ratio in its simplest form.

a 0.6 : 8 **b** 0.8 : 3 **c** 90 p : £3 **d** 750 m : 2 km
e 60 cm : 3 m **f** 2 m : 75 cm **g** 3 km : 240 m **h** £2.10 : 45 p
i 2.8 : 3.5 : 4.9 **j** 1.8 : 2.4 : 3.3 **k** 0.9 : 1.5 : 2.4 **l** 0.45 : 0.8 : 0.9

2 Express each of these ratios in the form $1 : n$.

a 3 : 15 **b** 7 : 56 **c** 5 : 45 **d** 6 : 42 **e** 13 : 52
f 2 : 5 **g** 4 : 9 **h** 5 : 16 **i** 10 : 17 **j** 20 : 43

3 The table gives details of the numbers of first and standard class passengers on a train between Birmingham and Lancaster. Copy and complete the table.

	First Class passengers	Standard Class passengers	Total number	Ratio	Proportion (First Class)	Proportion (Standard Class)
Birmingham to Wolverhampton			360	2 : 7		
Wolverhampton to Stafford			300		$\frac{3}{10}$	
Stafford to Crewe			260			$\frac{10}{13}$
Crewe to Wigan	60		330			
Wigan to Preston		275	350			
Preston to Lancaster	120			3 : 8		

4 At a village school all 456 pupils either walk, cycle or are driven by car to school in the respective ratio of 2 : 3 : 7. Find **i** the proportion **ii** the number who travel in each of the three ways.

2h Proportionality

example

A plank of wood is 60 cm long and has a mass of 1.35 kg.
Find the mass of a similar plank of length 80 cm.

The mass per centimetre length is $1.35 \div 60 = 0.0225$ kg
Therefore the mass of a plank of length 80 cm will be
$80 \times 0.0225\,\text{kg} = 1.8\,\text{kg}$

1 The table gives details of three people driving along the same stretch of motorway. Check if the ratio of distance to time figures are in direct proportion for each case.

	Distance travelled (km)				
	0	**72**	**126**	**144**	**180**
Mutso	0 h	1 h	1.75 h	2 h	2.5 h
Rosie	0 h	0.8 h	1.4 h	1.6 h	2 h
George	0 h	0.6 h	1.05 h	1.2 h	1.8 h

2 Jean makes a journey of 112 km in her car and finds that the car has consumed 7 litres of petrol.

a Find how much petrol the car would be expected to consume if she travelled **i** 96 km **ii** 128 km **iii** 200 km **iv** 152 km.

b How far could her car be expected to travel on
i 4 litres **ii** 7.5 litres **iii** 8.5 litres **iv** 5.5 litres of petrol?

3 'Frooties' are sweets which are sold in many different sized packets. A packet containing 40 sweets has a mass of 300 grams.

a Find the mass of a packet that contains **i** 32 sweets **ii** 60 sweets.

b Find the number of sweets in a packet of mass
i 90 grams **ii** 750 grams.

4 Tony is a long distance runner and when he trains he runs at a very steady pace. Copy and complete the table for his progress.

Distance (km)	0	5	8	10	12			22	25	
Time (minutes)	0	22.5				67.5	90			135

2i Proportion and scale

example

The distance between Lincoln and Newark on a map is 10 cm. What is the real distance between the places if the scale of the map is 1 : 250 000?

The real distance is $10 \times 250\,000$ cm $= 2\,500\,000$ cm $= 25\,000$ m
$= 25$ km

1 A map has a scale of 1 : 25 000.

a Find the real distance between villages that are
i 16 cm **ii** 9 cm **iii** 7 cm apart on the map.

b Find the distance on the map between road junctions that are
i 3 km **ii** 5 km **iii** 3.75 km apart.

2 Barney has a map of the town where he lives and its scale is 1 : 8000. Copy and complete the table.

	Real distance	Distance on map
Barney's house to the supermarket	2.4 km	
Barney's house to the 1st roundabout	1 km	
Barney's house to the post office		20 cm
Distance between the two roundabouts		9 cm

3 **a** A miniature railway has a track gauge of 36 cm. If the standard railtrack gauge is 144 cm, to what scale is the miniature railway built?

b The miniature railway has a steam locomotive of length 5.25 m, height 1.02 m and width 0.35 m. If this locomotive is a replica of a real one, what are the dimensions of the real one?

3a Angle problems

example

Find the three angles of the triangle and state what kind of triangle it is.

$x + 4x + 4x = 180°$, therefore $9x = 180°$, so $x = 20°$.

The three angles are therefore 20°, 80° and 80° and the triangle is acute angled and isosceles.

1 For each of these find the three angles of the triangle and state the kind of triangle.

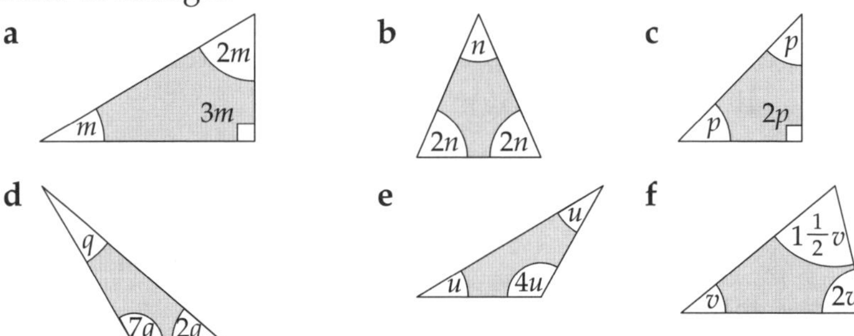

2 For each of these find the four angles of the quadrilateral and state the kind of quadrilateral.

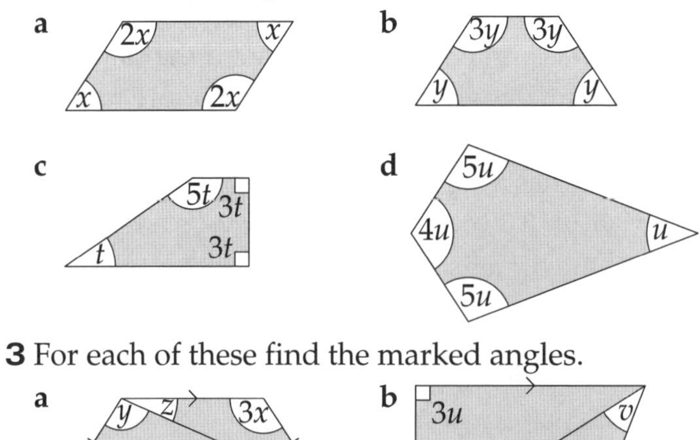

3 For each of these find the marked angles.

a

b

3b Angle properties of a polygon

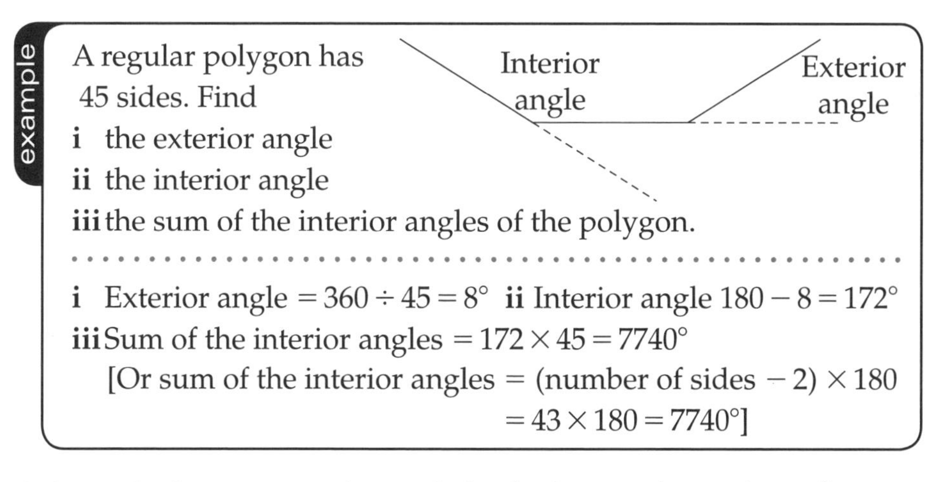

example

A regular polygon has 45 sides. Find

i the exterior angle

ii the interior angle

iii the sum of the interior angles of the polygon.

i Exterior angle $= 360 \div 45 = 8°$ ii Interior angle $180 - 8 = 172°$

iii Sum of the interior angles $= 172 \times 45 = 7740°$

[Or sum of the interior angles = (number of sides − 2) $\times 180$

$= 43 \times 180 = 7740°$]

1 A regular hexagon can be made by fitting six identical kites together. Copy the diagram and show how this can be done. Find the four angles for any one of the kites.

2 Copy and complete the table about regular polygons.

Number of sides	Number of symmetry axes	Order of rotational symmetry	Exterior angle	Interior angle	Sum of interior angles
9					
36					
16					
			24°		
			9°		
			7.5°		

3 Regular hexagons, squares and equilateral triangles can form a tessellation and the diagram shows how the pattern is started. Copy and continue the pattern until it includes at least four hexagons and triangles.

3c Circle properties

example

Find the marked angles, and state the value of $b + e$.

$a = b = (180 - 110) \div 2 = 70 \div 2 = 35°$,
because the triangle is isosceles.
$c = 180 - 110 = 70°$
$d = e = (180 - 70) \div 2 = 110 \div 2 = 55°$,
because again the triangle is isosceles.
$b + e = 35 + 55 = 90°$ (The angle in a semicircle)

1 a Draw an accurate copy of the diagram illustrated.

b Work out the area of the square.
(Area $= \frac{1}{2}$ of the product of the diagonal lengths.)

c Draw on your copy a circle of radius 5 cm which also has its centre at the centre of the square. What do you notice?

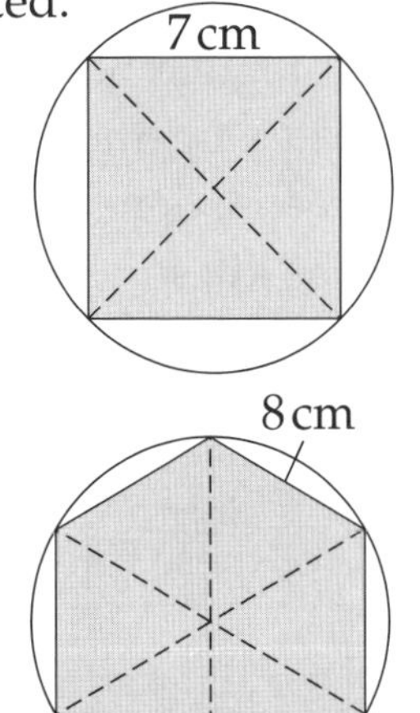

2 a Draw an accurate copy of the diagram illustrated.

b Draw on your copy a circle of radius 7 cm whose centre is also at the centre of the figure. What do you notice ?

3 a Find the marked angles.

b d, e and j are angles between a tangent and a chord. Look carefully to see which angles they are equal to. What do you notice?

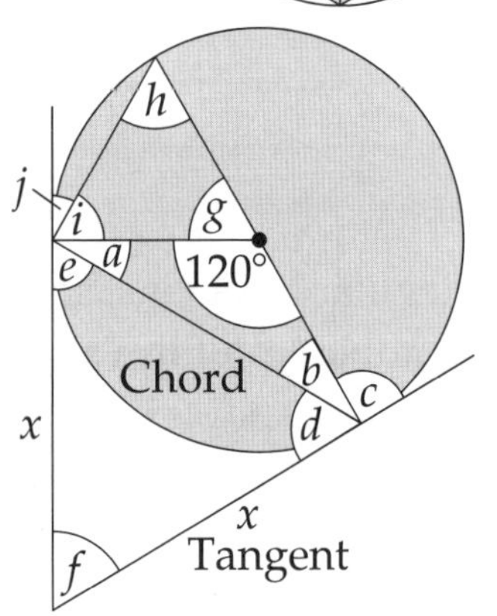

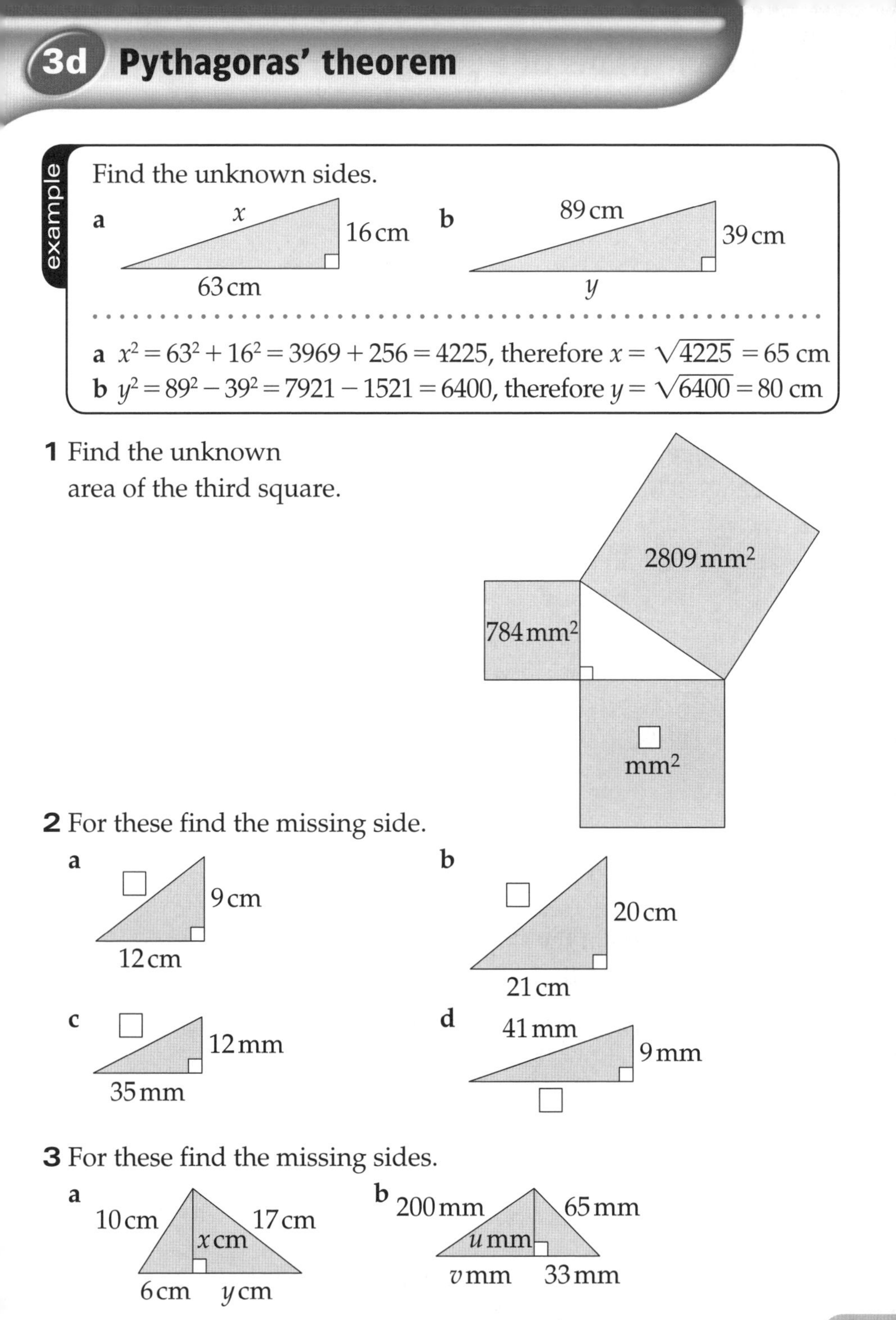

3d Pythagoras' theorem

example

Find the unknown sides.

a Right-angled triangle with sides 63 cm, 16 cm and hypotenuse x.

b Right-angled triangle with hypotenuse 89 cm, side 39 cm and side y.

a $x^2 = 63^2 + 16^2 = 3969 + 256 = 4225$, therefore $x = \sqrt{4225} = 65$ cm

b $y^2 = 89^2 - 39^2 = 7921 - 1521 = 6400$, therefore $y = \sqrt{6400} = 80$ cm

1 Find the unknown area of the third square.

2 For these find the missing side.

3 For these find the missing sides.

3e Applications of Pythagoras' theorem

example

Use Pythagoras' theorem to decide if the triangle is right angled.

3 cm 4 cm 2.6 cm

If the triangle is right angled 4^2 and $2.6^2 + 3^2$ would have to be equal, but $4^2 = 16$ and $2.6^2 + 3^2 = 6.76 + 9 = 15.76$. Therefore the triangle is not exactly right angled.

1 Use Pythagoras' theorem to decide if each of these triangles is right angled or not.

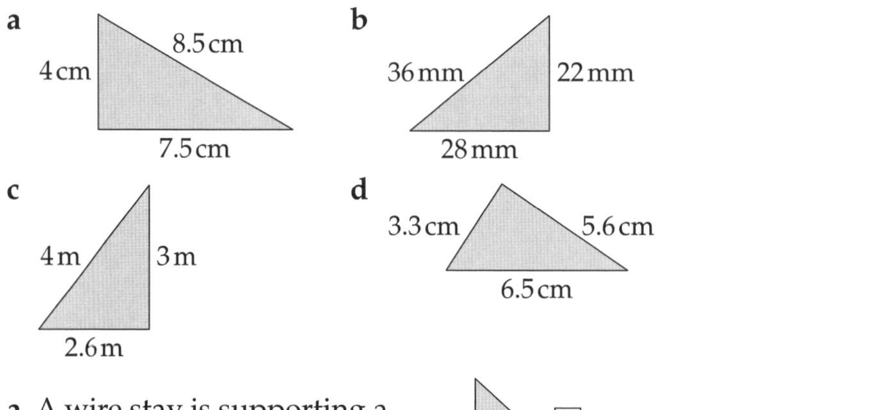

2 a A wire stay is supporting a radio mast.
Find the length of the stay.

b Find the width of the gate.

40 m
42 m
2.5 m
1.5 m

3 Find **i** the vertical height **ii** the area for each of these isosceles triangles.

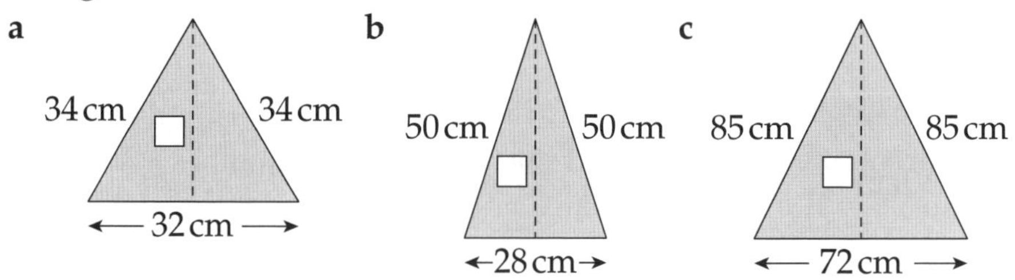

3f Constructing a triangle

example

Construct the triangle ABC in which AB = 3.6 cm, AC = 2.9 cm and BC = 2.5 cm. Measure the three angles in the triangle.

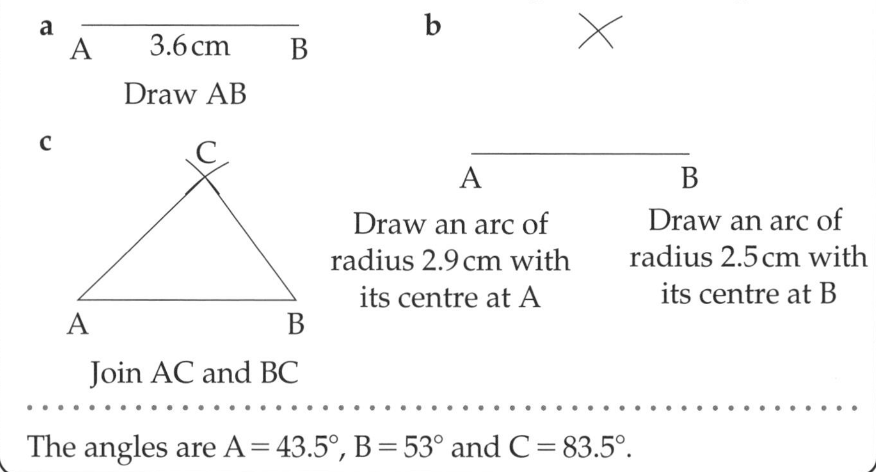

The angles are A = 43.5°, B = 53° and C = 83.5°.

1 Construct these triangles. Measure any side lengths and angles that are not given.

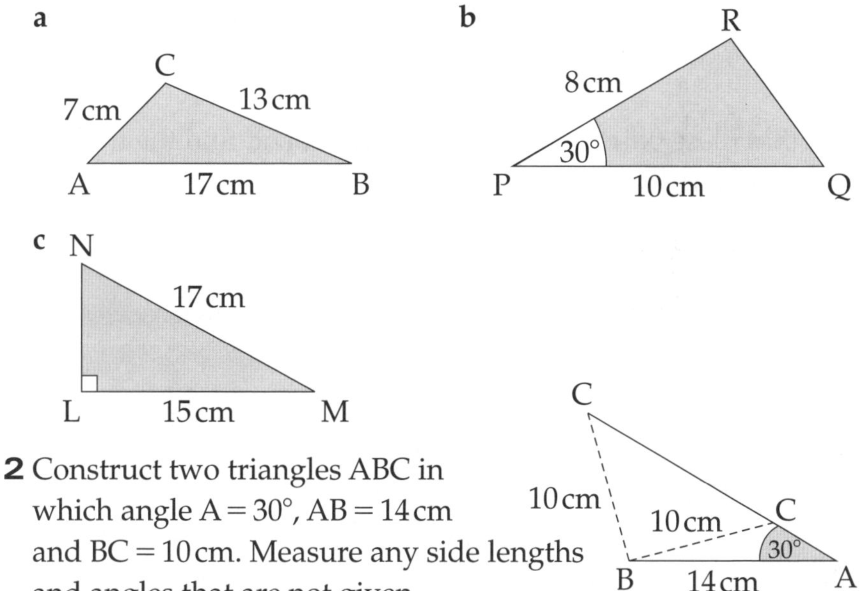

2 Construct two triangles ABC in which angle A = 30°, AB = 14 cm and BC = 10 cm. Measure any side lengths and angles that are not given.

3g Congruence

example

State whether or not the two triangles are congruent. Give a reason for your answer.

45 mm, 30°, 70 mm; 70 mm, 30°, 45 mm

No, the triangles are not congruent because the angle of 30° is not where the two given sides meet in the second triangle.

1 For these pairs of triangles state whether or not they are congruent. Give a reason for your answer in each case.

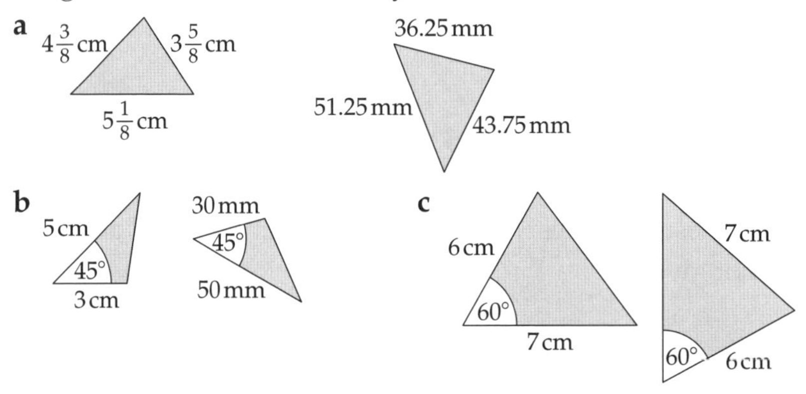

2 Given that these pairs of triangles are congruent, find the missing lengths and angles.

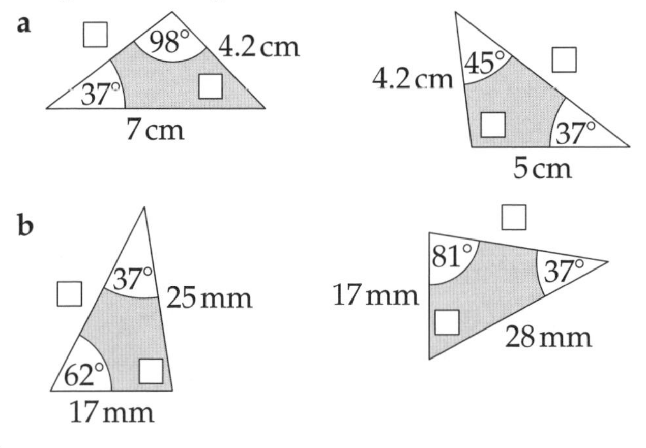

3h Loci

example

Draw the locus of the points which are 1 cm from the line illustrated.

5 cm

The locus consists of two lines which are parallel to the given line and 1 cm from it, together with two semicircles of radius 1 cm with their centres at each end of the line.

5 cm

1 cm

1 cm

1 Draw the locus of the points which are 1 cm from

a the square **b** the isosceles right-angled triangle.

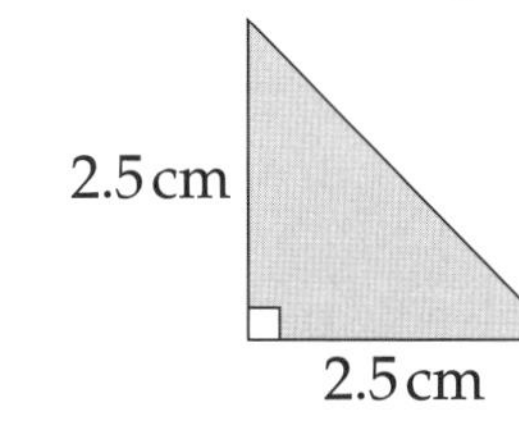

2 cm

2 A guard dog's rope is fastened to the midpoint of a wall which is 8 m long. Draw the locus of the area which encloses where the dog can walk if the rope is

a 4 m long **b** 8 m long.

Rope

8 m

3 Draw the locus of the path Tom walks when these instructions are followed and state the type of quadrilateral that he describes.

'Forward 7 m, turn clockwise through 90°, forward 4 m, turn clockwise through 60°, forward 4 m, turn clockwise through 90° and forward 7 m.'

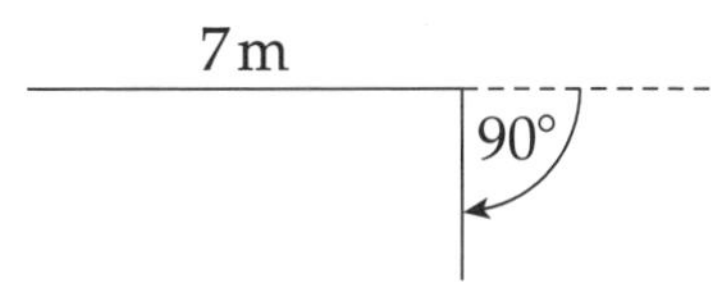

4a Consolidating linear equations

example

Solve the equation $5(t-4) = 2(t+5)$

$$5(t-4) = 2(t+5)$$

therefore $5t - 20 = 2t + 10$

therefore $5t - 2t = 10 + 20$

therefore $3t = 30$

so $t = 10$

1 Solve these equations. For each case find which part (**i**, **ii** or **iii**) has a different solution from the other two.

a **i** $12x + 25 = 73$ **ii** $15x - 28 = 17$ **iii** $9x - 31 = -4$

b **i** $5y - 12 = 2y + 15$ **ii** $9y - 65 = 2y - 9$ **iii** $13y + 16 = 4y + 97$

c **i** $5(z-7) = 3(z+5)$ **ii** $7(z+11) = 4(z+38)$ **iii** $7(z-9) = 5(z-1)$

d **i** $\frac{(t+42)}{3} = \frac{(t+126)}{7}$ **ii** $\frac{(t-5)}{5} = \frac{(t+4)}{8}$ **iii** $\frac{(t-13)}{4} = \frac{(t-3)}{9}$

2 The rectangle and the isosceles trapezium have the same perimeter. Find

a the value of y, and

b the common perimeter.

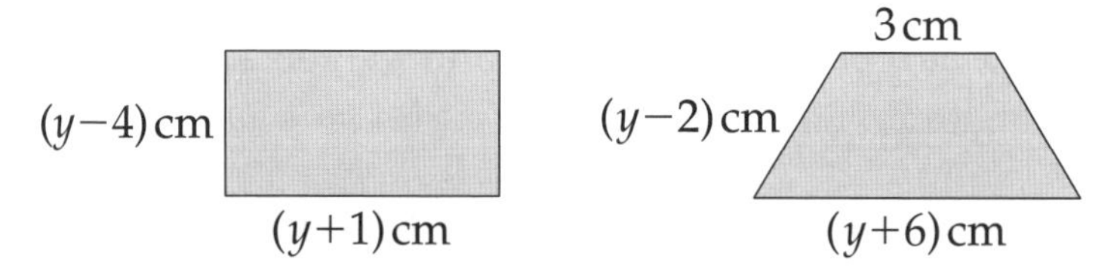

3 Rocco is m years old. He is 3 years older than his brother Tony and 7 years younger than his sister Juliana. If their grandmother's age is both 5 times more than Tony's and 3 times more than Juliana's, form an equation in m. Use your equation to find

a Rocco's age

b the age of each of the others.

4b Introducing simultaneous equations

example

Solve the simultaneous equations $3x + 2y = 11$ and $x - 2y = 1$.

Add the two equations together in order to eliminate y,

$$\begin{aligned} 3x + 2y &= 11 \\ x - 2y &= 1 \\ \hline 4x \quad &= 12 \end{aligned}$$ therefore $x = 3$

Substituting for x in the first equation gives,

$3 \times 3 + 2y = 11$

therefore $9 + 2y = 11$

therefore $2y = 11 - 9 = 2$

therefore $y = 1$

The solution therefore is $x = 3$ and $y = 1$.

1 Solve these pairs of simultaneous equations by adding.

a $3x + 2y = 17$
$5x - 2y = 7$

b $4x + 3y = 25$
$7x - 3y = 19$

c $8x + 3y = 46$
$2x - 3y = 4$

2 Solve these pairs of simultaneous equations by subtracting.

a $5x + 3y = 19$
$2x + 3y = 13$

b $7x + 2y = 31$
$3x + 2y = 19$

c $4x + 9y = 44$
$4x + 7y = 36$

3 The triangle has a perimeter of 32 cm and the rectangle has a perimeter of 40 cm. Find the values of x and y.

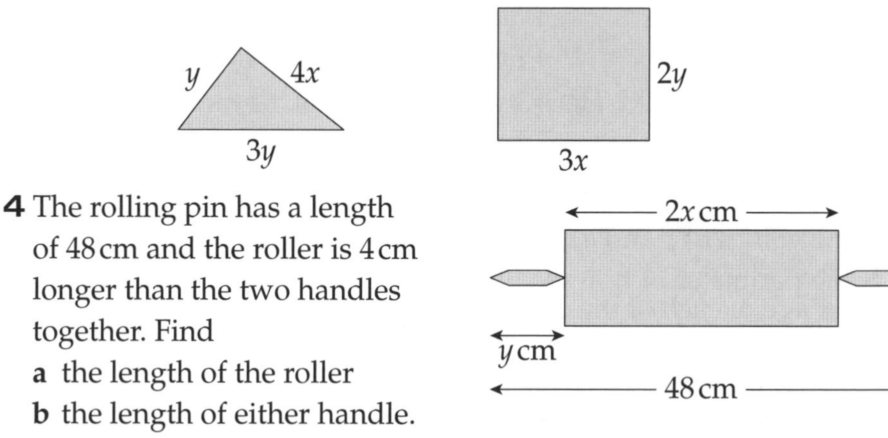

4 The rolling pin has a length of 48 cm and the roller is 4 cm longer than the two handles together. Find

a the length of the roller

b the length of either handle.

4c Further simultaneous equations

example

Solve the simultaneous equations $4x + 3y = 18$ and $5x + 2y = 19$.

$5x + 2y = 19$	Multiply the upper equation	$15x + 6y = 57$
$4x + 3y = 18$	by 3 and the lower equation	$8x + 6y = 36$
	by 2 in order to eliminate y	$7x = 21$
	by subtraction.	So $x = 3$

Substituting for x in the upper equation gives $15 \times 3 + 6y = 57$

therefore $45 + 6y = 57$

therefore $6y = 57 - 45 = 12$

therefore $y = 2$

The solution therefore is $x = 3$ and $y = 2$.

1 Solve these pairs of simultaneous equations by first multiplying one of the equations by a suitable factor.

a $4x + y = 12$, $5x + 2y = 18$ **b** $2x + y = 11$, $4x + 3y = 25$ **c** $3x + y = 11$, $5x + 4y = 23$

d $4x + y = 13$, $10x - 3y = 5$ **e** $6x + y = 22$, $7x - 4y = 5$ **f** $5x - y = 7$, $3x + 2y = 12$

2 Solve these pairs of simultaneous equations by first multiplying both equations by a suitable factor.

a $5x + 4y = 32$, $2x + 3y = 17$ **b** $4x + 3y = 20$, $2x + 5y = 24$ **c** $7x + 2y = 25$, $4x + 3y = 18$

d $5x + 3y = 19$, $7x - 2y = 8$ **e** $2x + 5y = 26$, $3x - 2y = 1$ **f** $3x + 4y = 31$, $4x - 3y = 8$

3 If the perimeter of triangle ABD is 19 cm and that of triangle ABC is 29 cm, find

a the values of p and q

b the perimeter of triangle BDC.

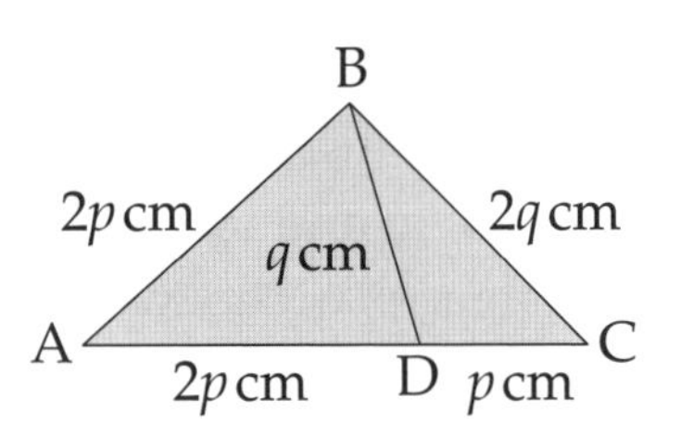

4d Constructing simultaneous equations

example

A miniature railway on a beach charges adults £x and children £y for a ride. One train sets off with 20 adults and 35 children on board and the conductor collects £130. The next train sets off with 15 adults and 40 children on board and the conductor collects £125. Find the values of x and y.

For the first train $20x + 35y = 130$ and
for the second train $15x + 40y = 125$.
Multiply the first equation by 3 and the second by 4 in order to be able to eliminate x by subtraction,

$$60x + 105y = 390$$
$$60x + 160y = 500$$
$$55y = 110$$ therefore $y = 2$,

and from the first equation $20x + 70 = 130$ which solves to give $x = 3$.

Therefore the solution is $x = 3$ (the charge is £3 for adults) and $y = 2$ (the charge is £2 for children).

1 A ferry operator charges £c for cars and £v for vans. One day it was used by 20 cars and 6 vans and the operator collected £142. On the next day it was used by 21 cars and 4 vans and for this the operator collected £133. Find the values of c and v.

2 Look at the triangles illustrated. Find the values of x and y and hence the size of all three angles in each triangle.

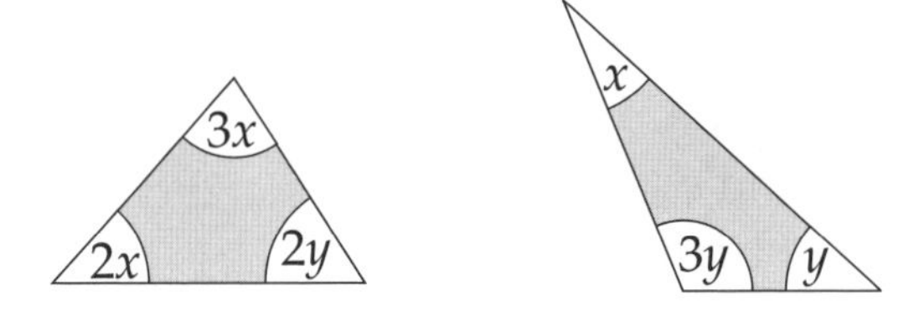

4e Introducing and solving inequalities

example

Represent each of these inequalities on a number line.

a $x \geq -2$ **b** $-3 < x \leq 6$

a −4 −2 0 2 4 6

● Indicates included
○ Indicates excluded

b −4 −2 0 2 4 6

1 Write the inequalities that these number lines represent.

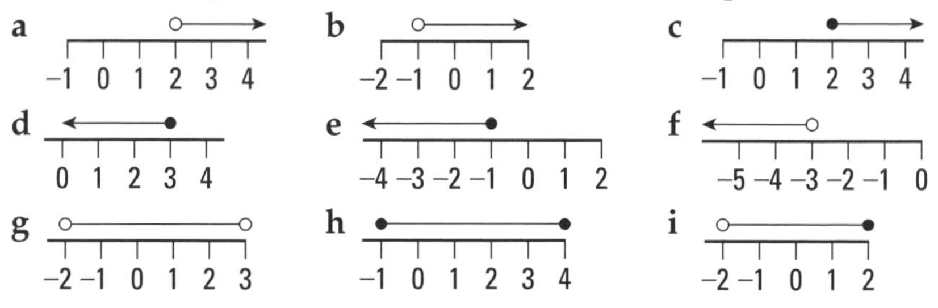

2 Represent each of these inequalities on a number line.

a $x > 1$ **b** $x > -3$ **c** $x \geq 4$

d $x \leq 2$ **e** $x \leq -3$ **f** $-3 < x < 2$

g $-2 \leq x \leq 3$ **h** $-1 \leq x < 4$ **i** $-3 < x \leq 5$

3 Solve these inequalities and draw each answer on a number line.

a $7x + 3 \leq 31$ **b** $8x - 23 < 3x - 8$ **c** $5x - 4 > 2x + 11$

d $6x + 5 > 2x + 13$ **e** $12x + 5 \leq 3x + 41$ **f** $16 - 3x \leq 7$

g $3(x - 1) < 2(x + 1)$ **h** $4(x + 2) \geq 3(x + 4)$

4 The rectangle has a greater perimeter than the isosceles triangle. Find the condition on x.

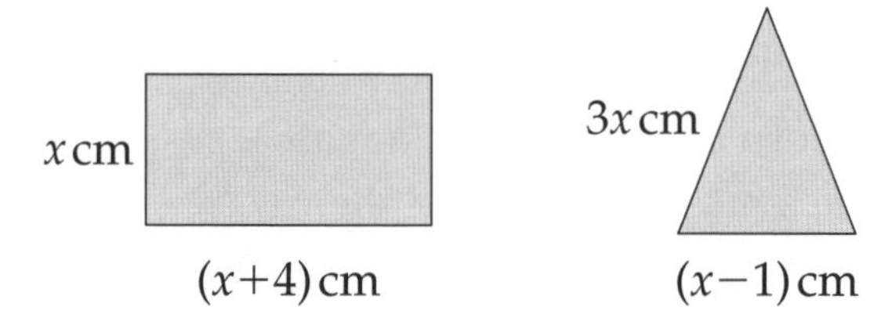

5 Look again at question **4**. There is another inequality condition that applies to x. What is it?

4f Solving equations using trial-and-improvement

example

Solve the equation $x^2 + x = 1000$ by trial and improvement.
Give your answer correct to 1 decimal place.

Try $x = 30$, this gives $30^2 + 30 = 930$ which is too low.
Try $x = 31$, this gives $31^2 + 31 = 992$ which is closer, but still too low.
Try $x = 31.1$, this gives $31.1^2 + 31.1 = 998.31$ which is very close, but again, still too low.
Try $x = 31.2$, this gives $31.2^2 + 31.2 = 1004.64$ which is too high.

998.31 is, however, closer to 1000 than 1004.64 so 31.1 is the solution correct to 1 decimal place.

1 Find exact solutions to these equations by trial and improvement.

a $x^2 + 3x = 700$ **b** $x^2 - 5x = 864$ **c** $x^3 + 2x^2 = 2016$
d $x^3 - 3x^2 = 4046$ **e** $x^3 - x = 9240$ **f** $x^3 + x = 6878$
g $2^x = 4096$ **h** $3^x = 2187$

2 Find solutions to these equations by trial and improvement. Give your answers correct to 1 decimal place.

a $x^2 + 2x = 50$ **b** $x^2 - 3x = 60$ **c** $x^3 + 3x^2 = 1000$
d $x^3 - 2x^2 = 1200$ **e** $x^3 - x = 1500$ **f** $x^3 + x = 2000$
g $x^3 + 2x = 1600$ **h** $x^3 - 3x = 900$

3 Look at the diagram opposite. Find

a the value of x
b the distance from Watford to Glasgow.

Glasgow
x^2 km
650 km
Watford
x km
London

4 Robbie's new born baby sister has a mass of m kg, Robbie's mass is m^2 kg and their mother's mass is m^3 kg. If all three are together on a scale the reading is 84 kg. Find

a the value of m **b** Robbie's mass **c** their mother's mass.

5a Using statistical methods

example

Zeke thinks that the country's top football clubs have slowly lost interest in the FA Cup competition.

a Would he require primary or secondary data to test this hypothesis?

b How could he collect his data?

c What might have made him think of this hypothesis?

a and **b** His data could be of either kind. He may have kept his own record over several years which listed the cup winning team and their league position for the same season. These data are also available from the FA.

c Perhaps he believes that the top clubs have become more interested in European competitions.

For each of these explain

a whether the hypothesis proposer will have to collect primary or secondary data

b how the data might be collected

c what might have made the proposer think of the hypothesis.

1 The works manager at a factory thinks that his workers who travel in by bus are getting more and more punctual despite the fact that road congestion seems to be getting worse.

2 Zodia thinks that as students progress from Year 7 to Year 11 at school they tend to be absent less.

3 Tnisha thinks that students who have a long journey to school arrive more punctually than those who live within walking distance.

4 A medical research worker thinks that if people sleep less they are more frequently absent from work.

5 Barbara thinks that car-carrying trains are getting more and more business in recent years.

5b Designing a survey or experiment

example

Matthew is an archery enthusiast. Peter would like to know how many bull's eyes Matthew is likely to score in 10 shots.

a Will Peter have to carry out an experiment or a survey in order to investigate?

b How should he carry out his investigation?

a Peter will have to perform an experiment, because he will have to record Matthew's results from several shots.

b Probably the best way to carry out his investigation is to see how many bull's eyes Matthew scores in 10 shots several times over. Better still, every set of 10 shots should be fired at different times rather than all at once.

For each of these

a explain whether the investigation will require an experiment or a survey

b describe how the investigation could be carried out.

1 Jodie is a high jumper. Does she perform better on warmer days?

2 In a certain town road congestion is bad. The council would like to know whether people would like things to be improved by
i providing bus lanes **ii** reopening a railway line, or **iii** both.

3 Joza is a sprinter and she thinks that she is a better performer than Deana, but the other girls in the school do not agree. The games teacher wants to settle the argument.

4 Many from the UK who drive in mainland Europe seem to find it an inconvenience driving on the right-hand side of the road. The Ministry of Transport would like to do something about it and decide to ask people whether they would like to
i have the UK changed to right-hand side driving, or
ii have cars fitted with controls that could be moved to the other side of the dashboard.

Data collection

example

Elaine works for a train operating company and she thinks that many passengers feel that the fares they pay are too high. She goes to a London station during the morning peak hour and asks several hundred people what they think. Why might she obtain biased information and how could she improve matters?

Most of the people she asked would probably have been commuters, so long-distance travellers would have been under represented. She needs to take samples of about the same number of people at other times of the day.

1 The Headmaster of Willow Grange School has an idea that pupils would like to see prefects done away with in schools and give privileges, such as some freedom of hours, to all of the more senior pupils instead. He therefore asks all of the sixth form pupils at his school what they think. Give two reasons why this is a biased sample. Suggest how he could get better information.

2 Jean is in Year 11 at her school and she thinks that ever since she was in Year 7 the number of lessons in which pupils are taught by supply teachers has been increasing. She still has copies of her timetables for all of her five years at the school and she studies them to see if she is right. Why might her conclusion be very biased? What could she do to make her conclusion better?

3 A government official thinks if a company loses a lot of business during a recession it is better to make all employees suffer a pay cut rather than making some people redundant and/or asking older workers to take early retirement. He waits at the main entrance to an industrial estate one morning and asks the first 100 people to arrive what they think. Suggest reasons why his sample may be biased. Suggest ways in which he could improve his questioning.

Frequency diagrams

example

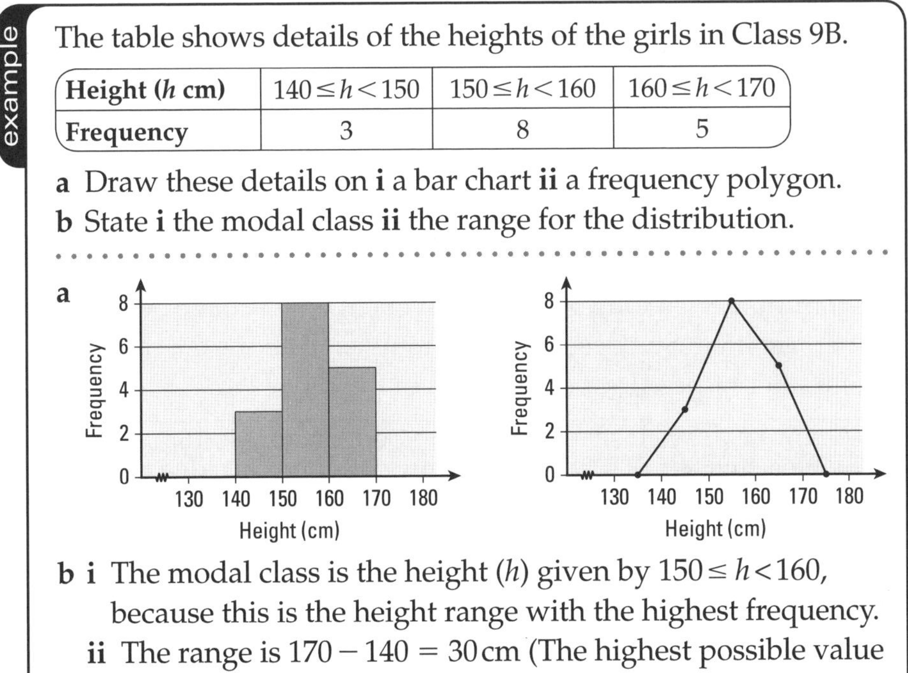

The table shows details of the heights of the girls in Class 9B.

Height (h cm)	$140 \le h < 150$	$150 \le h < 160$	$160 \le h < 170$
Frequency	3	8	5

a Draw these details on **i** a bar chart **ii** a frequency polygon.

b State **i** the modal class **ii** the range for the distribution.

a

b i The modal class is the height (h) given by $150 \le h < 160$, because this is the height range with the highest frequency.

ii The range is $170 - 140 = 30$ cm (The highest possible value minus the lowest possible value)

1 The table gives details of the masses of the boys in Class 9A.

a Draw these details on **i** a bar chart **ii** a frequency polygon.

b State **i** the modal class and **ii** the range for the distribution.

Mass (m kg)	$45 \le m < 50$	$50 \le m < 55$	$55 \le m < 60$	$60 \le m < 65$
Frequency	2	5	6	3

2 The bar chart shows the distribution for the masses of the girls in the same class as the boys in question **1**. Use this information and that from question **1** to draw **i** a bar chart **ii** a frequency polygon that shows the mass distribution for the whole class.

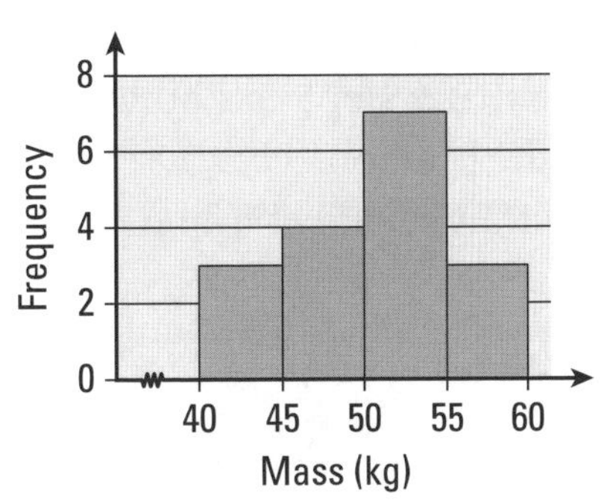

5e Line of best fit

example

The games teacher at Holly Lane School records the best high jump and long jump records for his four best performers on this scatter diagram.

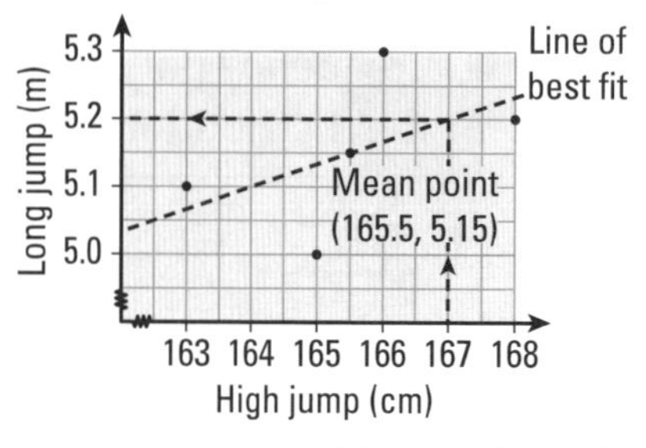

A new boy says his best high jump performance is 167 cm. Use your scatter diagram to predict his best long jump performance.

From the scatter diagram it can be seen that his best long jump record might be 5.2 m.

1 Anwar collects the money for boat hiring on a pleasure park lake. He thinks that more people hire boats on warmer days. Here are some data that he collected over six days.

Midday temperature (°C)	12	14	16	18	20	22
Number of people	40	60	50	55	45	65

a Draw a scatter diagram and add a line of best fit.

b Why would it be unwise to make predictions using this diagram?

2 A medical researcher asked some workers about how much they usually slept and how many days off work they had during the previous year. Draw a scatter diagram of their details and a straight line of best fit.

	Anne	Yasmin	Rosa	Tony	Chan
Hours of sleep	4	5	6	7	8
Days off work last year	24	18	13	9	6

Time series

example

The graph shows the mean number of books that were borrowed from a school library during each of the three terms over a three-year period. Comment on and give any reasons for

a the termly variation

b the overall trend.

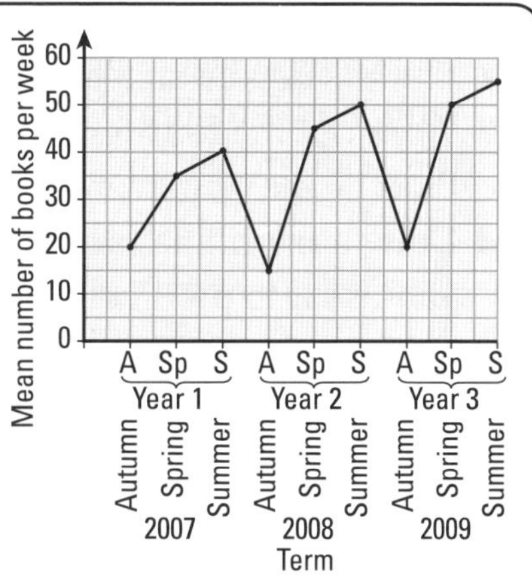

a Later in the school year more books are borrowed because both internal and external examinations are held in the summer term.

b The overall trend is upwards. This could be due to the number of pupils in the school increasing or examination syllabuses including more coursework.

1 The graph shows the mean number of cars that are parked in a station's car park by 09:00 h each morning over two years. Comment on and give possible reasons for

a any variations within the three-month periods

b the overall trend.

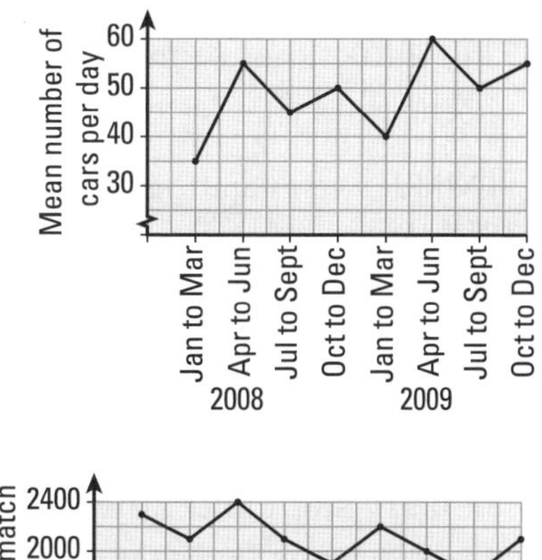

2 The graph shows how a football club's average home attendances varied over three seasons. Comment on and give possible reasons for

a any variations between the seasons

b the overall trend.

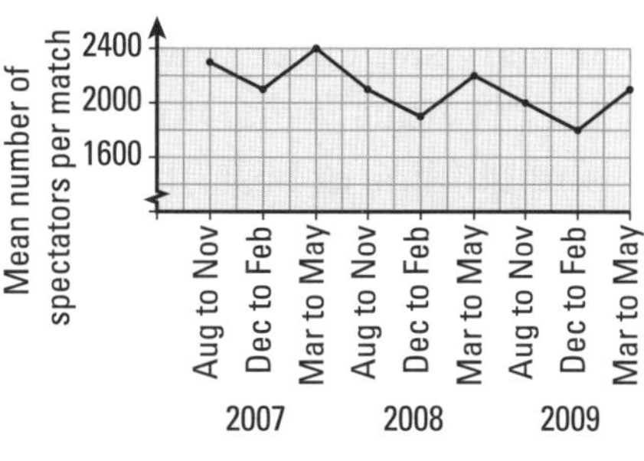

5f² Moving averages

For all of these questions follow this procedure.

a Plot the details on a graph.

b Work out the four-term moving averages.

c Plot the moving averages on your graph.

d Draw a trend line for the moving averages on your graph and use it to predict the moving average for January 2009 to December 2009.

e Find an estimate of the relevant quantity for October to December 2009.

	Jan to Mar 2008	Apr to Jun 2008	Jul to Sep 2008	Oct to Dec 2008	Jan to Mar 2009	Apr to Jun 2009	Jul to Sep 2009
1 The mean number of people using a swimming pool per day	60	90	150	60	80	110	170
2 The mean rainfall per day where Sushila lives	28 cm	24 cm	20 cm	24 cm	24 cm	20 cm	16 cm
3 The mean amount of money Jake makes per day selling ice	£100	£150	£250	£120	£80	£130	£230

5g The mean

example

Jake records how many pupils travelled on his school bus over the 75 days of the Autumn Term.

	Number of pupils (n)		
	$10 \le n < 15$	$15 \le n < 20$	$20 \le n < 25$
Number of days	15	36	24

Find an estimate for the mean number of pupils per day.

The mid-interval values are used to find an estimate for the total
$(12.5 \times 15) + (17.5 \times 36) + (22.5 \times 24) = 1357.5$
So an estimate for the mean is $1357.5 \div 75 = 18.1$

1 The table give details of the masses of the boys and girls in Year 9 at Hatchend School.

	Mass (m kg)						
	$40 \le m < 45$	$45 \le m < 50$	$50 \le m < 55$	$55 \le m < 60$	$60 \le m < 65$	$65 \le m < 70$	$70 \le m < 75$
Number of boys	10	10	20	28	20	10	2
Number of girls	15	25	30	25	19	5	1

Find an estimate for the mean mass of **i** the boys, and **ii** the girls. (An assumed mean of 42.5 is a convenient one to use if you prefer that method.)

2 The table gives details of the English and Mathematics test results for the Year 9 students at Larch Lane School.

	Mark				
	$0 \le m < 20$	$20 \le m < 40$	$40 \le m < 60$	$60 \le m < 80$	$80 \le m < 100$
English (No. of students)	15	60	70	45	10
Mathematics (No. of students)	30	30	70	40	30

Find an estimate for the mean mark for **i** English, and **ii** Mathematics.

6a Measures

example

Shani stands on a weighing machine and the reading is 45 kg. To what degree of accuracy is this reading and what is the range of possible values for it?

It is correct to two significant figures so the range of possible values that her mass could be is 44.5 kg to 45.5 kg.

1 State the degree of accuracy and range of possible values for these.

a 53 cm **b** 76 ml **c** 324 kg **d** 266 mm
e 8 litres **f** 5 tonnes **g** 3.6 m^2 **h** 7.1 litres
i 6.0 m^3 **j** 3.76 kg **k** 8.21 m **l** 2.325 km

2 The diagram shows Candace's way to her school. State the degree of accuracy and the range of values for each distance shown.

Candace's front gate — Bus stop — Bus stop — School gate

← 125 m → ← 3.8 km → ← 75 m →

3 Reshmi looks at a map and it shows 40 km for the distance from Leeds to York. She is not sure whether the range of values for the figure is 39.5 to 40.5 km or 35 to 45 km. What do you think?

4 Convert these metric measurements to the units indicated.

a 2.5 km to m **b** 3.6 m to cm **c** 10.2 cm to mm
d 2.25 tonnes to kg **e** 3.44 kg to g **f** 10.21 litres to cm^3
g 5 m^2 to cm^2 **h** 136 cm^2 to mm^2 **i** 4.5 ha to m^2
j 0.27 m^3 to cm^3 **k** 5300 m to km **l** 870 cm to m

5 Use the metric to imperial conversion table in your Student's Book to make these conversions.

a 3.6 gallons to litres **b** 5 pints to litres
c 10.5 kg to pounds (lb) **d** 25 oz to grams
e 36 feet to metres **f** 18 inches to cm
g 55 miles to km **h** 13.5 litres to gallons

6b Dimensions

example

If someone told you that the formulae for the surface area and volume of the prism shown were $bh + 3b^2$ and $\frac{1}{2}b^2h$, but they could not remember which one was which, how could you find out for certain?

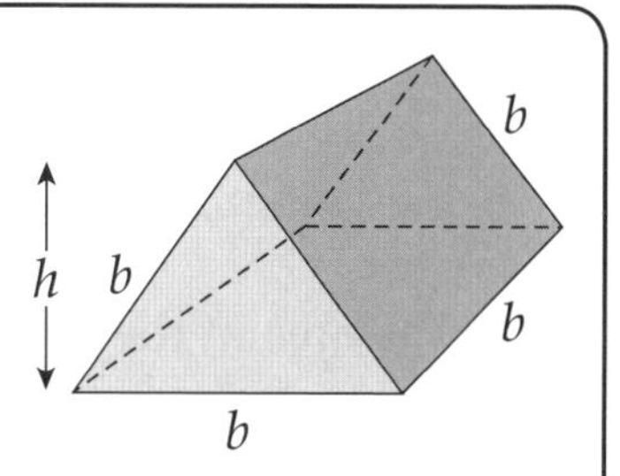

The formula $bh + 3b^2$ can be written as $b \times h + 3b \times b$, from which it can easily be seen that only two dimensions (i.e. two letters) are multiplied together in either term. Therefore this is the formula for the surface area because area is a two-dimensional quantity.
The formula $\frac{1}{2}b^2h$ can be written as $\frac{1}{2} \times b \times b \times h$ from which it can easily be seen that three dimensions are multiplied together. Therefore this is the formula for the volume because volume is a three-dimensional quantity.

1 Here are six formulae, **a** to **f**, without their subjects. Match them with the subjects **i** to **vi** that are given with the diagrams.

a $\pi r^2 l$ **b** $4\pi r^2$ **c** πr^2 **d** $2\pi r$ **e** $\frac{4}{3}\pi r^3$ **f** $6l^2$

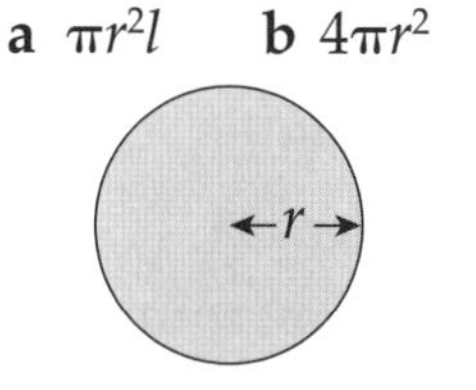

i Circumference of circle
ii Area of circle

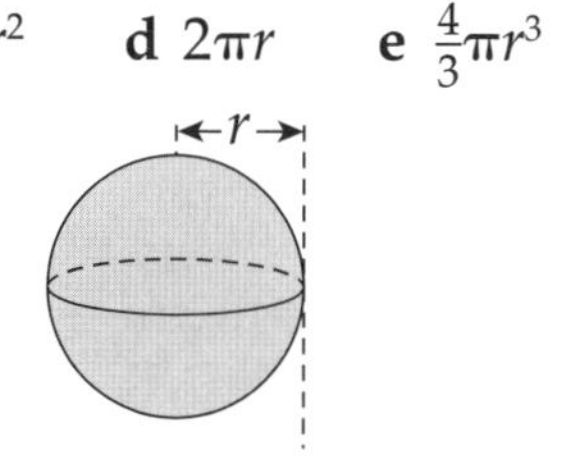

iii Surface area of sphere
iv Volume of sphere

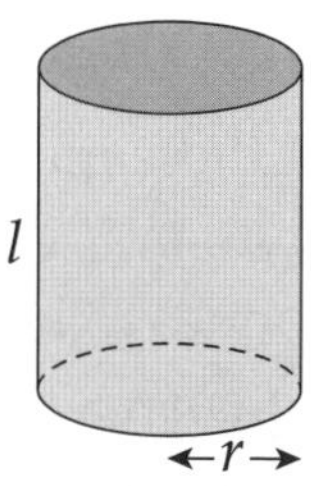

v Volume of cylinder

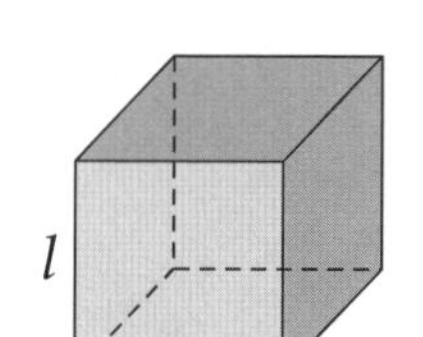

vi Surface area of cube

6c Length, area and volume

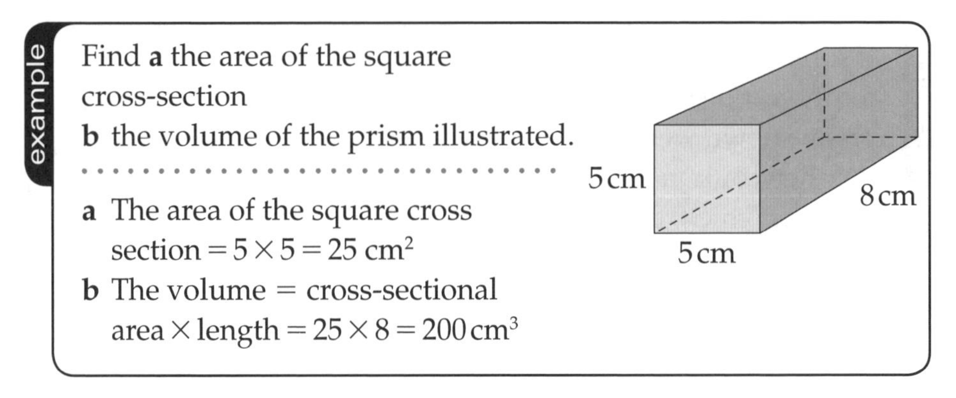

example

Find **a** the area of the square cross-section

b the volume of the prism illustrated.

a The area of the square cross section $= 5 \times 5 = 25\ \text{cm}^2$

b The volume = cross-sectional area $\times$ length $= 25 \times 8 = 200\ \text{cm}^3$

(Where required, assume that $\pi = 3.14$.)

1 Find **i** the cross sectional area, and **ii** the volume of these prisms.

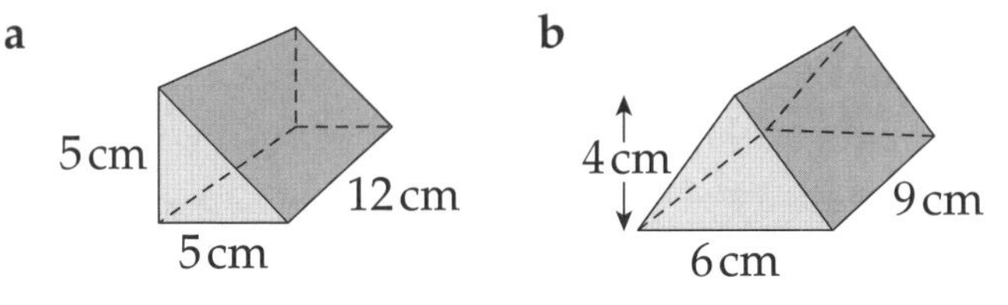

2 Find **i** the area of the circular cross section, and **ii** the volume.

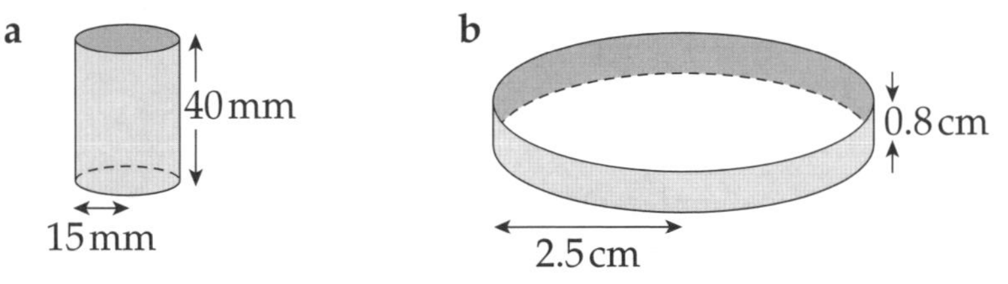

3 **a** Find the area of the inscribed circle of the square.

b Find the area of the circumcircle of the rectangle.

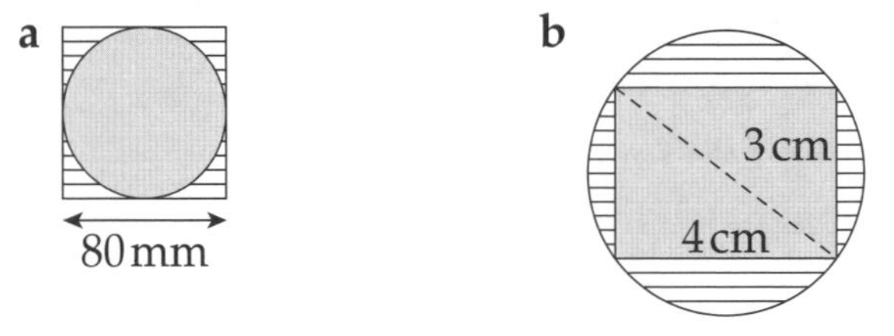

Arcs and sectors

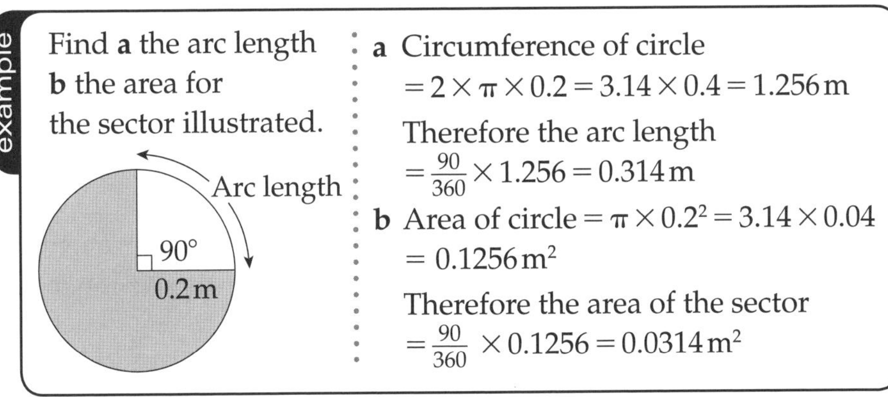

Find **a** the arc length **b** the area for the sector illustrated.

a Circumference of circle $= 2 \times \pi \times 0.2 = 3.14 \times 0.4 = 1.256\,\text{m}$

Therefore the arc length $= \frac{90}{360} \times 1.256 = 0.314\,\text{m}$

b Area of circle $= \pi \times 0.2^2 = 3.14 \times 0.04 = 0.1256\,\text{m}^2$

Therefore the area of the sector $= \frac{90}{360} \times 0.1256 = 0.0314\,\text{m}^2$

(Where required assume that $\pi = 3.14$.)

1 Copy and complete the table about circles.

Radius (r)	Diameter (d)	Circumference	Area
4 cm			
	6 cm		
		188.4 cm	
			7.065 m²

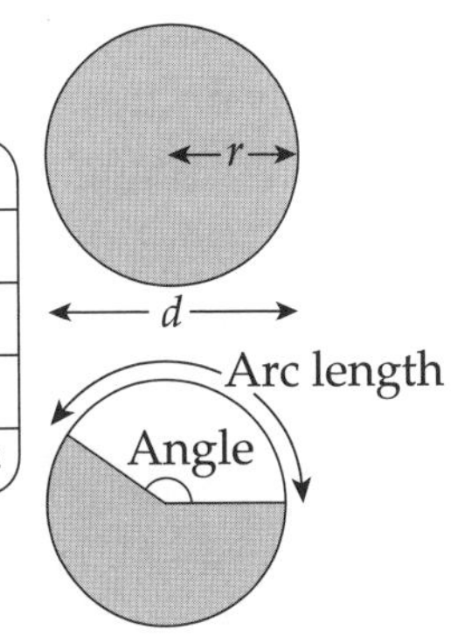

2 Copy and complete the table about sectors.

Sector angle	Radius (r)	Circumference	Arc length	Area of circle	Area of sector of circle
60°	15 cm				
45°	12 cm				
120°	9 cm				
150°	60 mm				

3 Find the **a** perimeter **b** the area for **i** the lawn **ii** the vegetable patch in Rapinda's garden.

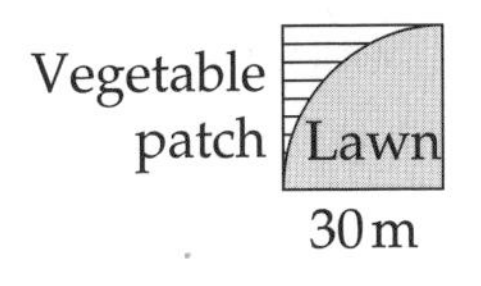

6e Compound measures

example

Find the average speed, in km/h, of a motorway coach that travels 165 km from Newcastle to Leeds in 2 h 45 min.

Speed = distance ÷ time = $165 \div 2\frac{45}{60}$ (because 45 min = $\frac{45}{60}$ h)

= 60 km/h

1 Find the average speed, in metres per second, for these runners.

a Ayo sprints 100 m in 12.5 seconds.

b Zoey completes a 400 m race in 62.5 seconds.

c Jisanne completes a 1500 m race in 4 min 10 s.

2 Find the average speed, in kilometres per hour, for these journeys.

a A train travels 190 km from London to Bristol in 1 h 15 min.

b Charmaine drives her car 154 km from London to Leicester in 1 h 45 min.

c Ronnie rides his bike 45 km from London to Guildford in 2 h 15 min.

3 a A wooden block has a mass of 7.2 kg and its dimensions are 30 cm, 20 cm and 15 cm.

Find

i its mass in grams

ii its volume in cm^3

iii its density in grams per cubic centimetre

iv its volume in m^3

v its density in kilograms per cubic metre.

b Find the mass of another block of the same kind of wood if its volume is

i 5000 cm^3

ii 0.002 m^3.

7a Standard form for large numbers

example

a Write 2.5×10^4 as an ordinary number.
b Write 396 000 in standard form.

a $2.5 \times 10^4 = 25\,000$ (The decimal point has to be moved 4 places to the right.)
b $396\,000 = 3.96 \times 10^5$ (The decimal point must go between the first two digits when the number is expressed in standard form, but its place in the ordinary number is 5 places to the right of that.)

1 Write these as ordinary numbers.

a 3×10^4 **b** 4×10^6 **c** 8.2×10^2 **d** 9.1×10^5
e 4.73×10^4 **f** 6.94×10^3 **g** 1.356×10^5 **h** 4.229×10^7
i 6.231×10^2 **j** 3.4581×10^3

2 Write these in standard form.

a 700 000 **b** 3000 **c** 76 000 **d** 520
e 3 930 000 **f** 15 600 **g** 223 100 **h** 86 140 000
i 749.6 **j** 8536.1 **k** 39.68 **l** 42

3 Write these in standard form.

a The distance from the Earth to the Moon is 390 000 km.
b The distance from the Earth to the Sun is 150 000 000 km.
c The circumference of the Earth is 40 000 km.
d The speed of sound is 1200 km/h.
e One gram of hydrogen occupies a volume of 11 200 cm^3.
f The distance from the Sun to the planet Pluto is 5 920 000 000 km.

4 Write these in standard form.

a 28×10^3 **b** 43×10^5 **c** 16.4×10^4 **d** 39.2×10^6
e 351×10^2 **f** 911×10^4 **g** 0.52×10^7 **h** 0.67×10^6

5 A swimming pool has length 1.95×10^3 cm and width 9.5×10^2 cm. Find its perimeter in **a** centimetres, and **b** metres.

7b Standard form for small numbers

example

a Express 2.7×10^{-2} as a decimal.
b Express 0.000 21 in standard form.

a $2.7 \times 10^{-2} = 0.027$ (The decimal point has to be moved 2 places to the left.)
b $0.000\,21 = 2.1 \times 10^{-4}$ (The decimal point must go between the first two digits when the number is expressed in standard form, but its place in the ordinary number is 4 places to the left of that.)

1 Work out these.

a $531 \div 10^2$ **b** $6500 \div 10^3$ **c** $24\,000 \div 10^5$ **d** $12 \div 10^3$ **e** $26 \div 10^4$
f 55×10^{-2} **g** 81.6×10^{-3} **h** 3.2×10^{-4} **i** 5.6×10^{-5} **j** 0.54×10^{-3}

2 Express these as a decimal.

a 2×10^{-3} **b** 5×10^{-5} **c** 3.6×10^{-2} **d** 4.2×10^{-4}
e 6.32×10^{-6} **f** 9.15×10^{-3} **g** 6.256×10^{-5} **h** 9.857×10^{-2}
i 6.352×10^{-1} **j** 1.001×10^{-4}

3 Express these in standard form.

a 0.0005 **b** 0.003 **c** 0.000 081 **d** 0.000 0045
e 0.000 594 **f** 0.007 76 **g** 0.013 46 **h** 0.006 051
i 0.6727 **j** 0.99 **k** 0.3

4 Express these in standard form.

a Ultrasonic waves of wavelength 0.0095 m are used in depth sounding.
b Light waves of wavelength 0.000 06 cm are emitted from yellow street lights.
c A salt grain, which is cubic in shape, has a side length of 0.004 cm.
d A grain of sand has a volume of 0.000 15 mm^3.

5 A piece of adhesive tape of width 5×10^{-2} cm is stuck onto a piece of paper of width 1.0×10^{-2} cm. Find the combined thickness.

7c Powers and operations

example

Simplify $\frac{10^8 \times 10^{-4} \times 10^{-1}}{10^7}$ giving your answer as a single power of 10.

$\frac{(10^8 \times 10^{-4} \times 10^{-1})}{10^7} = 10^3 \div 10^7$ (on adding the indices in the numerator)

$= 10^{-4}$ (on subtracting the indices)

For question **1**, **2** and **3** simplify all parts, giving your answer as a single power of the number.

1 **a** $3^2 \times 3^5 \times 3^3$ **b** $8^2 \times 8^3 \times 8^4$ **c** $5^4 \times 5^2 \times 5^{-3}$
d $4^4 \times 4^{-2} \times 4^3$ **e** $6^4 \times 6^3 \times 6^{-2}$ **f** $2^5 \times 2^{-2} \times 2^{-7}$
g $9^5 \div 9^2$ **h** $8^3 \div 8^5$ **i** $7^6 \div 7^{-2}$

2 **a** $\frac{3^2 \times 3^4 \times 3^3}{3^5}$ **b** $\frac{4^5 \times 4^1 \times 4^{-2}}{4^2}$ **c** $\frac{5^7 \times 5^{-3} \times 5^{-1}}{5^2}$ **d** $\frac{6^8 \times 6^{-2} \times 6^{-3}}{6^6}$
e $\frac{2^2 \times 2^3 \times 2^6}{2^5 \times 2^2}$ **f** $\frac{7^3 \times 7^6 \times 7^{-2}}{7^2 \times 7^3}$ **g** $\frac{4^7 \times 4^{-2} \times 4^{-1}}{4^5 \times 4}$ **h** $\frac{5^8 \times 5^{-1} \times 5^{-2}}{5 \times 5^3}$

3 **a** $(4^2)^5$ **b** $(5^3)^2$ **c** $(2^{-3})^4$ **d** $(6^{-1})^5$
e $(7^2)^{-3}$ **f** $(8^{-3})^{-2}$ **g** $(10^{-4})^{-1}$

4 Work out these.

a $\frac{(7+3)^2}{(7-5)^3}$ **b** $\frac{(5^2+5)^2}{(2^3-2)^2}$ **c** $\frac{(4^2+5) \times (3^2+7)}{6^2-4}$

d $\frac{\sqrt{(6^2+8^2)} \times (3^3-7)}{\sqrt{5^2-3^2}}$ **e** $\frac{\sqrt{13^2-12^2} \times (2^4-1)}{\sqrt{29^2-21^2}}$

5 Find

a the volume

b the surface area

of the wooden plank illustrated.

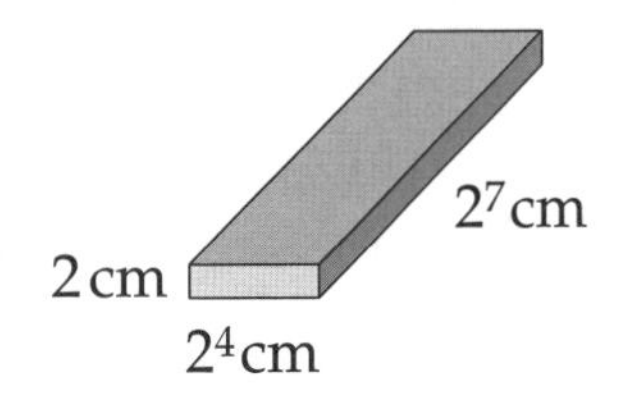

7d Approximation

example

Evaluate $\frac{1.5 \times 3.57}{0.125}$. Give your answer

i exactly **ii** to 1 significant figure **iii** to 2 significant figures.

i $\frac{1.5 \times 3.57}{0.125} = 5.355 \div 0.125 = 42.84$

ii 4$\underline{2}$.84 is 40 to 1 significant figure because 2 is less than 5, and is therefore ignored.

iii 42.$\underline{8}$4 is 43 to 2 significant figures because 8 is greater than 5, so the 2 is rounded up to 3.

1 Round these numbers to

i 1 significant figure **ii** 2 significant figures

iii 3 significant figures.

a 3863 **b** 52 492 **c** 637.1 **d** 32.68 **e** 75.91

f 8.237 **g** 9.845 **h** 0.9362 **i** 0.051 87 **j** 0.007 294

2 Round these numbers to 3 significant figures. Give your answers

i in standard form **ii** as an ordinary number.

a 5.367×10^5 **b** 6.2149×10^3 **c** 8.6304×10^{-3}

3 Work out these. Give your answers

i to 1 significant figure **ii** to 2 significant figures.

a $\frac{36 + 92}{25 \times 5}$ **b** $\frac{107 + 121.96}{225 \div 7.5}$ **c** $\frac{530 - 123}{175 \div 14}$

d $\frac{70.75 - 5.125}{28 \times 7.5}$ **e** $\frac{235 + 440 - 45}{1.2^2}$

4 Work these out approximately after first rounding every number to 1 significant figure.

a $\frac{512 \times 16.8}{52.5}$ **b** $\frac{(78.57 \times 3.29)}{6.3}$ **c** $\frac{39.6 \times 13.2}{24.75}$ **d** $\frac{40.5 \times 0.385}{23.1 \times 1.5}$

5 Write down the upper and lower bounds for these figures.

a Helen's mass is 66.3 kg. (3 sf)

b The diameter of a washer is 20.25 mm (4 sf).

c The 'absolute zero' temperature is -273.2 °C (4 sf).

7e Calculating with decimals

example

a Find **i** the perimeter and **ii** the area of the isosceles triangle.

b Find the width of the paddling pool

7.5 m

Area = 27 m^2 □

3.5 cm　3.7 cm　2.4 cm

a i The perimeter = 2.4 + 3.7 + 3.7 = 9.8 cm (The decimal points are aligned when the numbers are added.)

ii The area = $\frac{1}{2} \times$ base $\times$ height = $0.5 \times 2.4 \times 3.5 = 4.200$ or 4.2 cm^2. ($5 \times 24 \times 35 = 4200$, but the calculation included three figures after a decimal point. Therefore three figures must also come after the decimal point in the answer.)

b The width = area ÷ length = 27 ÷ 7.5 = 270 ÷ 75 = 54 ÷ 15
= 18 ÷ 5 = $3\frac{3}{5}$ = 3.6 m

For questions **1**, **2** and **3**, work out all parts by any appropriate method.

1 a i 12.57 + 36.39 + 21.05　**ii** 15.64 + 39.76 + 14.7
iii 23.02 + 13.39 + 33.6
b i 103.4 + 69.37 + 25.53　**ii** 115.6 + 78.2 + 5.5
iii 92.18 + 75.12 + 32
c i 153.2 + 37.21 − 94.01　**ii** 133.22 + 29.58 − 66.3
iii 194 + 36.2 − 133.7

2 a i 45.25×2.2　**ii** 66.3×1.5　**iii** 39.78×2.5
b i 128×0.16　**ii** 85.75×0.24　**iii** 58.8×0.35
c i 140×0.36　**ii** 23×2.2　**iii** 720×0.07

3 a i 15.12 ÷ 2.7　**ii** 25.2 ÷ 4.5　**iii** 18.81 ÷ 3.3
b i 5.304 ÷ 0.85　**ii** 5.75 ÷ 0.92　**iii** 4.68 ÷ 0.75
c i 133.25 ÷ 13　**ii** 162.4 ÷ 16　**iii** 235.75 ÷ 23

4 Find **i** the perimeter and **ii** the area of a yard with length 64 m and width 29.25 m.

7f Recurring decimals with reciprocals

example

Find the reciprocal of 6.4. Give your answer as
i a fraction, and **ii** a decimal.

i The reciprocal is $\frac{1}{6.4} = \frac{10}{64} = \frac{5}{32}$ **ii** $\frac{5}{32} = 5 \div 32 = 0.156\,25$

1 Write each decimal as a fraction in its simplest form.

a 0.45 **b** 0.95 **c** 0.35 **d** 0.32 **e** 0.9
f 1.6 **g** 1.4 **h** 2.2 **i** 3.55 **j** 4.05

2 Change these fractions to decimals.

a $\frac{11}{20}$ **b** $\frac{3}{20}$ **c** $\frac{12}{25}$ **d** $\frac{9}{25}$ **e** $\frac{3}{8}$
f $\frac{7}{8}$ **g** $\frac{9}{5}$ **h** $\frac{13}{10}$ **i** $\frac{29}{25}$ **j** $\frac{56}{25}$

3 Change these fractions to decimals. Give your answers correct to four decimal places.

a $\frac{2}{7}$ **b** $\frac{5}{7}$ **c** $\frac{1}{7}$ **d** $\frac{7}{12}$ **e** $\frac{11}{12}$
f $\frac{1}{9}$ **g** $\frac{4}{9}$ **h** $\frac{2}{11}$ **i** $\frac{6}{11}$ **j** $\frac{1}{12}$

4 Write these recurring decimals as fractions in their simplest form.

a 0.222 22 **b** 0.777 77 **c** 0.888 88 **d** 0.555 55
e 0.416 66 **f** 0.272 72 **g** 0.090 90 **h** 0.818 18
i 0.133 33 **j** 0.466 66 **k** 0.733 33 **l** 0.208 33

5 Find the reciprocal for each of these. Give each answer as
i a fraction **ii** a decimal.

a 20 **b** 50 **c** 40 **d** 3.2
e 6.25 **f** 1.5625 **g** 250 **h** 800

6 Find the reciprocal for each of these. Give each answer as a whole number or a mixed number.

a 0.04 **b** 0.0125 **c** 0.0625 **d** 0.32
e 0.08 **f** 0.625 **g** 0.005 **h** 0.000 625

7 A water tank contains 1 m^3 of water. How many watering cans of capacity 0.002 m^3 can it fill?

7g Using numbers written in index form

example

a Find the HCF and the LCM of 12 and 42.
b Work out $(6 \times 10^3) \times (5 \times 10^2)$. Give your answer in standard form.

---

a Express the numbers as a product of their prime factors.
$12 = 2 \times 6 = 2 \times \underline{2} \times \underline{3}$ and $42 = 2 \times 21 = \underline{2} \times \underline{3} \times 7$.
The HCF is the product of the common factors (underlined), so it is $\underline{2} \times \underline{3} = 6$.
The LCM is the product of all the factors, but the common ones (underlined) are only included once. Therefore the LCM is $2 \times \underline{2} \times \underline{3} \times 7 = 84$.
b $(6 \times 10^3) \times (5 \times 10^2) = 30 \times 10^5 = 3.0 \times 10^6$. (The decimal point must go between the first two figures.)

1 Write each of these numbers as a product of its prime factors.

a 210	**b** 330	**c** 546	**d** 910	**e** 1155	**f** 132
g 220	**h** 84	**i** 840	**j** 280	**k** 616	**l** 252

2 Find the HCF and the LCM of these numbers.

a 54 and 90	**b** 72 and 108	**c** 96 and 144	**d** 80 and 112
e 105 and 140	**f** 135 and 180	**g** 30, 40 and 50	**h** 12, 18 and 30
i 16, 20 and 24	**j** 18, 45 and 60	**k** 25, 30 and 45	**l** 24, 30 and 42

3 Work out these. Give your answers in standard form.

a $(3 \times 10^3) \times (4 \times 10^2)$	**b** $(5 \times 10^4) \times (7 \times 10^3)$
c $(3 \times 10^5) \times (8 \times 10^1)$	**d** $(4 \times 10^5) \times (3 \times 10^{-2})$
e $(5 \times 10^6) \times (4 \times 10^{-3})$	**f** $(6 \times 10^4) \times (5 \times 10^{-2})$
g $(3 \times 10^5) \div (5 \times 10^2)$	**h** $(4 \times 10^6) \div (5 \times 10^4)$
i $(3 \times 10^4) \div (4 \times 10^2)$	**j** $(3 \times 10^6) \div (4 \times 10^{-2})$
k $(2 \times 10^4) \div (5 \times 10^{-2})$	**l** $(1 \times 10^3) \div (4 \times 10^{-1})$

7h Indices and surds

example

a Simplify $\sqrt{500}$ as much as possible.
b Write $\sqrt[3]{15}$ in index form.

a $\sqrt{500} = \sqrt{100 \times 5} = 10\sqrt{5}$ **b** $\sqrt[3]{15} = 15^{\frac{1}{3}}$

1 Calculate the following leaving your answers in surd form.

a $\sqrt{5} \times \sqrt{6}$ **b** $\sqrt{7} \times \sqrt{11}$ **c** $\sqrt{10} \times \sqrt{13}$ **d** $\sqrt{2} \times \sqrt{17}$
e $\sqrt{3} \times \sqrt{19}$ **f** $\sqrt{7} \times \sqrt{31}$ **g** $\sqrt{13} \times \sqrt{11}$ **h** $\sqrt{7} \times \sqrt{23}$
i $\sqrt{17} \times \sqrt{13}$ **j** $\sqrt{11} \times \sqrt{23}$

2 Write these in their simplest form.

a $\sqrt{20}$ **b** $\sqrt{44}$ **c** $\sqrt{28}$ **d** $\sqrt{45}$ **e** $\sqrt{63}$
f $\sqrt{135}$ **g** $\sqrt{80}$ **h** $\sqrt{112}$ **i** $\sqrt{150}$ **j** $\sqrt{250}$

3 Calculate the following leaving your answers in surd form.

a $3\sqrt{2} \times 7\sqrt{3}$ **b** $6\sqrt{5} \times 3\sqrt{7}$ **c** $2\sqrt{11} \times 5\sqrt{3}$
d $7\sqrt{6} \times 11\sqrt{5}$ **e** $15\sqrt{5} \times 6\sqrt{2}$ **f** $2\sqrt{13} \times 7\sqrt{5}$
g $5\sqrt{11} \times 3\sqrt{7}$ **h** $3\sqrt{15} \times 4\sqrt{13}$ **i** $5\sqrt{14} \times 2\sqrt{5}$
j $7\sqrt{17} \times 3\sqrt{5}$

4 Write these using index notation.

a $\sqrt{10}$ **b** $\sqrt{50}$ **c** $\sqrt{90}$ **d** $\sqrt[3]{20}$ **e** $\sqrt[3]{100}$ **f** $\sqrt[3]{10}$

5 Work out these.

a $64^{\frac{1}{2}}$ **b** $144^{\frac{1}{2}}$ **c** $81^{\frac{1}{2}}$ **d** $64^{\frac{1}{3}}$
e $125^{\frac{1}{3}}$ **f** $1000^{\frac{1}{3}}$ **g** $512^{\frac{1}{3}}$ **h** $343^{\frac{1}{3}}$

6 Calculate these leaving your answer in index form.

a $5^{\frac{1}{3}} \times 5^2$ **b** $3^{\frac{1}{2}} \times 3^3$ **c** $6^{\frac{1}{2}} \times 6^5$ **d** $7^{\frac{1}{3}} \times 7^4$
e $10^{\frac{1}{3}} \times 10^3$ **f** $12^{\frac{1}{3}} \times 12$ **g** $15^{\frac{1}{2}} \times 15$ **h** $11^{\frac{1}{2}} \times 11^0$

7 Find **i** the area, and **ii** the diagonal length of the rectangle.

$(170\sqrt{2})$ mm

$(14\sqrt{50})$ mm

8a Revisiting simultaneous equations

example

By using values of x from -1 to 2, solve the simultaneous equations $y = 2x$ and $y = x + 1$.

$x =$	-1	0	1	2
$y\ (= 2x)$	-2	0	2	4
$y\ (= x + 1)$	0	1	2	3

It can be seen from the graph that the solution is $x = 1$ and $y = 2$.

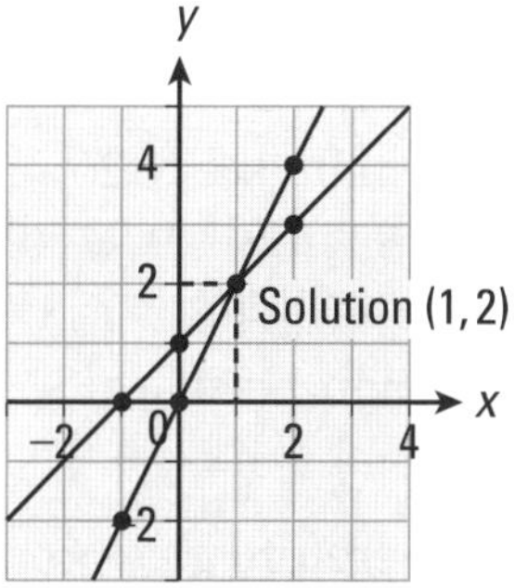

1 Solve these pairs of simultaneous equations using a graph. For each pair of equations draw a grid with $-6 \le x \le 8$ and $-6 \le y \le 8$.

a $y = 2x - 1$ $\quad y = x + 1$ $\quad$ (Use values of x from -2 to 3)
b $y = 2x - 2$ $\quad y = x + 2$ $\quad$ (Use values of x from -2 to 5)
c $y = x - 1$ $\quad y = \frac{1}{2}x + 2$ $\quad$ (Use values of x from -4 to 8)
d $y = x + 2$ $\quad y = \frac{1}{2}x + 3$ $\quad$ (Use values of x from -6 to 6)
e $y = 2x$ $\quad y = 3 - x$ $\quad$ (Use values of x from -2 to 4)
f $y = 2x + 4$ $\quad y = 1 - x$ $\quad$ (Use values of x from -4 to 2)
g $x + y = 3$ $\quad y = \frac{1}{2}x - 3$ $\quad$ (Use values of x from -2 to 8)
h $x + y = -3$ $\quad y = 2x + 3$ $\quad$ (Use values of x from -4 to 2)

2 The Gray family go into a cafe. They order 2 teas and one coffee and their bill is £5. The Johnson family then order 2 teas and 2 coffees and their bill is £7. Find **i** by algebra, and **ii** by a graph, the cost of a tea (£x) and a coffee (£y).
Your graph axes should be $-1 \le y \le 5$ and $0 \le x \le 4$.

8b The gradient of straight-line graphs

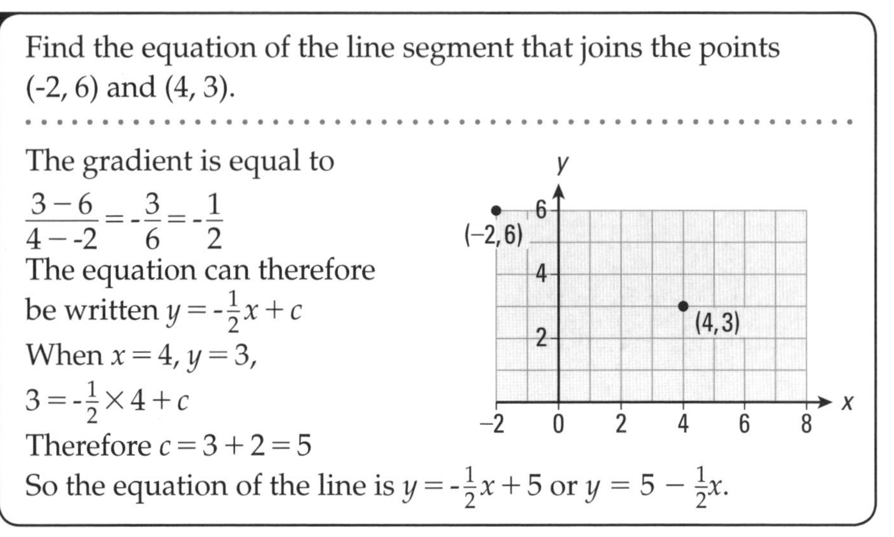

Find the equation of the line segment that joins the points (-2, 6) and (4, 3).

The gradient is equal to

$\frac{3-6}{4--2} = -\frac{3}{6} = -\frac{1}{2}$

The equation can therefore be written $y = -\frac{1}{2}x + c$

When $x = 4$, $y = 3$,

$3 = -\frac{1}{2} \times 4 + c$

Therefore $c = 3 + 2 = 5$

So the equation of the line is $y = -\frac{1}{2}x + 5$ or $y = 5 - \frac{1}{2}x$.

1 Find the gradient of the line segment joining these pairs of points.

a (1, 4) and (5, 12) **b** (2, 1) and (4, 11) **c** (-1, 3) and (2, 12)

d (-2, -1) and (1, 11) **e** (2, 10) and (6, 2) **f** (4, 8) and (7, -7)

g (-1, 3) and (1, -5) **h** (-4, 5) and (-1, -4)

2 Find the equations of these lines in the form $y = mx + c$.

a The line has a gradient of 3 and a y intercept at (0, 1).

b The line has a gradient of -2 and a y intercept at (0, 3).

c The line has a gradient of 2 and passes through the point (3, 4).

d The line has a gradient of -4 and passes through the point (1, -2).

e The line passes through the points (1, 4) and (3, 8).

f The line passes through the points (-1, -4) and (4, 11).

g The line passes through the points (-2, 7) and (1, 1).

h The line passes through the points (-5, 8) and (4, -1).

3 A quadrilateral ABCD is formed by joining the points A (0, 4), B (3, 0), C (0, -4) and D (-7, 0).

a Find the gradient of each of its edges.

b What kind of quadrilateral is it?

8c Parallel and perpendicular lines

example

Find the equation of the line which crosses the line $y = 2x$ perpendicularly at the point (2, 4).

The gradient of the line is $-\frac{1}{2}$, so the equation can be written $y = -\frac{1}{2}x + c$, but $y = 4$ if $x = 2$, so $4 = -1 + c$ therefore $c = 5$.
Hence the equation of the line is $y = -\frac{1}{2}x + 5$.

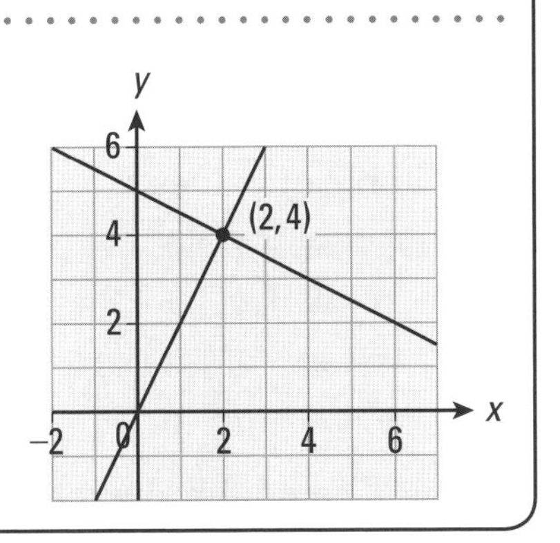

1 Copy and complete the table.

Equation of the line	Gradient of the line	Gradient of any line that is perpendicular to the given line
$y = 2x - 3$		
$y = \frac{1}{2}x + 2$		
$y = 4 - 3x$		
$y = 1 - \frac{1}{5}x$		

2 Find the equations for these lines.

a The line that is perpendicular to $y = 2x - 1$ and crosses it at (2, 3)
b The line that is perpendicular to $y = 3x - 2$ and crosses it at (3, 7)
c The line that is perpendicular to $y = -\frac{1}{4}x + 12$ and crosses it at (4, 11)
d The line that is perpendicular to $y = 8 - 2x$ and crosses it at (2, 4)
e The line that is perpendicular to $y = \frac{1}{3}x + 2$ and crosses it at (3, 3)
f The line that is perpendicular to $y = 6 - x$ and crosses it at (4, 2).

3 A triangle ABC is formed by joining A (3, 1), B (4, 5) and C (20, 1).

a Find the gradient of each side of the triangle.
b Is the triangle right angled?

8d Quadratic graphs

example

a Using values of x from -2 to 2, plot a graph of $y = x^2 - 1$.

b Find from your graph

i the minimum value of y

ii the equation of the symmetry axis of the curve.

a Table of values

x	=	-2	-1	0	1	2
x^2	=	4	1	0	1	4
-1	=	-1	-1	-1	-1	-1
y	=	3	0	-1	0	3

Symmetry axis $x = 0$
(y axis)

b i The minimum value of y is -1, when $x = 0$.

ii The equation of the symmetry axis is $x = 0$ (the y axis).

1 For equations **a** $y = x^2 - 2x$ and **b** $y = x^2 + 2x - 3$

i complete a table of values for $-4 \le x \le 2$ and draw a graph

ii use your graph to find the minimum value of y

iii use your graph to find the equation of the symmetry axis of the curve.

2 The rectangle illustrated has area A given by $A = x(4 - x)$ or $4x - x^2$.

a Calculate A for values of x from -1 to 5 and draw a graph.

b Find

i the maximum value of A

ii the value of x when A has its maximum value.

iii What do you notice about the rectangle when x has this maximum value?

8e Cubic graphs

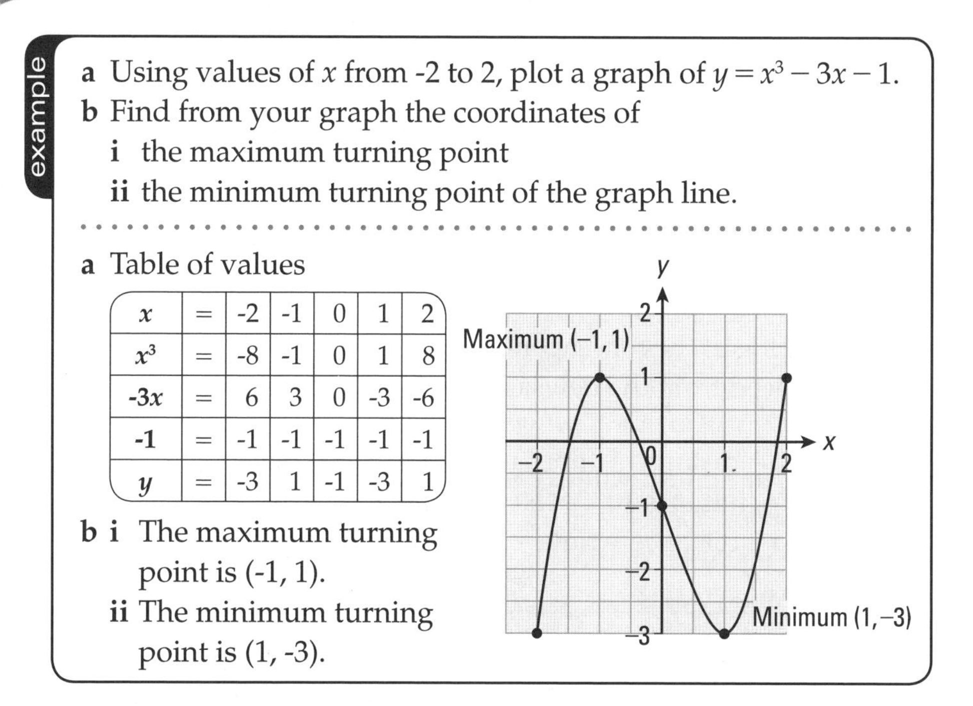

a Using values of x from -2 to 2, plot a graph of $y = x^3 - 3x - 1$.

b Find from your graph the coordinates of

i the maximum turning point

ii the minimum turning point of the graph line.

a Table of values

x	=	-2	-1	0	1	2
x^3	=	-8	-1	0	1	8
$-3x$	=	6	3	0	-3	-6
-1	=	-1	-1	-1	-1	-1
y	=	-3	1	-1	-3	1

b i The maximum turning point is (-1, 1).

ii The minimum turning point is (1, -3).

1 For equations **a** $y = x^3 - 12x$ and **b** $y = x^3 + 3x^2 - 9x$

i complete a table of values for $-5 \leq x \leq 3$ and draw a graph

ii use your graph to find the coordinates of the maximum and minimum turning points.

2 a Draw on your graph for part **a** in question **1** the line $y = x + 12$. Write down the coordinates of the three points where this line crosses the curve on your graph.

b Draw on your graph for part **b** in question **1** the line $y = x + 24$. Write down the coordinates of the three points where this line crosses the curve.

3 The volume (V) of a cuboid is given by $V = x^2(6 - x)$ or $6x^2 - x^3$.

a Calculate V for values of x from -2 to 6 and draw a graph.

b Find **i** the maximum value of V

ii the value of x when V has its maximum value.

8f Distance–time graphs

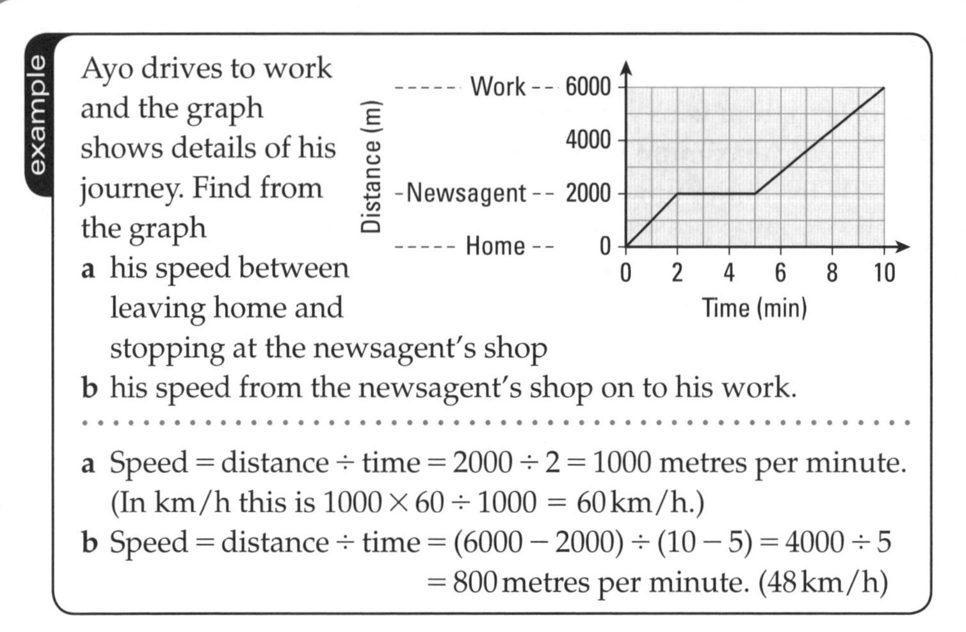

example

Ayo drives to work and the graph shows details of his journey. Find from the graph

a his speed between leaving home and stopping at the newsagent's shop

b his speed from the newsagent's shop on to his work.

a Speed = distance ÷ time = 2000 ÷ 2 = 1000 metres per minute.
(In km/h this is $1000 \times 60 \div 1000 = 60$ km/h.)

b Speed = distance ÷ time = (6000 − 2000) ÷ (10 − 5) = 4000 ÷ 5
= 800 metres per minute. (48 km/h)

1 Jainie walks with her daughter to school, having stopped at a shop on the way, and then walks back home. The graph shows details of the walk.

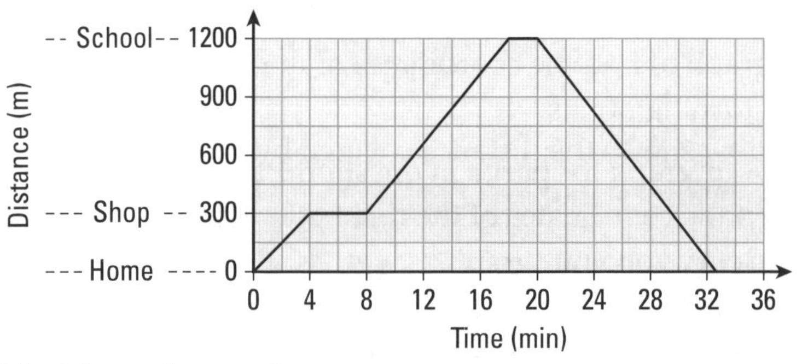

Find from the graph

a the distance from the shop where they stopped to the school.

b the time that they spent

i at the shop **ii** walking from the shop to the school.

c her walking speed (in metres per minute and km/h) when she walks from

i her home to the shop **ii** the shop to the school.

8g Real-life graphs

example

A digital clock is disconnected from the mains but the figures do not disappear immediately because there is a time delay circuit within the clock. The table, however, shows how the voltage does drop with time. Plot these details on a graph.
If the figures on the clock do go out when the voltage drops to 100 volts, find the time for which they are still visible.

Time (minutes)	0	10	20	30	40	50	60
Voltage	240	170	120	80	60	40	30

It can be seen from the graph that the voltage will drop to 100 volts after 25 minutes.

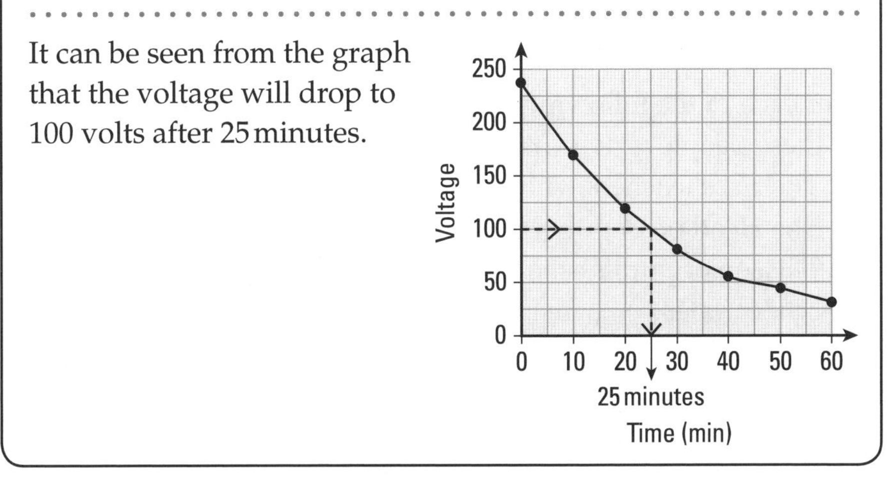

1 The table below shows the distance covered by a train travelling between two nearby stations.

Time (minutes)	0	1	2	3	4	5	6
Distance covered (km)	0	0.25	1	2	3	3.75	4

Plot these figures on a graph (distance against time). Find from your graph the time taken and the distance covered when the train
a reached a steady speed **b** had its brakes applied.

9a Prediction and uncertainty

example

Tnisha and Marcus are going on a long train journey. Tnisha says that they will have to take food for the journey, but Marcus thinks that they should have meals on the train. What are the advantages and disadvantages of their two ideas? Should they think about any outcome that may happen on the way?

Prepared food would be much cheaper but it can be inconvenient to carry it for a long way and it might not keep. One possible outcome is that a long delay may occur, so they should take money for food in case of that.

1 For each of the following, describe how big a problem it would be if these people arrived at school late.

- **a** The class teachers who call the registers
- **b** The Head or Deputy Head
- **c** The senior pupils who take the names of latecomers at the school gates.

2 How big a problem would it be if you planned to do these things and were delayed in getting there?

- **a** Play for your team in a football match
- **b** Referee a football match
- **c** Be a linesman at a football match
- **d** Watch a football match.

For questions 3 and 4 discuss the advantages and disadvantages of the options. Give details of any outcomes that could affect any option.

3 You need to get to an interview in central London. What are the benefits and risks involved in travelling by train or being driven by a parent?

4 A family are going on holiday to America: two parents, their two young children and two elderly grand parents. Health insurance costs £50 per person. Discuss who, if any one, should take out insurance.

9b Independent events

example

Jacob takes the penalties for his football team and the probability that he scores from one of his kicks is $\frac{2}{3}$. If he has to take two penalties in a match, what is the probability that he scores from the first one and fails from the second?

Assuming the events to be independent, the probability is $\frac{2}{3} \times \frac{1}{3} = \frac{2}{9}$

1 State, with reason(s), whether these pairs of events are independent or not.

a A person visiting a doctor is **i** suffering from headaches **ii** living under stress.

b A person visiting a doctor is **i** suffering from an ear infection **ii** a long distance runner.

c A fair dice is thrown and the score is **i** a prime number **ii** a factor of 7.

d Two fair dice are thrown together and the total score is **i** a triangular number **ii** a multiple of 4.

2 In Class 9A, $\frac{3}{5}$ of the pupils are boys, $\frac{2}{3}$ of all the pupils walk to school and all of the others cycle. Find the probability that a pupil picked at random

a is a boy who walks to school

b is a girl who cycles to school.

If there are 30 pupils in the class, find the actual numbers for parts **a** and **b**.

3 a If a fair dice is thrown find the probability that the score is

i a square number

ii a triangular number

iii a prime number.

b If a fair dice is thrown twice, find the probability that the outcome is

i a square number followed by a triangular number

ii a triangular number followed by a prime number.

Tree diagrams

example

Marlon has a choice of two routes to school and he may find any of the gates open or closed. Draw a tree diagram to show his possible outcomes. Show on your diagram paths through it which include only one open gate.

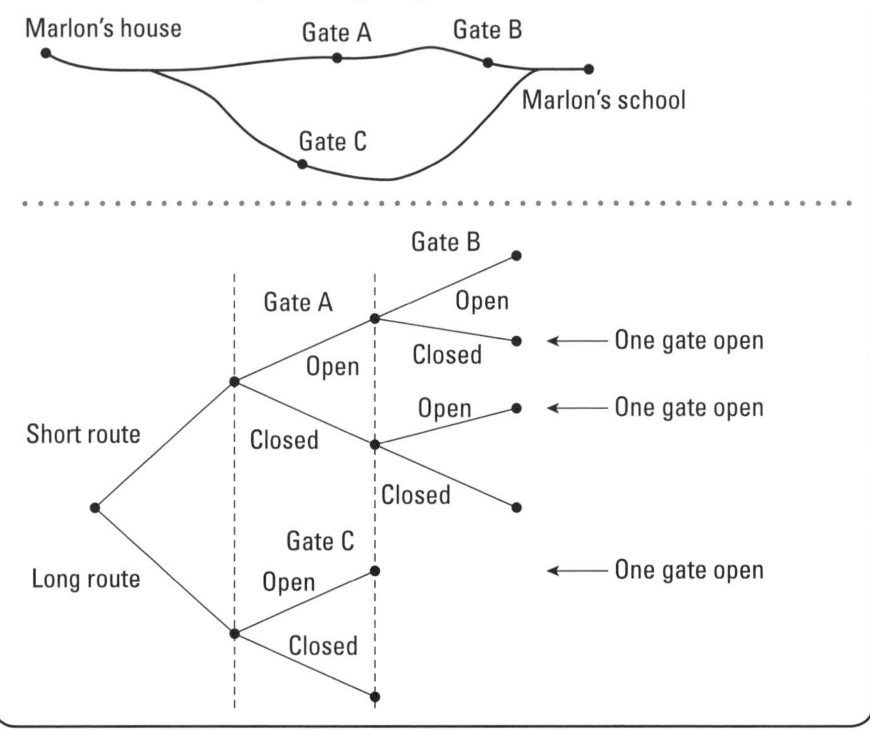

1 Eva travels home from work by train and her husband waits for her at the station with their car. Her train may be on time or late and her husband may be either waiting or late. Draw a tree diagram to show the four possible outcomes.

2 Martin drives to work. He passes three sets of traffic lights on the way and he may or may not be stopped at any of them. Draw a tree diagram to show the eight possible outcomes. Show on your diagram the paths which show that he is stopped

i once **ii** twice.

9d Probability of combined events

example

Wayne cycles to school and he passes a level crossing on the way. There is a probability of $\frac{1}{5}$ that he will find the gates closed. If the gates are closed there is a probability of $\frac{5}{6}$ that one train only will pass, otherwise two trains will pass. Draw a tree diagram to show the outcomes and find the probability that he is stopped for

i one train to pass **ii** two trains to pass.

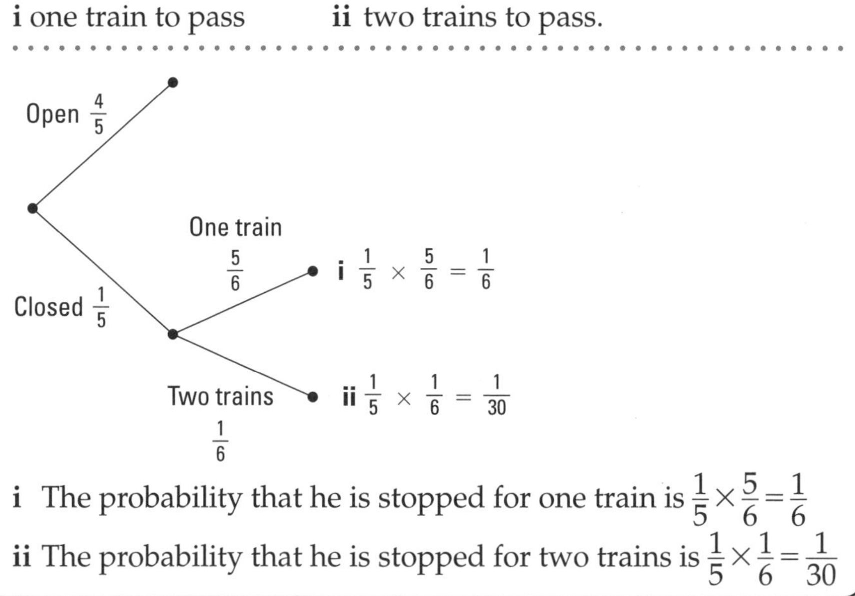

i The probability that he is stopped for one train is $\frac{1}{5} \times \frac{5}{6} = \frac{1}{6}$

ii The probability that he is stopped for two trains is $\frac{1}{5} \times \frac{1}{6} = \frac{1}{30}$

Questions **1** and **2** refer to the tree diagrams you drew for questions **1** and **2** in Homework 9c.

1 The probability that Eva's train is late is $\frac{1}{6}$ and the probability that her husband arrives late is $\frac{1}{4}$. Find the probability of all four outcomes.

2 The probabilities for Martin being stopped at each of the three sets of traffic lights are $\frac{4}{5}$, $\frac{3}{4}$ and $\frac{2}{3}$.

a Find the probability of all eight outcomes.

b What do you notice about the sum of the probabilities?

9e Experimental probability

example

Josiah takes the penalties for his football team. Last season there were six matches in which he had kicks to take. The table shows his record.

Number of kicks in the match	2	1	1	1	2	1
Number of successes	2	0	1	1	1	0

Find the probability that he scores from a penalty kick according to this record.

Total number of kicks $= 2 + 1 + 1 + 1 + 2 + 1 = 8$
Total number of successes $= 2 + 1 + 1 + 1 = 5$
Therefore his probability of scoring is $\frac{5}{8}$.

1 Ronnie takes the 'shot at goal' kicks for his rugby team and his record in a six-round cup contest is shown.

Number of shots	3	2	4	5	5	2
Number of goals	2	1	2	3	4	2

Find the probability that he scores from a kick according to this record.

2 Afiya throws a dice until she obtains a six. She repeats this 30 times. The numbers of throws required to obtain a six each time is shown.

4 8 5 6 4 7 6 5 6 7 6 9 7 6 5 5 8 9 6 5 5 5 7 6 7 4 8
9 10 6

Find the probability that she has to make

i 4 throws　　**ii** 6 throws
iii 9 throws　　**iv** 10 throws before she obtains a six.

9e² Simulations

example

Look at the queue history graphs in your Student's Book. The description tells you about how different they are, but can you see any similarities?

Yes, there is perhaps one. They all start off with zero people in the queue followed by a growth in queue length and then a shortening.

1 a Using the random number generator on your calculator simulate the arrivals and departures in a queue for 10 time steps and plot a graph of the queue length using the following probabilities.

i

	0	1	2	3	4
Arrivals	0.2	0.25	0.3	0.15	0.1
Departures	0.1	0.1	0.2	0.3	0.3

ii

	0	1	2	3	4
Arrivals	0.2	0.25	0.3	0.15	0.1
Departures	0.3	0.3	0.2	0.1	0.1

iii

	0	1	2	3	4
Arrivals	0.2	0.25	0.3	0.15	0.1
Departures	0.3	0.1	0.3	0.2	0.1

b Comment on any differences you notice between the three cases.

10a Transformations

example

State the translation that maps
a A onto B **b** B onto C
c C onto D.

a A reflection in the line $y = x$.
b A rotation of 180° about (0, 0).
c A translation of $\begin{pmatrix}10\\1\end{pmatrix}$
(10 units in the x direction and 1 unit in the y direction.)

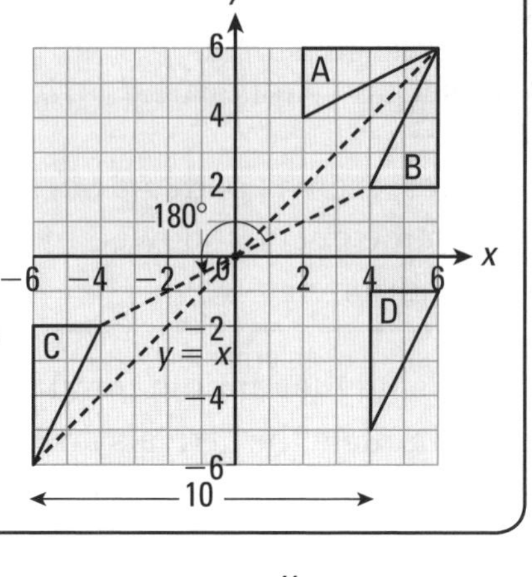

1 a Copy the diagram shown.
i Reflect A in the line $y = x$ and label the image B.
ii Reflect B in the x axis and label the image C.
iii Reflect C in the line $y = -x$ and label the image D.
iv Reflect D in the y axis and label the image E.
v Reflect E in the line $y = x$ and label the image F.
vi Reflect F in the x axis and label the image G.
vii Reflect G in the line $y = -x$ and label the image H.

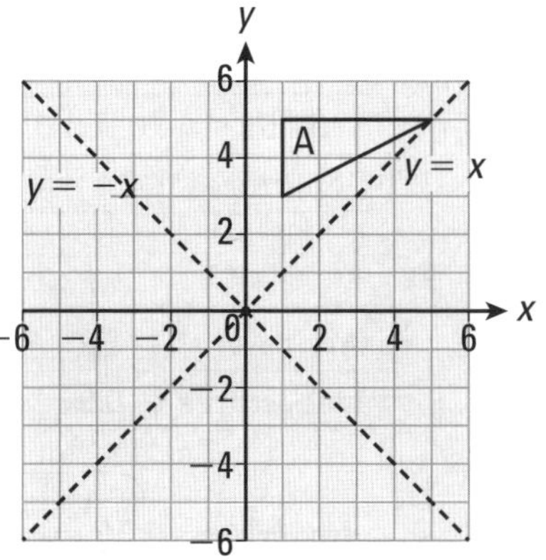

b What reflection maps A onto **i** D **ii** H **iii** F?
c What reflection maps C onto **i** F **ii** H?
d What is **i** A **ii** B **iii** C **iv** D mapped onto by a rotation of 180° about (0, 0)?
e What is **i** A **ii** G **iii** E **iv** C mapped onto by a 90° anticlockwise rotation about (0, 0)?
f What is **i** B **ii** D **iii** F **iv** H mapped onto by a 90° clockwise rotation about (0, 0)?

10b Enlargements 1

example

Copy the diagram shown. With respect to the centre of enlargement shown, draw on an enlargement of the reference figure with a scale factor of **a** 2 **b** $\frac{1}{2}$.

The diagram shows the two images in both size and position.

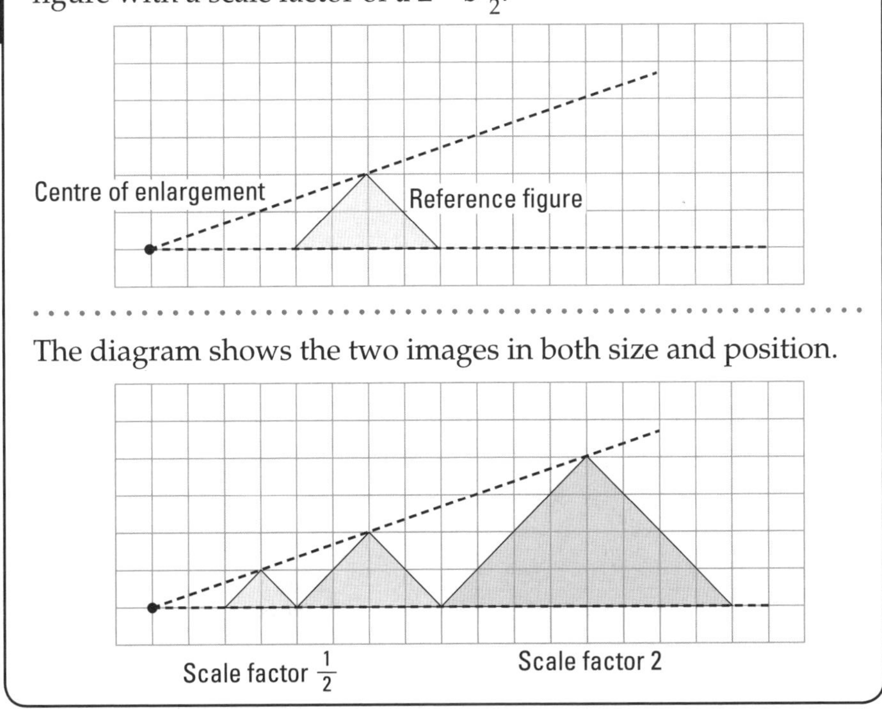

1 Copy the diagram and, with respect to the centre of enlargement shown, draw on an enlargement of the reference figure for each of the scale factors stated.

a 2

b $\frac{1}{2}$

c $\frac{1}{3}$

d $1\frac{1}{2}$

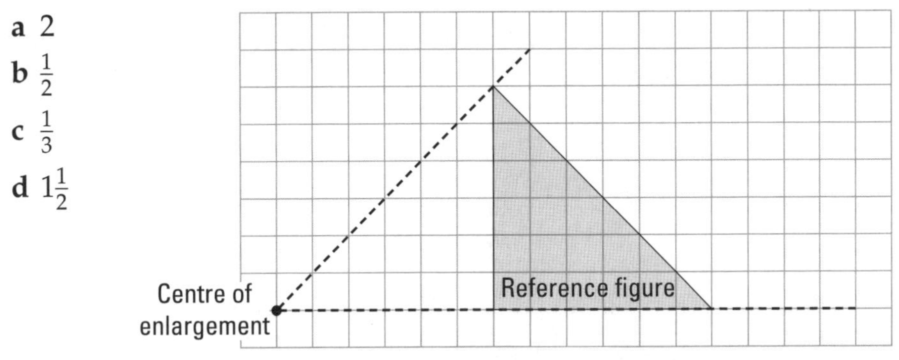

10c Enlargements 2

example

Copy the diagram shown. Mark on the centre of enlargement and state the scale factor with respect to the reference figure for the other two.

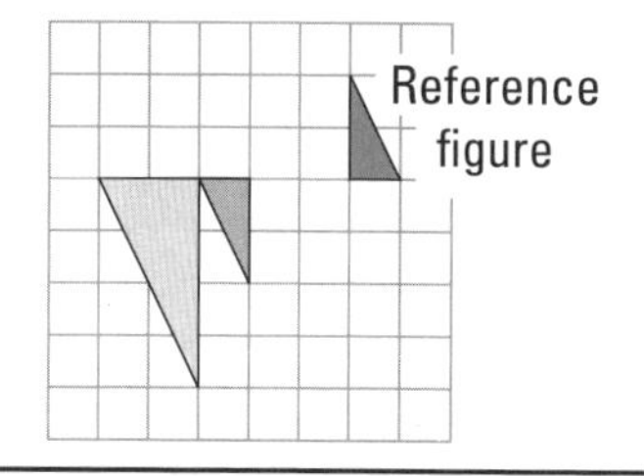

The centre of enlargement is shown. The scale factors of the other two figures are −2 and −1. (Note the negative signs because the figures are inverted.)

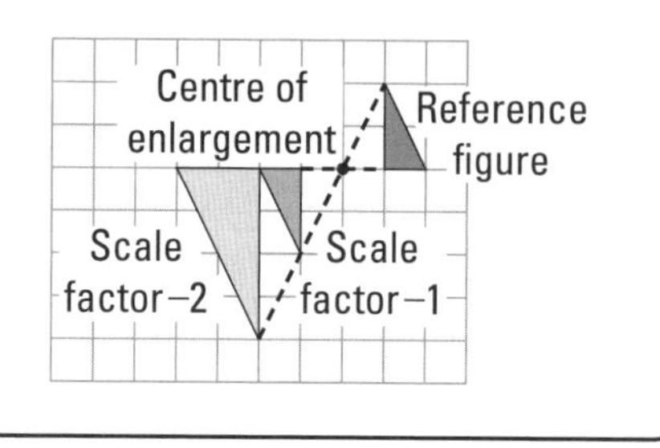

1 a Copy the given diagram and mark on the centre of enlargement.

b State the scale factors for each of the enlargements.

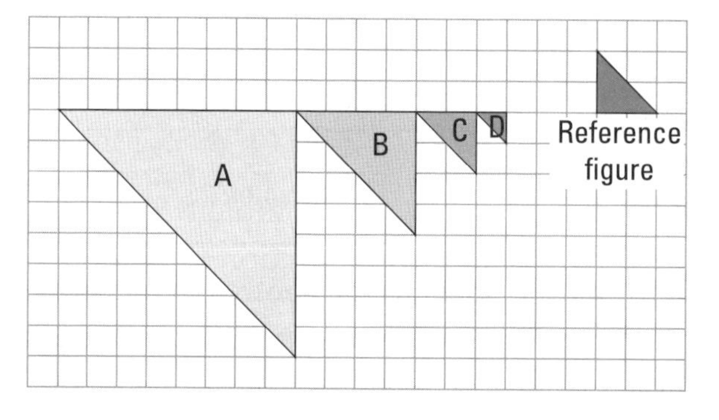

2 Copy the diagram and, with respect to the centre of enlargement shown, draw on an enlargement of the reference figure for each of the scale factors stated.

a -1 **b** -2

c -3 **d** $-\frac{1}{2}$

e $-1\frac{1}{2}$.

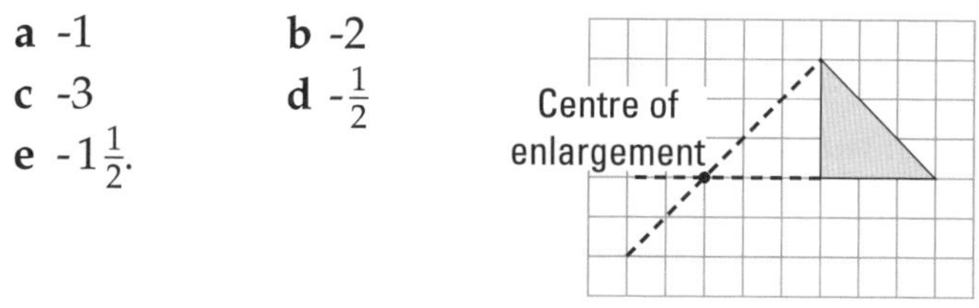

10d Maps and scale drawings

example

Zeke has a toy car of length 6 cm. If it is a model to a scale of 1 : 60, what is the length of its real counterpart?

The length of the real car = $6 \times 60 = 360$ cm or 3.6 m.

1 Zodia is going to build a dog's kennel. She has made a drawing of it to a scale of 1:5 and the dimensions on her drawing are length 18 cm, width 15 cm, wall height 10 cm and eves height 9 cm. What will be the dimensions of the real kennel when she has made it?

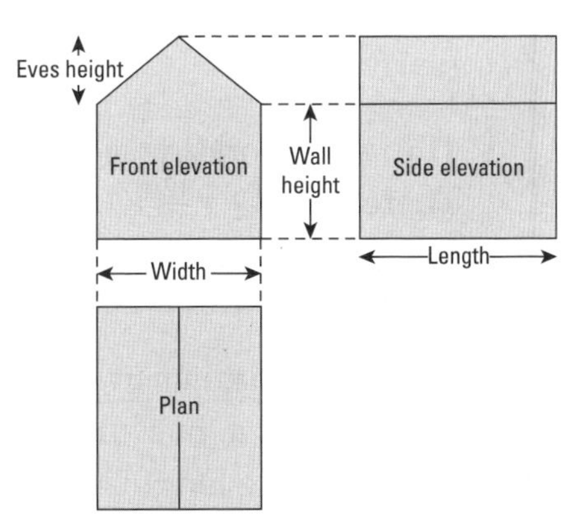

2 Josiah has built a garden hut and its dimensions are length 3 m, width 2.5 m, wall height 2.4 m and eves height 1 m. Before he built it he had made a drawing of it using a scale of 1 : 25. What were the dimensions on his drawing?

3 A map has a scale of 1 : 400 000. Copy and complete the table which shows details of the distance from London to 10 places.

Place	Distance on map	Real distance (km)	Place	Distance on map (cm)	Real distance
Southend	15 cm		Oxford		84 km
Biggleswade	18 cm		Guildford		48 km
Woking	10 cm		Hatfield		32 km
Watford	7 cm		Chelmsford		56 km
Waddesdon	17 cm		Dorking		36 km

4 Marcus has a model railway with a track gauge of 18 mm. If the standard Network Rail gauge is 144 cm, what is the scale of Marcus's model?

Similar shapes

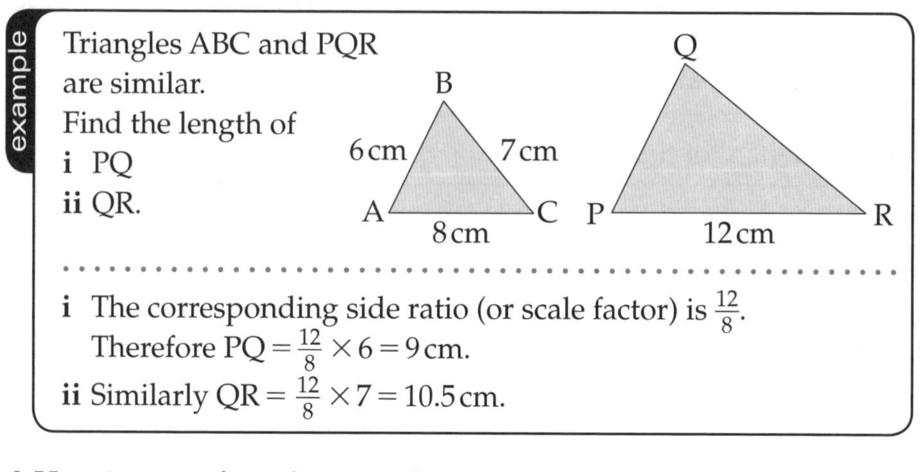

example

Triangles ABC and PQR are similar.
Find the length of
i PQ
ii QR.

i The corresponding side ratio (or scale factor) is $\frac{12}{8}$.
Therefore $PQ = \frac{12}{8} \times 6 = 9$ cm.
ii Similarly $QR = \frac{12}{8} \times 7 = 10.5$ cm.

1 Here is a set of similar triangles.
For the triangles **a**, **b**, **c** and **d**, find
i the missing side lengths **ii** the scale factor with respect to this reference triangle.

6 cm, 10 cm, 8 cm

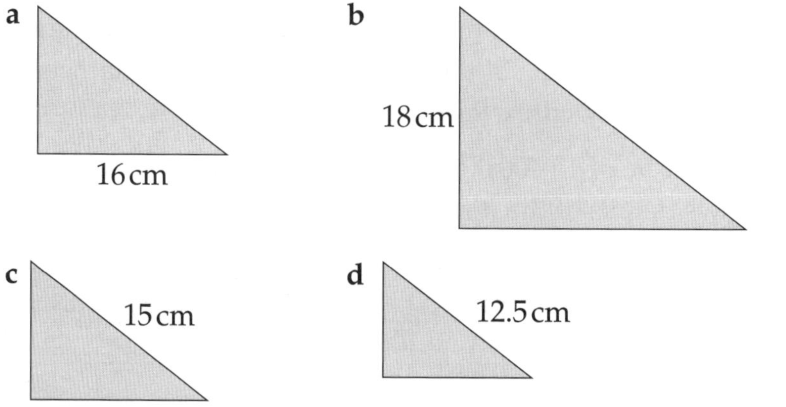

2 P and Q have the coordinates (2, 2) and (14, 18).
  a Find the coordinates of the midpoint of PQ.
  b Use Pythagoras' theorem to find the length of PQ.

3 The triangles in question **1** are right angled.
  a Find the area of all five triangles.
  b How are the areas related to the scale factors?

11a Index laws 1

example

Simplify $\frac{3x^3 \times 4x}{6x^2}$

$\frac{3x^3 \times 4x}{6x^2} = (3x^3 \times 4x) \div 6x^2 = 12x^4 \div 6x^2 = 2x^2$

(The indices are added for multiplication and subtracted for division.)

1 Evaluate these.

a 7^2 **b** 4^3 **c** 10^5 **d** 3^4 **e** 2^6

f $(-2)^4$ **g** $(-2)^3$ **h** $(-3)^3$ **i** $(-3)^2$ **j** $(-2)^5$

k $(-5)^2$ **l** $(-5)^3$ **m** $(-10)^3$ **n** $(-10)^2$ **o** $(-10)^6$

2 Simplify these expressions, leaving your answers in index form.

a $2^3 \times 2^5$ **b** $3^2 \times 3^4$ **c** $5^3 \times 5^6$ **d** $6^3 \times 6$

e $8^7 \div 8^2$ **f** $7^6 \div 7^3$ **g** $(2^4)^3$ **h** $(3^2)^4$

i $(x^3)^5$ **j** $(y^2)^4$ **k** $a^6 \div a^2$ **l** $b^9 \div b^4$

m $c^5 \div c$ **n** $d^3 \times d^2$ **o** $u^4 \times u^5$ **p** $v \times v^6$

3 Simplify these expressions, leaving your answers in index form.

a $3x^2 \times 4x^5$ **b** $6y^3 \times 5y^6$ **c** $24z^9 \div 6z^4$ **d** $35t^{10} \div 7t^7$

e $(3u^3)^2$ **f** $(2v^4)^3$ **g** $8p^3 \times 3p^2 \times 2p^4$ **h** $3q^5 \times 2q^3 \times 5q^4$

i $6r^3 \times 5r^2 \times 4r$ **j** $\frac{8m^2 \times 3m^4}{6m^3}$ **k** $\frac{12n^3 \times 2n^2}{8n^4}$

4 Write a simplified expression for the area of these two figures. If they both have the same area find the value of x.

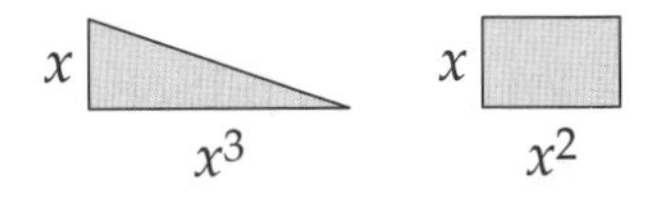

5 Write a simplified expression for the volume of these two solids. If they both have the same volume find the value of y.

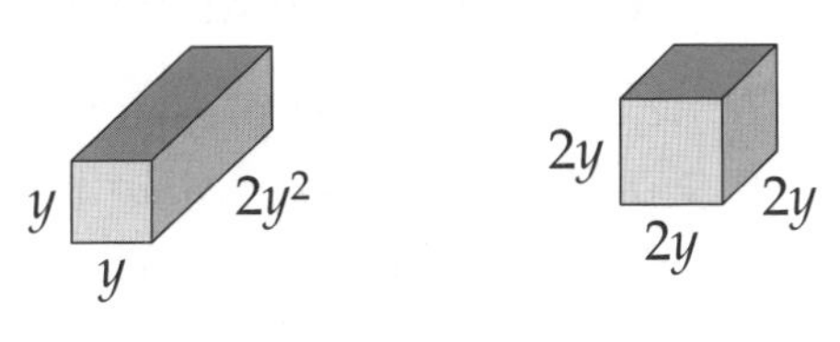

11b Index laws 2

example

Simplify $\dfrac{a^{-\frac{3}{4}} \times a^{-1}}{a^{\frac{1}{4}}}$

$\dfrac{a^{-\frac{3}{4}} \times a^{-1}}{a^{\frac{1}{4}}} = a^{-1\frac{3}{4}} \div a^{\frac{1}{4}} = a^{-1\frac{3}{4}-\frac{1}{4}} = a^{-2}$

(The indices are added for multiplication and subtracted for division.)

1 Evaluate these.

a $16^{\frac{1}{2}}$ **b** $36^{\frac{1}{2}}$ **c** $25^{\frac{1}{2}}$ **d** $27^{\frac{1}{3}}$ **e** $125^{\frac{1}{3}}$

f $64^{\frac{1}{3}}$ **g** 2^{-2} **h** 2^{-3} **i** 5^{-3} **j** 5^{-2}

k 8^{-2} **l** 8^{-1} **m** 10^{-1} **n** 10^{-3} **o** 10^{-4}

2 Simplify these expressions, leaving your answer in index form.

a $2^6 \times 2^{-2}$ **b** $6^5 \times 6^{-3}$ **c** $5^3 \times 5^{-7}$ **d** $8^2 \times 8^{-5}$ **e** $(3^2)^{-4}$

f $(2^3)^{-5}$ **g** $(2^{-2})^4$ **h** $(4^{-5})^2$ **i** $(x^{-3})^2$ **j** $(y^4)^{-2}$

k $z^5 \times z^{-2}$ **l** $t^4 \times t^{-7}$ **m** $u^2 \div u^{-5}$ **n** $v^4 \div v^{-6}$ **o** $w \div w^{-5}$

3 Simplify these expressions, leaving your answer in index form.

a $8^{\frac{1}{2}} \times 8^{\frac{3}{2}}$ **b** $7^{\frac{1}{3}} \times 7^{\frac{5}{3}}$ **c** $4^{\frac{2}{3}} \times 4^{-\frac{1}{3}}$ **d** $5^{\frac{4}{3}} \times 5^{-\frac{2}{3}}$

e $2^{\frac{1}{3}} \times 2^{-\frac{2}{3}}$ **f** $6^{\frac{1}{4}} \times 6^{-\frac{3}{4}}$ **g** $(2^2)^{\frac{1}{4}}$ **h** $(x^3)^{\frac{1}{4}}$

i $(y^2)^{-\frac{1}{3}}$ **j** $(z^{-1})^{-\frac{1}{2}}$ **k** $t^{-1} \times t^{-\frac{1}{2}}$ **l** $u^{-2} \times u^{\frac{3}{2}}$

m $v^{\frac{3}{2}} \times v^{-\frac{1}{2}}$ **n** $p^{-1} \div p^{-\frac{1}{2}}$ **o** $q^{\frac{1}{2}} \div q^{-\frac{1}{2}}$ **p** $r \div r^{-\frac{1}{3}}$

4 Write a simplified expression for the area of these two figures. If they both have the same area find the value of x.

5 Write a simplified expression for the area of these two figures. If they both have the same area find the value of y.

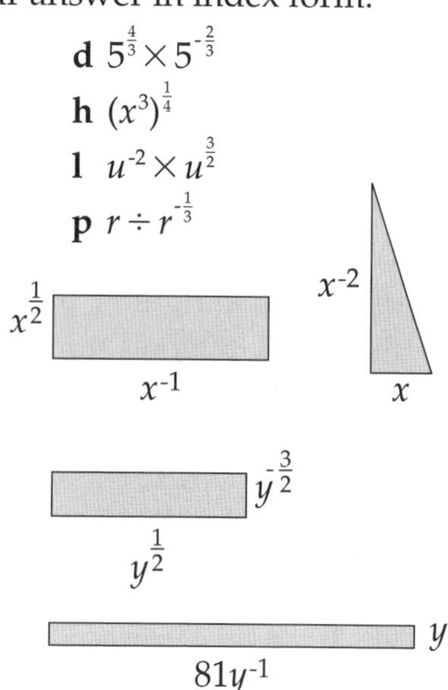

11c Multiplying linear expressions

example

Expand and simplify this expression: $(x+1)(x-7)$

$(x+1)(x-7) = x(x-7) + 1(x-7) = x^2 - 7x + x - 7 = x^2 - 6x - 7$

For questions **1**, **2**, **3** and **4**, expand and simplify each expression.

1 **a** $(x+5)(x+3)$ **b** $(y+7)(y+4)$ **c** $(z+6)(z+2)$ **d** $(t+7)(t+1)$
e $(u+4)(u+9)$ **f** $(v+3)(v+8)$ **g** $(w+1)(w+10)$ **h** $(m+7)^2$
i $(n+4)^2$ **j** $(p+1)^2$

2 **a** $(x-4)(x-3)$ **b** $(y-5)(y-4)$ **c** $(z-3)(z-2)$ **d** $(p-5)(p-1)$
e $(q-5)(q-7)$ **f** $(r-4)(r-6)$ **g** $(u-1)(u-9)$ **h** $(v-3)^2$
i $(w-10)^2$ **j** $(m-12)^2$

3 **a** $(x+5)(x-3)$ **b** $(y+9)(y-2)$ **c** $(z+7)(z-4)$ **d** $(t+5)(t-1)$
e $(p+6)(p-5)$ **f** $(q+2)(q-8)$ **g** $(r+3)(r-7)$ **h** $(s+1)(s-10)$
i $(u+4)(u-4)$ **j** $(v+9)(v-9)$

4 **a** $(x+3)(x+2)+(x+5)(x+1)$ **b** $(y-2)(y-4)+(y-1)(y-3)$
c $(z-1)(z-5)-(z-4)(z-3)$ **d** $(t+3)(t+2)-(t+1)(t+4)$
e $(u+5)(u-3)+(u-1)(u+2)$ **f** $(v+2)(v-5)+(v-4)(v+1)$
g $(p+1)(p-3)-(p-5)(p+2)$ **h** $(q+4)(q-1)-(q-6)(q+1)$

In questions **5**, **6** and **7**, two figures with the same area are illustrated. Find

i an expression for the area for both figures
ii the value of the letter.

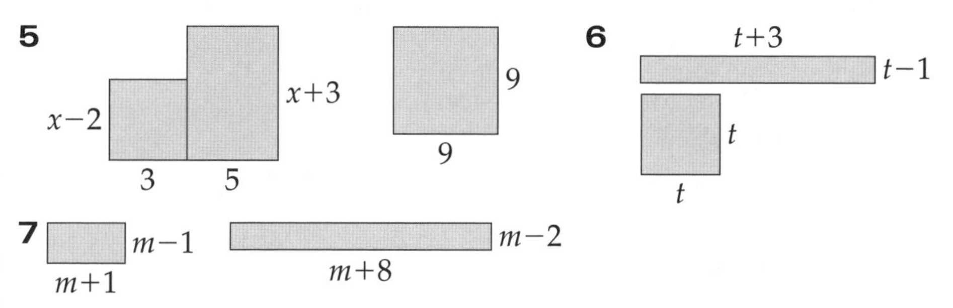

11c² Factorising expressions

example

Factorise $4x^2 - 36xy$.

$4x^2 - 36xy = 4x(x - 9y)$
(4x is the highest common factor of both terms.)

For questions **1** to **5**, fully factorise each expression.

1 **a** $3x + 15$ **b** $5y + 20$ **c** $4z - 12$ **d** $6t - 18$
e $8u - 40$ **f** $7v - 42$ **g** $9w - 36$ **h** $12p - 60$

2 **a** $4xy + 3x$ **b** $5uv + 8v$ **c** $2pq - 5q$ **d** $7mn - 4m$ **e** $8rs - r$
f $tu - 5t$ **g** $3xyz - 5xy$ **h** $2pqr + 7qr$ **i** $4tuv + 3tv$ **j** $5abc - ab$

3 **a** $6xy + 9x$ **b** $15uv + 10v$ **c** $16pq - 12q$ **d** $21mn - 14m$
e $18rs - 9r$ **f** $5yz - 20y$ **g** $6tu - 6u$ **h** $8qrs + 24qr$
i $18xyz + 12xy + 24xz$ **j** $15tuv + 10tu - 5uv$

4 **a** $x^2 + 5x$ **b** $y^2 + 9y$ **c** $3z^2 + 4z$ **d** $9u^2 + 12u$
e $10v^2 - 25v$ **f** $12t^2 - 18st$ **g** $27xy - 18y^2$ **h** $30uv + 20u^2$
i $10abc + 15ab^2 + 20ac^2$ **j** $8xyz + 12xy^2 - 4yz^2$

5 **a** $x^2 - 64$ **b** $y^2 - 36$ **c** $z^2 - 121$ **d** $t^2 - 144$
e $4u^2 - 49$ **f** $4v^2 - 81$ **g** $9p^2 - 25$ **h** $9q^2 - 100$
i $16r^2 - 9$ **j** $16r^2 - 1$ **k** $x^2 - y^2$ **l** $4x^2 - 9y^2$

6 **a** The volume of the cuboid illustrated is $(4x^2 - 36y^2)\,\text{cm}^3$. Find the missing side lengths.
b Find the volume of the cuboid if $x = 4\,\text{cm}$ and $y = 1\,\text{cm}$.

4 cm

7 **a** Find a fully factorised expression for the perimeter of the triangle illustrated.
b If $m = 2$ and $n = 1$, find
i the perimeter
ii the area of the triangle.

$2mn$ cm
(m^2+n^2) cm
(m^2-n^2) cm

11d Identities

example

Show that $7x + 3(x + 10)$ is identical to $10(x + 3)$.

$7x + 3(x + 10) = 7x + 3x + 30 = 10x + 30 = 10(x + 3)$

The two expressions are therefore equal to each other for all values of x.

1 Find the value of the required variable in each of these formula.

a $A = lb$ — Find A if $l = 10.5$ and $b = 4$

b $P = 2a + b$ — Find P if $a = 4.5$ and $b = 6$

c $A = \pi r^2$ — Find A if $\pi = 3.14$ and $r = 15$

d $v = u + at$ — Find v if $u = 5$, $a = 10$ and $t = 0.4$

e $A = \frac{1}{2}h(a + b)$ — Find A if $h = 12$, $a = 13$ and $b = 7.5$

f $V = \frac{4}{3}\pi r^3$ — Find V if $\pi = 3.14$ and $r = 6$.

2 Solve these equations. Find which part **i, ii** or **iii** has a different answer from the other two.

a **i** $4x + 7 = 31$ **ii** $3(x + 9) = 42$ **iii** $12x - 17 = 43$

b **i** $42 - 5y = 27$ **ii** $8(10 - y) = 56$ **iii** $5(16 - y) = 60$

c **i** $8z - 3 = 2z + 21$ **ii** $9z - 40 = 3z - 10$ **iii** $12z + 5 = 3z + 41$

d **i** $9(t - 5) = 5(t + 3)$ **ii** $11(t - 7) = 8(t - 4)$ **iii** $5(t + 2) = 2(t + 23)$

3 Prove that these are identities.

a $12(x + 13) \equiv 12x + 156$

b $9(y - 15) \equiv 9y - 135$

c $3(z + 11) + 4(z - 3) \equiv 7(z + 3)$

d $7(t + 8) + 3(t + 18) \equiv 10(t + 11)$

e $3(u - 5) + 5(u - 21) \equiv 8(u - 15)$

f $12(v - 3) - 7(v + 2) \equiv 5(v - 10)$

g $15(m - 3) - 8(m - 10) \equiv 7(m + 5)$

h $20(n + 5) - 17(n + 2) \equiv 3(n + 22)$

For questions **4** and **5**, check whether the pair of figures illustrated have the same area for all values of x.

4

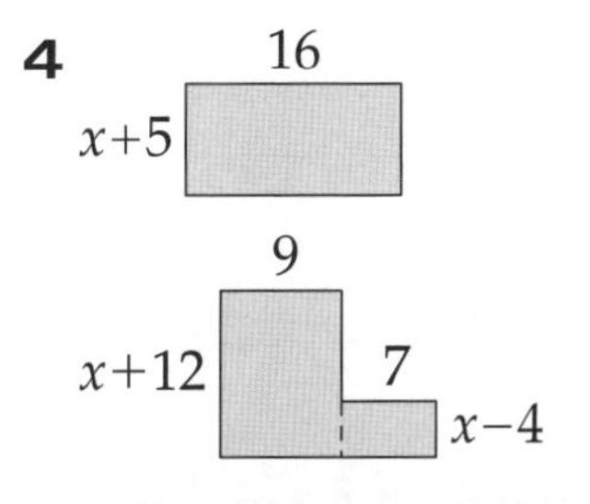

5

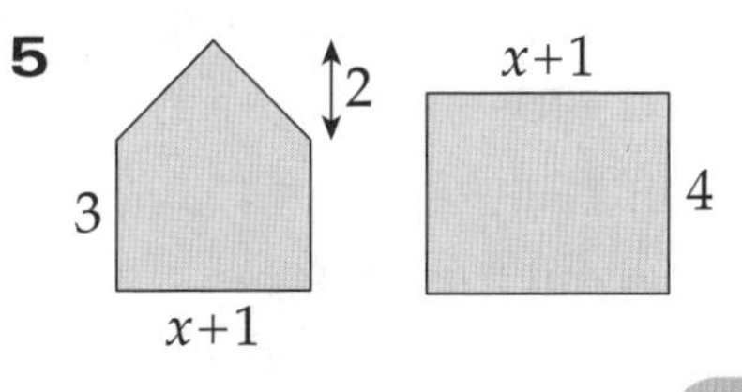

11e Formulae

Use the formula $V = \pi r^2 l$ to find the volume of the cylinder. ($\pi = 3.14$)

$V = 3.14r^2l = 3.14 \times 2^2 \times 5 = 62.8\,\text{cm}^3$

1 Use the formula $S = bh + l(b + h + s)$ to find the surface area of these triangular prisms.

a $b = 4\,\text{cm}$, $h = 3\,\text{cm}$, $s = 5\,\text{cm}$, $l = 10\,\text{cm}$.

b $b = 12\,\text{cm}$, $h = 5\,\text{cm}$, $s = 13\,\text{cm}$, $l = 20\,\text{cm}$.

c $b = 15\,\text{cm}$, $h = 8\,\text{cm}$, $s = 17\,\text{cm}$, $l = 30\,\text{cm}$.

d $b = 21\,\text{mm}$, $h = 20\,\text{mm}$, $s = 29\,\text{mm}$, $l = 40\,\text{mm}$.

2 a Use the formula $S = 2\pi r(r + l)$ to find the surface area of these cylinders.

i $r = 5\,\text{cm}$, $l = 10\,\text{cm}$ **ii** $r = 10\,\text{cm}$, $l = 30\,\text{cm}$

iii $r = 20\,\text{mm}$, $l = 40\,\text{mm}$ **iv** $r = 15\,\text{cm}$, $l = 5\,\text{cm}$

v $r = 0.2\,\text{m}$, $l = 0.5\,\text{m}$

b Use the formula $V = \pi r^2 l$ to find the volume of the same cylinders ($\pi = 3.14$).

3 A square pond of side length 6 cm has concrete paths of width x cm on two sides of it. Show that the total area of the concrete paths is $(x^2 + 12x)\,\text{m}^2$. Find this area if $x = 2\,\text{m}$.

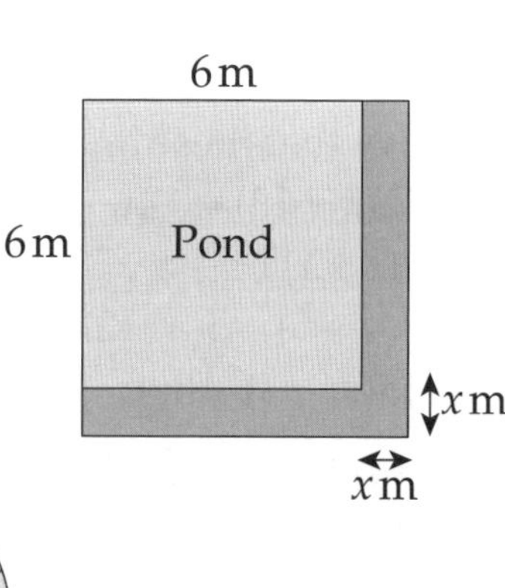

4 A square lawn is surrounded by shingle paths as shown.

a Show that the total area of the shingle paths is $25(\pi - 2)\,\text{m}^2$.

b Using $\pi = 3.14$, work out this area.

11f Changing the subject of a formula

example

Make a the subject of $3(a+b)=c$.

$3(a+b)=c$, therefore $3a+3b=c$, so $3a=c-3b$, hence $a=\frac{c}{3}-b$.

1 Make x the subject of these equations.

a $x+a=b$ **b** $x-m=n$ **c** $x+3p=5p$ **d** $x-2q=6q$
e $x+a=b+c$ **f** $x+m=n-p$ **g** $x-t=u+v$ **h** $x-a=b-c$

2 Make y the subject of these equations.

a $py=q$ **b** $\frac{y}{a}=b$ **c** $my=n+p$ **d** $py=q-r$
e $ay+b=c$ **f** $my-n=p$ **g** $\frac{y}{a}+b=c$ **h** $\frac{y}{m}-n=p$
i $y(a+b)=c$ **j** $y(m-n)=p$ **k** $y(a+b)=c$ **l** $y(p-q)=r$

3 Make a the subject of these equations.

a $p=q(a-b)$ **b** $m=n(a+b)$ **c** $5(a+m)=n$
d $4(a-b)=c$ **e** $180(a-2)=S$ **f** $\frac{1}{3}(a+b+c)=d$
g $2(a-b+c)=m$ **h** $4(a-b-c)=n$ **i** $6(a+b-c)=p$

4 a The formula $v=u+at$ connects the variables, initial velocity (u), final velocity (v), acceleration (a) and time (t). Make t the subject of the formula.

b If a car travelling at 5 m/s accelerates at a rate of $1.25\,\text{m/s}^2$ to 30 m/s, how long will it take to do so?

5 a The formula $V=v\left(1+\frac{t}{273}\right)$ connects the variables, volume (V) of a gas at fixed pressure and temperature (t°C) and its volume at 0°C (v). Make t the subject of the formula.

b Find the temperature if V equals

i $\frac{4v}{3}$ **ii** $\frac{8v}{7}$.

6 The surface area of a cuboid is given by the formula $S=2x^2+4xy$. Make y the subject of the formula to find y if $S=170\text{ cm}^2$ and $x=5$ cm.

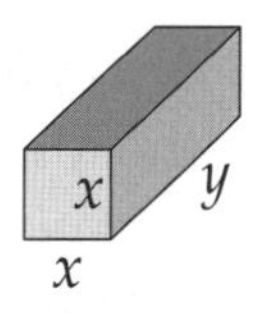

11g Further changing the subject of a formula

example

Make x the subject of $7 - \sqrt{x} = y$.

$7 - \sqrt{x} = y$, therefore $7 - y = \sqrt{x}$, so $(7 - y)^2 = x$, or $x = (7 - y)^2$

1 Make x the subject of these equations.

a $m = n - x$ **b** $p = qr - x$ **c** $u^2 = c - x$ **d** $a = b - 3x$

e $c = d - 8x$ **f** $p = q(r - x)$ **g** $m = \frac{1}{n}(p - x)$ **h** $t = \frac{u}{v}(w - x)$

i $a = \frac{bc}{d}(e - x)$ **j** $p = \frac{q}{rs}(t - x)$

2 Make y the subject of these equations.

a $\frac{p}{y} = q$ **b** $\frac{a}{y} = \frac{b}{c}$ **c** $\frac{m}{ny} = p$ **d** $\frac{tu}{vy} = w$

e $\frac{a}{y} - b = c$ **f** $\frac{a}{y} + b = c$ **g** $m = n - \frac{p}{y}$ **h** $ab = c - \frac{d}{y}$

i $p = \frac{q}{y + r}$ **j** $a = \frac{b}{y - c}$ **k** $t = \frac{u}{v - y}$ **l** $a = \frac{bc}{d - y}$

3 Make p the subject of these equations.

a $p^2 = a$ **b** $p^2 + b = c$ **c** $p^2 - d = e$ **d** $up^2 = v$

e $m - p^2 = n$ **f** $u - p^2 = -v$ **g** $\sqrt{p} = a$ **h** $\sqrt{p} + b = c$

i $\sqrt{p} - 3 = q$ **j** $r = 5 - \sqrt{p}$ **k** $a = b - \sqrt{p}$

4 Make x the subject of these equations.

a $6x + a = 2x + b$ **b** $8x - c = 3x + d$

c $10x - m = 7x - n$ **d** $12x + p = 7x - q$

5 a The power in watts of an electrical appliance (P), the voltage (V) and the current drawn (I amps) are related by the formula $P = VI$. Make I the subject of this formula.

b The mains voltage is 240 volts. Find the current drawn by

i a light bulb of power 120 watts **ii** a heater of power 960 watts

6 a The length of the unequal side of an isosceles triangle is given by the formula $x = P - 2l$, where P is the perimeter. Make l the subject of this formula.

b Find l for $P = 15$ cm and $x = 3$ cm.

l l x

12a Interpreting graphs

example

Three coins were tossed together 40 times over and the table shows the results. Draw a histogram and a frequency polygon of the results and comment on the shape of the distribution.

Number of heads	0	1	2	3
Frequency	6	14	16	4

The distribution is nearly symmetric. An axis of symmetry could nearly be drawn down its centre.

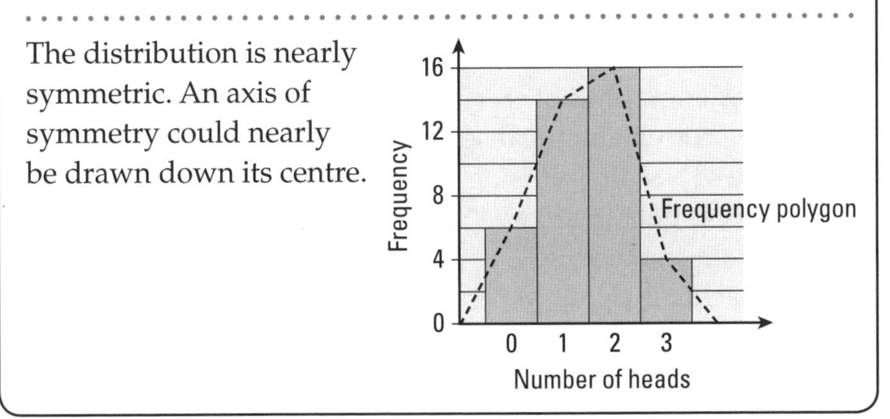

For questions **1** and **2**, draw a histogram and a frequency polygon of the details and comment on the shape of the distribution.

1 The table shows details of the heights of the students in Class 9B.

Height range (cm)	$140 < h \le 145$	$145 < h \le 150$	$150 < h \le 155$	$155 < h \le 160$	$160 < h \le 165$
Number of students	5	7	4	3	1

2 The table shows details of the masses of the students in Class 9B.

Mass range (kg)	$35 < m \le 40$	$40 < m \le 45$	$45 < m \le 50$	$50 < m \le 55$	$55 < m \le 60$
Number of students	2	2	5	7	4

Correlation

example

A headteacher thinks that more students arrive late as the week goes on. Here are some data that he collected one week. Plot his data on a scatter graph and comment on the correlation. Do the data suggest that the headteacher is right?

Day	Mon	Tues	Wed	Thurs	Fri
Number late	21	25	17	28	25

The scatter graph shows positive correlation because the line of best fit is a rising line. These data therefore might suggest that the headteacher is right. (More data would be needed to confirm.)

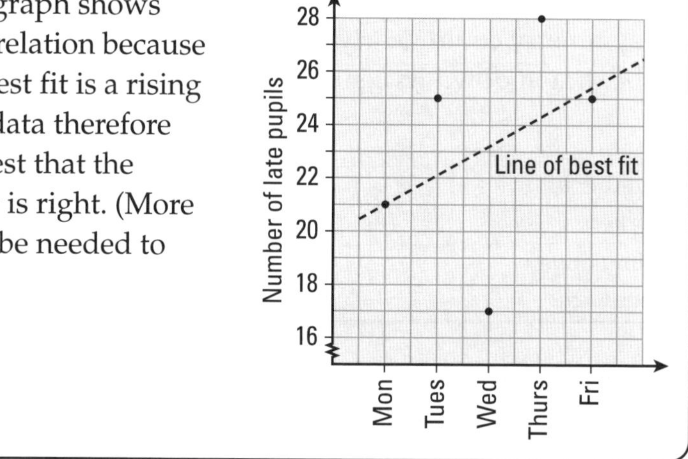

1 Zoey thinks that as the summer goes on the weather actually improves To test her claim she collects rainfall details for where she lives over a 15-week period from the start of June to mid-September.
Plot the data on a scatter graph and comment on the correlation. State whether or not Zoey's claim appears to be correct. Mention any other details that you think would help in checking the conclusion further and why.

Week number	1	2	3	4	5	6	7	8	9	10	11	12	13	14	15
Average rainfall (cm)	14	13	14	11	10	13	11	12	15	10	9	8	12	9	7

12c Cumulative frequency

For questions **1** and **2**

a copy and complete the table and draw a cumulative frequency graph. (In question 1, the graph is started for you.)

b find from your graph

i the median **ii** the upper and lower quartiles

iii the interquartile range for the distribution.

1 The table shows details of how far the 24 workers at a London office have to travel to work.

	Distance travelled (km)								
	$0 < d \leq 10$	$10 < d \leq 20$	$20 < d \leq 30$	$30 < d \leq 40$	$40 < d \leq 50$	$50 < d \leq 60$	$60 < d \leq 70$	$70 < d \leq 80$	$80 < d \leq 90$
Number of workers	1	1	2	2	6	6	4	1	1
Cumulative frequency	1	2							

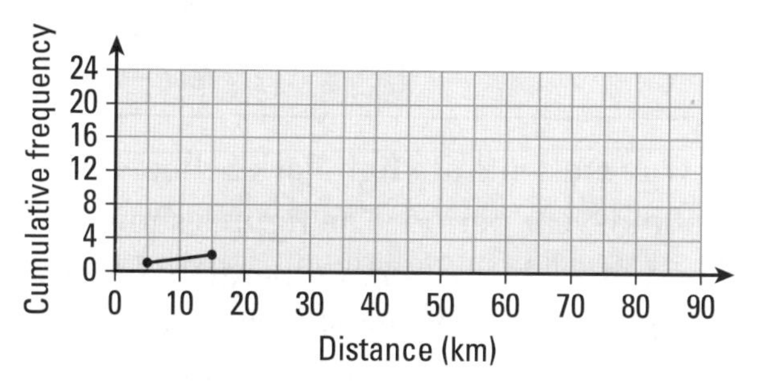

2 The table shows the ages of the 20 girls who play for a hockey club.

	Age (years)								
	$15 \leq a < 16$	$16 \leq a < 17$	$17 \leq a < 18$	$18 \leq a < 19$	$19 \leq a < 20$	$20 \leq a < 21$	$21 \leq a < 22$	$22 \leq a < 23$	$23 \leq a < 24$
Number of girls	1	1	3	5	5	2	1	1	1
Cumulative frequency									

12d Analysing data

example

A post office supervisor thinks that letter mail is a declining business. In order to check her idea she has recorded the average number of letters per day that her office has delivered over a four-year period. Plot her figures on a graph and comment on the trend. Can you explain the trend?

Year	2005	2006	2007	2008
Average number of letters per day	300	320	270	260

There is, as the supervisor says, a downward trend. It is probably due to increased use of e-mails and cheaper telephone charges.

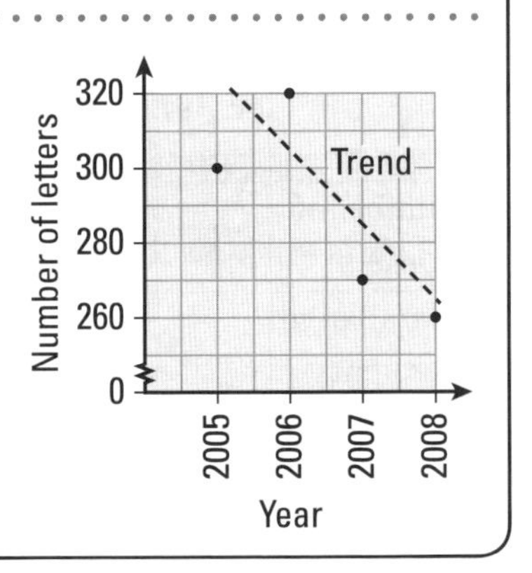

1 Details are shown of the way students at High Park School have travelled to school over a four-year period. The figures shown are percentages of the total and the data are given separately for boys and girls. Draw two graphs, similar to the ones in the example in your Student Book, to show these data. Can you explain the trends? Can you see any obvious differences between how the boys and the girls travel? If so, explain your answer.

	Boys				Girls			
	2005	2006	2007	2008	2005	2006	2007	2008
Walk	25	25	30	40	15	20	25	30
Cycle	20	25	25	35	25	20	25	40
Driven by car	35	35	20	10	40	45	25	20
Bus	20	15	25	15	20	15	25	10

12e Comparing distributions

example

The games teacher at Holly Hill School records the performances of Louis and Jacob, his best two long jumpers. The results for ten jumps each are shown. Comment on the differences between their performances.

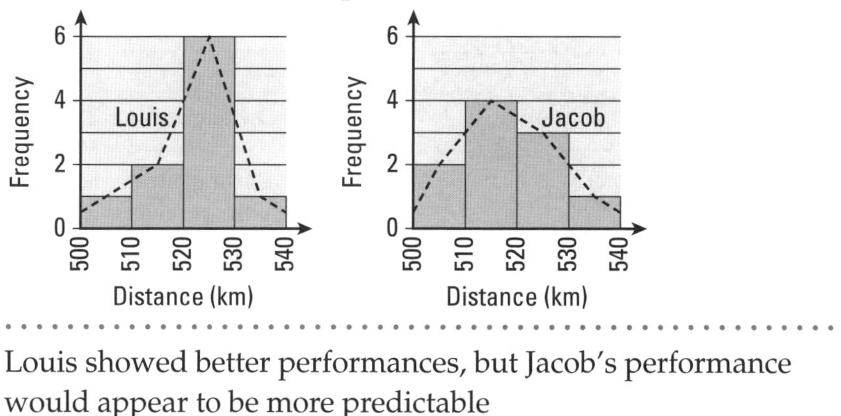

Louis showed better performances, but Jacob's performance would appear to be more predictable

1 a The table shows the mass distributions for the boys and girls in Class 9C. Draw a histogram and frequency polygon for both and comment on any differences that you notice between the two distributions.

	Mass range (kg)							
	$30 < m \le 35$	$35 < m \le 40$	$40 < m \le 45$	$45 < m \le 50$	$50 < m \le 55$	$55 < m \le 60$	$60 < m \le 65$	$65 < m \le 70$
No. of boys	0	0	3	4	6	2	0	0
No. of girls	1	1	2	2	3	3	2	1

b Repeat part **a** for the height distributions for the boys and girls in Class 9C.

	Height range (cm)					
	$145 < h \le 150$	$150 < h \le 155$	$155 < h \le 160$	$160 < h \le 165$	$165 < h \le 170$	$170 < h \le 175$
Number of boys	1	1	2	3	5	3
Number of girls	2	2	5	3	2	1

12e² Box plots

The masses of eight children were collected. The data were grouped and a cumulative frequency graph was drawn.

a From the graph, find **i** the median **ii** the upper and lower quartiles **iii** the interquartile range for the distribution.

b Show the distribution on a box plot.

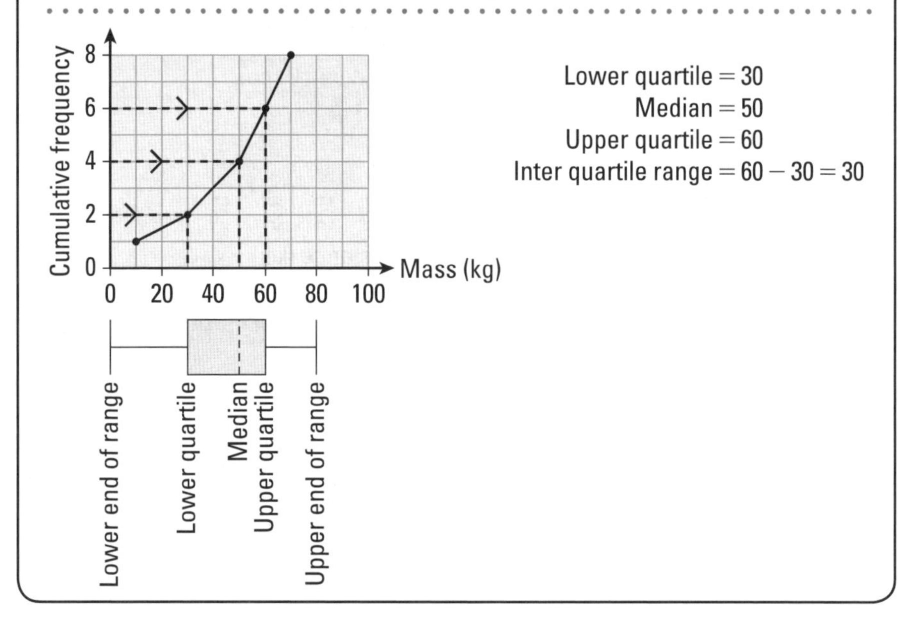

1 The table shows details of the masses of sixteen dogs that were staying at a boarding kennels.

a Copy and complete the table and draw a cumulative frequency graph.

b Find from your graph **i** the median **ii** the upper and lower quartiles **iii** the interquartile range.

c Show your answers to part **b** on a box plot.

	Mass range (kg)						
	$0 < m \le 10$	$10 < m \le 20$	$20 < m \le 30$	$30 < m \le 40$	$40 < m \le 50$	$50 < m \le 60$	$60 < m \le 70$
Number of dogs	1	2	2	3	3	2	3
Cumulative frequency							

12f Examining statistical results

example

An excursion train for 300 executives runs from London to Brighton and back. Some of the executives sit in standard class seats, others in first class seats and some spend the journey in the restaurant car. The comparison bar chart shows the details. Display the details for the outward train on a pie chart.

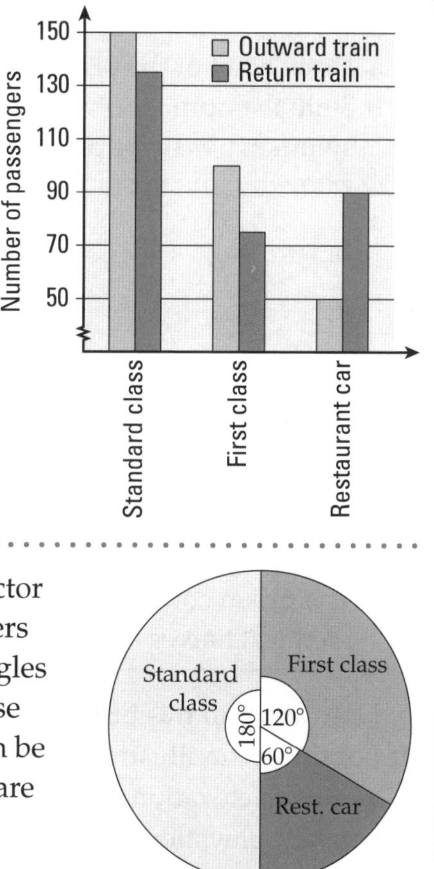

For the outward journey the sector angle for standard class travellers equals $\frac{150}{300} \times 360$ or 180°. The angles for first class travellers and those who sit in the restaurant car can be worked out similarly and they are equal to 120 and 60°.

1 The Year 9 and Year 10 students at a London school were asked which football team they supported. Their answers are summarized in the table.

	Arsenal	Spurs	Chelsea	Fulham	West Ham United
Number (Year 9)	20	40	30	15	15
Number (Year 10)	24	30	36	12	18

Display these details on

a a comparative bar chart **b** a pair of pie charts.

13a 3-D shapes

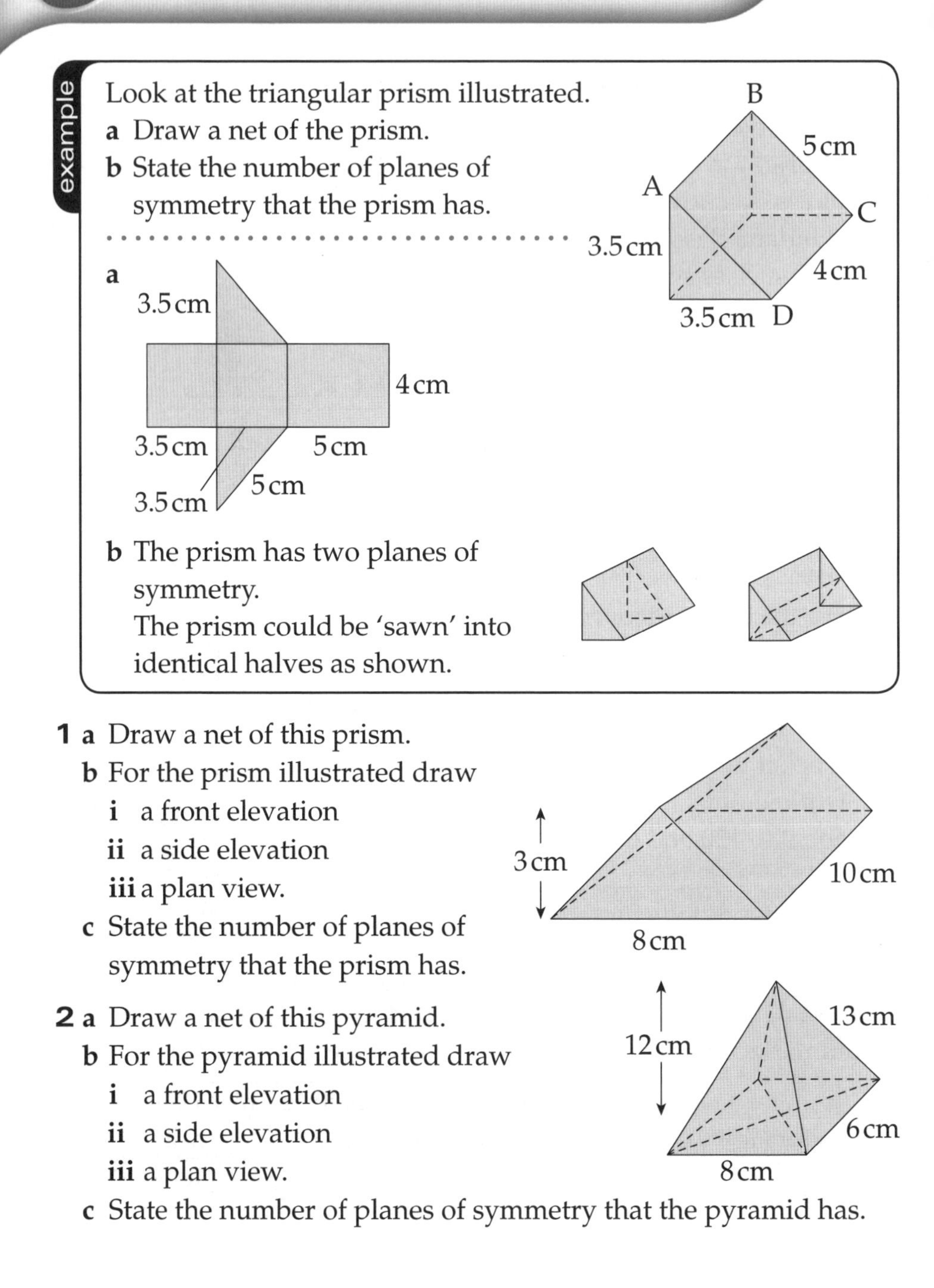

example

Look at the triangular prism illustrated.

a Draw a net of the prism.

b State the number of planes of symmetry that the prism has.

a

b The prism has two planes of symmetry.
The prism could be 'sawn' into identical halves as shown.

1 **a** Draw a net of this prism.

b For the prism illustrated draw

 i a front elevation

 ii a side elevation

 iii a plan view.

c State the number of planes of symmetry that the prism has.

2 **a** Draw a net of this pyramid.

b For the pyramid illustrated draw

 i a front elevation

 ii a side elevation

 iii a plan view.

c State the number of planes of symmetry that the pyramid has.

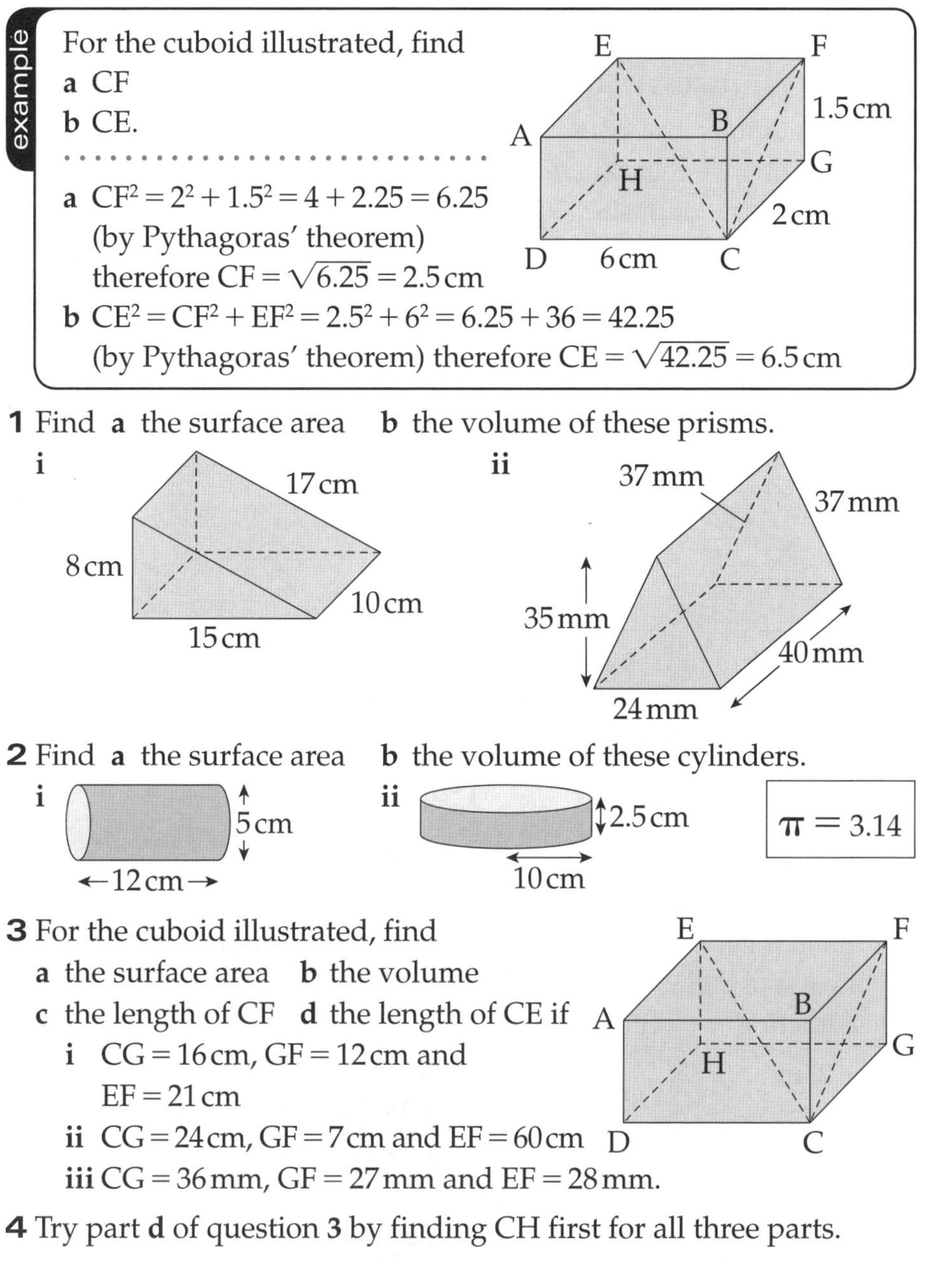

example

For the cuboid illustrated, find

a CF

b CE.

a $CF^2 = 2^2 + 1.5^2 = 4 + 2.25 = 6.25$
(by Pythagoras' theorem)
therefore $CF = \sqrt{6.25} = 2.5$ cm

b $CE^2 = CF^2 + EF^2 = 2.5^2 + 6^2 = 6.25 + 36 = 42.25$
(by Pythagoras' theorem) therefore $CE = \sqrt{42.25} = 6.5$ cm

1 Find **a** the surface area **b** the volume of these prisms.

i **ii**

2 Find **a** the surface area **b** the volume of these cylinders.

i **ii**

$\pi = 3.14$

3 For the cuboid illustrated, find

a the surface area **b** the volume

c the length of CF **d** the length of CE if

i CG = 16 cm, GF = 12 cm and EF = 21 cm

ii CG = 24 cm, GF = 7 cm and EF = 60 cm

iii CG = 36 mm, GF = 27 mm and EF = 28 mm.

4 Try part **d** of question **3** by finding CH first for all three parts.

5 A tin beans has a radius of 6 cm and a height of 12.5 cm. Find the area of the label which fits exactly around it.

Trigonometry 1

example

Give, as a fraction, the value of
i sin A **ii** cos A **iii** tan A.

53 mm
28 mm
A
45 mm

i $\sin A = \dfrac{\text{opposite}}{\text{hypotenuse}} = \dfrac{28}{53}$ **ii** $\cos A = \dfrac{\text{adjacent}}{\text{hypotenuse}} = \dfrac{45}{53}$

iii $\tan A = \dfrac{\text{opposite}}{\text{adjacent}} = \dfrac{28}{45}$

1 For each of these triangles, state which side is **i** the hypotenuse **ii** the side opposite angle A **iii** the side adjacent to angle A.

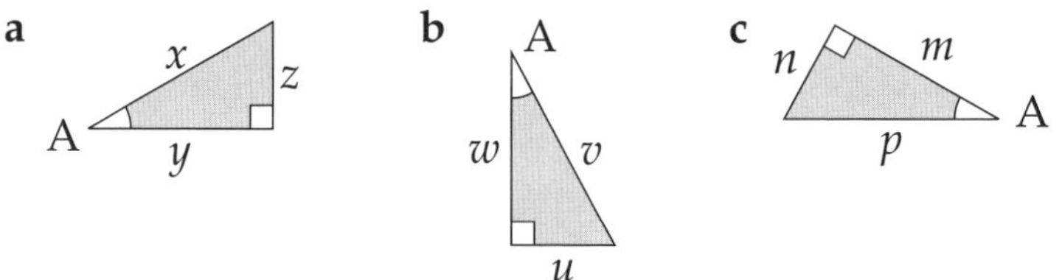

2 For each of these triangles, give the value of tan x as
i a fraction **ii** an exact decimal.

a
9 cm
x
40 cm

b
12 cm
x
16 cm

3 For each of these triangles, give the value of sin z as
i a fraction **ii** a decimal.

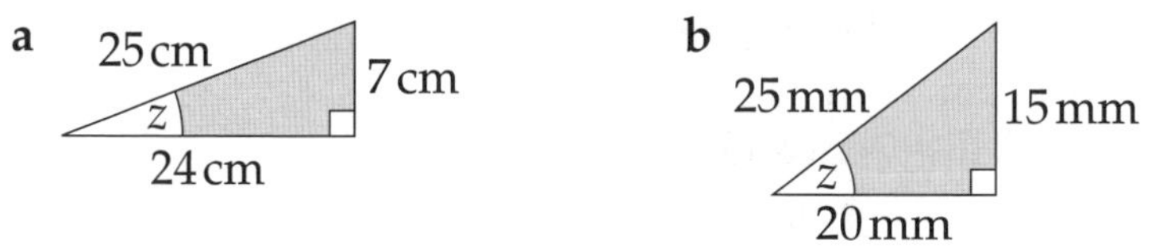

4 Look again at the triangles in question **3**. For each one give the value of cos z as
i a fraction **ii** a decimal.

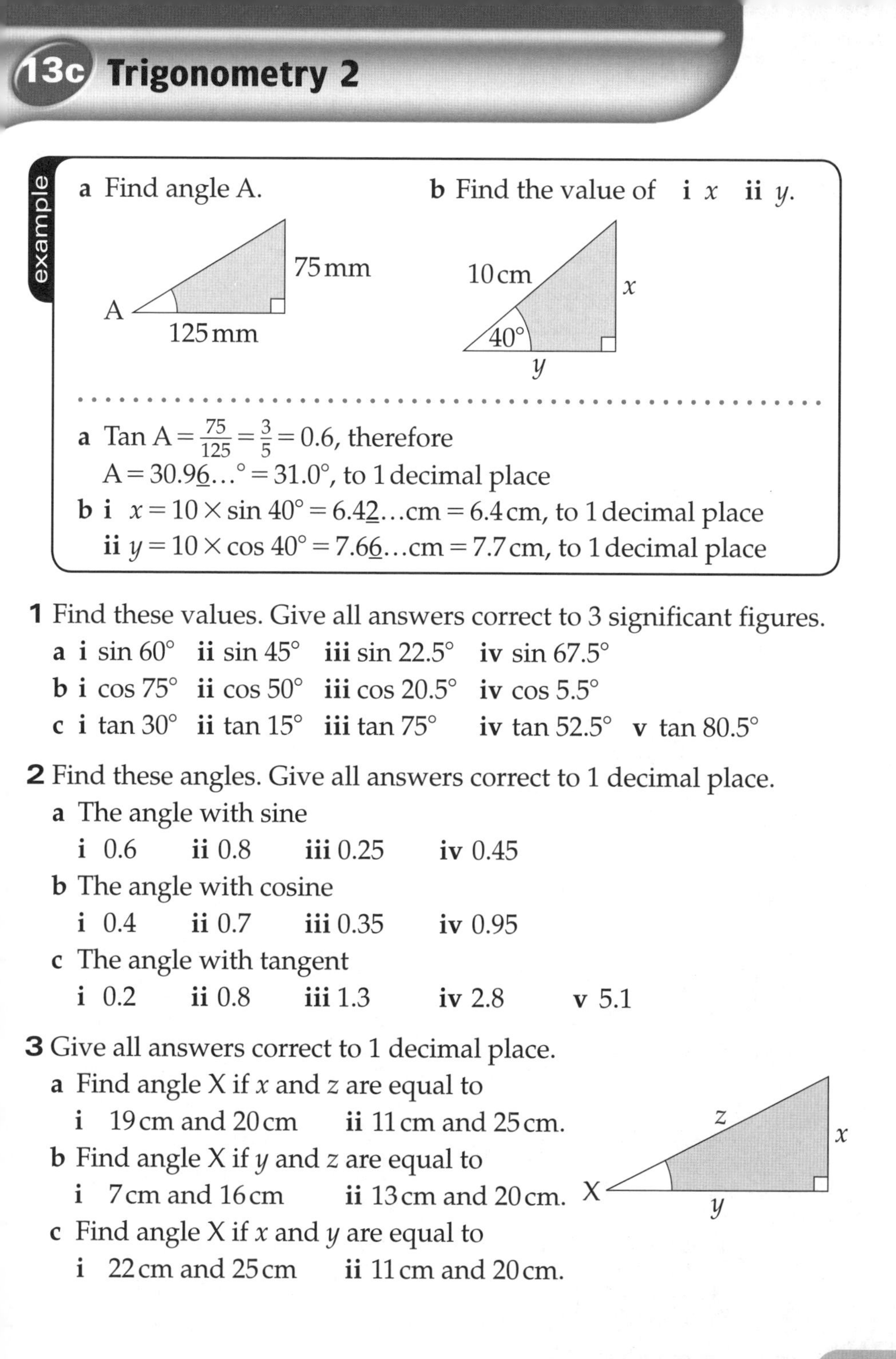

13c Trigonometry 2

example

a Find angle A.

75 mm

A

125 mm

b Find the value of **i** x **ii** y.

10 cm

x

40°

y

a $\text{Tan A} = \frac{75}{125} = \frac{3}{5} = 0.6$, therefore
$A = 30.9\underline{6}\ldots° = 31.0°$, to 1 decimal place

b i $x = 10 \times \sin 40° = 6.4\underline{2}\ldots\text{cm} = 6.4\,\text{cm}$, to 1 decimal place
ii $y = 10 \times \cos 40° = 7.6\underline{6}\ldots\text{cm} = 7.7\,\text{cm}$, to 1 decimal place

1 Find these values. Give all answers correct to 3 significant figures.

a i sin 60° **ii** sin 45° **iii** sin 22.5° **iv** sin 67.5°
b i cos 75° **ii** cos 50° **iii** cos 20.5° **iv** cos 5.5°
c i tan 30° **ii** tan 15° **iii** tan 75° **iv** tan 52.5° **v** tan 80.5°

2 Find these angles. Give all answers correct to 1 decimal place.

a The angle with sine
i 0.6 **ii** 0.8 **iii** 0.25 **iv** 0.45
b The angle with cosine
i 0.4 **ii** 0.7 **iii** 0.35 **iv** 0.95
c The angle with tangent
i 0.2 **ii** 0.8 **iii** 1.3 **iv** 2.8 **v** 5.1

3 Give all answers correct to 1 decimal place.

a Find angle X if x and z are equal to
i 19 cm and 20 cm **ii** 11 cm and 25 cm.
b Find angle X if y and z are equal to
i 7 cm and 16 cm **ii** 13 cm and 20 cm.
c Find angle X if x and y are equal to
i 22 cm and 25 cm **ii** 11 cm and 20 cm.

z

x

X

y

13d Bearings

Jana walks 250 m South and then 350 m East to get to Amelia's house. Find

a the bearing of Amelia's house from Jana's

b the bearing of Jana's house from Amelia's.

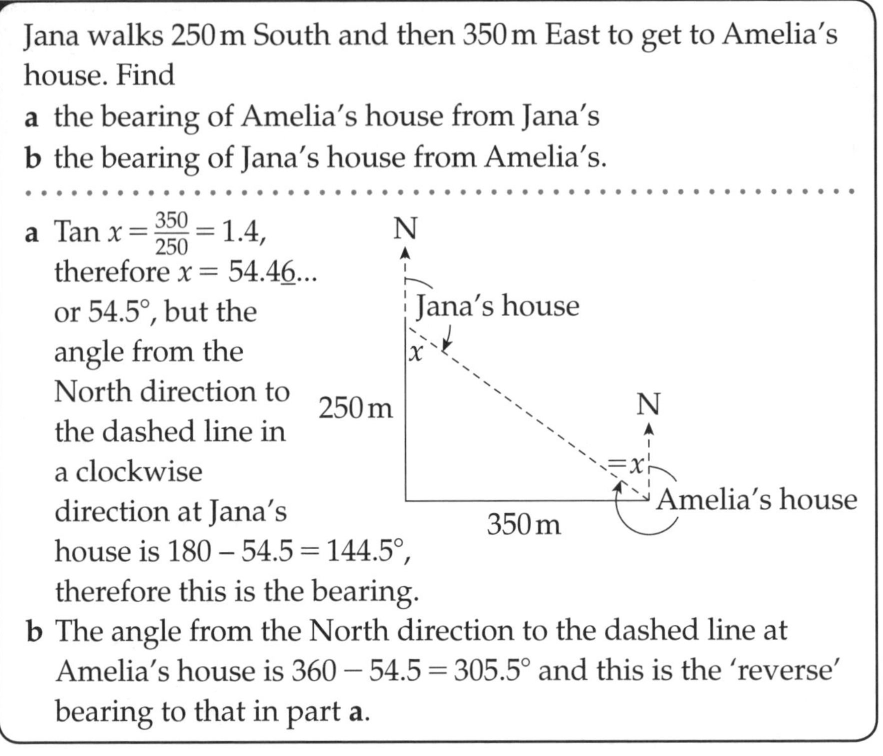

a Tan $x = \frac{350}{250} = 1.4$, therefore $x = 54.4\underline{6}...$ or 54.5°, but the angle from the North direction to the dashed line in a clockwise direction at Jana's house is 180 – 54.5 = 144.5°, therefore this is the bearing.

b The angle from the North direction to the dashed line at Amelia's house is 360 – 54.5 = 305.5° and this is the 'reverse' bearing to that in part **a**.

1 Look at the town map carefully. Give the bearing from the Town Centre to the

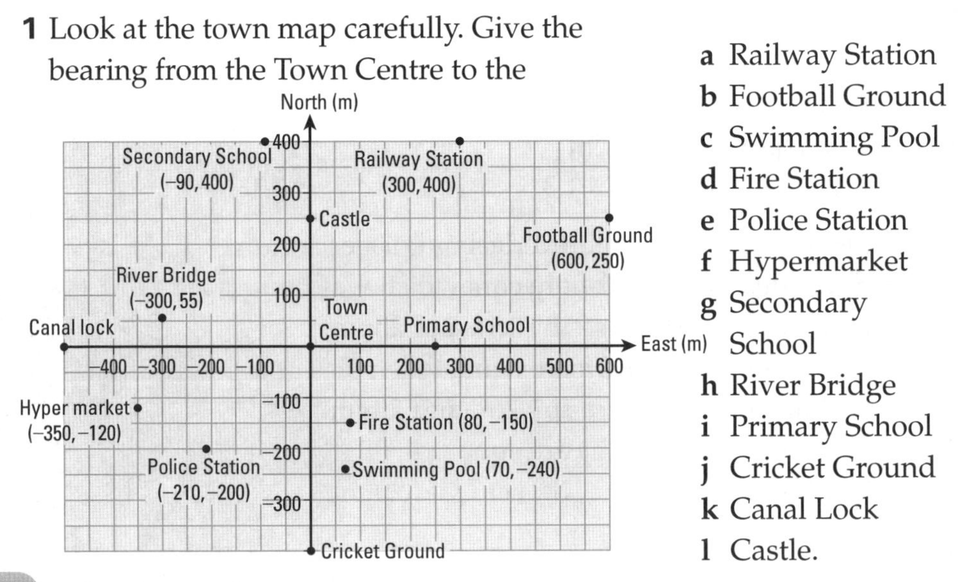

a Railway Station
b Football Ground
c Swimming Pool
d Fire Station
e Police Station
f Hypermarket
g Secondary School
h River Bridge
i Primary School
j Cricket Ground
k Canal Lock
l Castle.

14a Percentage problems

example

Jim buys a bike for £200, but it depreciates by 10% per annum. How much is it worth after 2 years?

After 1 year its value is 90% of £200 or $\frac{90}{100} \times £200$, which is £180. Therefore after 2 years its value is 90% of £180 or $\frac{90}{100} \times £180$, which is £162.

1 The table shows details of price reductions at a sale. Copy and complete the table.

Article	Original price	Percentage reduction	Actual reduction	Sale price
Television	£360	20%		
Set of chairs	£70	15%		
Table	£120			£90
Cooker	£320			£280
Cabinet		12%		£132
Microwave oven		16%		£75.60
Lawn mower	£350		£31.50	£75.60
Bike	£220		£17.60	

2 Calculate these percentage changes.

a The value of a house after 5 years which was bought for £200 000 and its value increases by 10% per annum.

b The value of a holiday home after 3 years which was bought for £80 000 and its value increases by 5% per annum.

c The value of a car after 4 years which was bought for £20 000 and its value decreases by 10% per annum.

d The value of a van after 4 years which was bought for £15 000 and its value decreases by 20% per annum.

14b Proportional reasoning

example

A photograph of dimensions 12 cm by 10 cm is enlarged. If the length of the enlargement is 15 cm, what is its width?

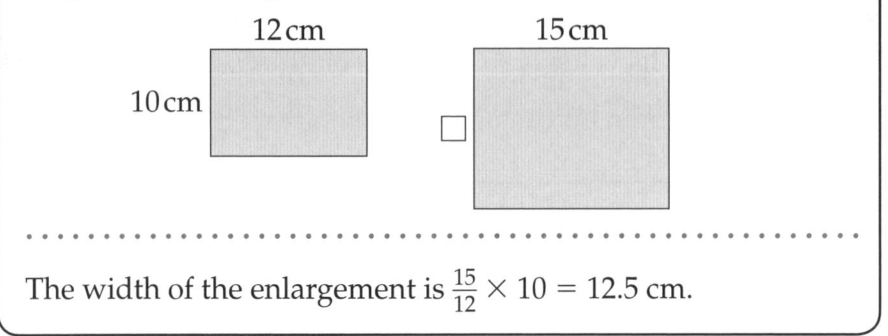

The width of the enlargement is $\frac{15}{12} \times 10 = 12.5$ cm.

1 The triangles illustrated are similar. Find
i the side length ratio of the large one with respect to the small one
ii the values of a and b.

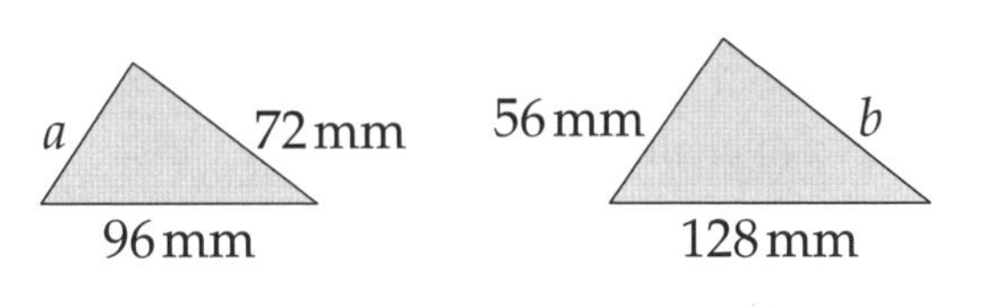

2 In a sale all the prices in a shop are reduced by the same percentage. If a carpet is reduced in price from £200 to £175 find
a the sale price of a keyboard which normally costs £340.
b the original price of a refrigerator which is priced at £157.50 in the sale.

3 **a** If a train consumes 1 litre of diesel for every 400 m it travels, find how much it uses for each of these journeys.
i London to Newport, 220 km **ii** London to Oxford, 102 km
b If the journey from London to Newport takes 1 h 50 minutes, find how much diesel it consumes in 1 hour.

4 A school bus is carrying girls and boys in the ratio 5 : 2. It stops at North Park Girls' School where $\frac{2}{3}$ of the girls get off. If nobody else joins the bus, what is the ratio of girls to boys left on board?

14c Estimation and approximation

example

Shani pours some milk into a jug up to the 400 ml mark, but the markings are only correct to the nearest 10 ml. Find

i the upper and lower bounds for the amount of milk that she has poured into the jug

ii the maximum percentage error with respect to the nominal value.

i The upper and lower bounds are $400 + 5 = 405$ ml and $400 - 5 = 395$ ml.

ii The maximum percentage error is $\frac{5}{400} \times 100 = 1.25\%$.

1 Work out these

i exactly

ii to a rough estimate by rounding every number to 1 significant figure.

a $\frac{(24 \times 2.8)}{25.6}$ **b** $\frac{(3.6 \times 5.76)}{0.32}$ **c** $\frac{(455 \times 0.84)}{12.74}$

d $\frac{(56 \times 1.62)}{(1.05 \times 4.32)}$ **e** $\frac{(1.728 \times 315)}{(0.625 \times 19.2)}$ **f** $\frac{(453.6 \times 28.35)}{(2.592 \times 0.45)}$

2 For these, find **i** the upper and lower bounds for the quantity

ii the maximum percentage error with respect to the nominal value.

a A running track is measured to be 100 m long correct to the nearest metre.

b Zoey pours 500 g of flour onto her scales, but they are only correct to the nearest 10 g.

c Eshe puts 50 litres of petrol into her car's tank but the gauge at the garage is only correct to the nearest 0.1 litre.

d A carpet fitter measures the area of a room to be 40 m^2, but this figure is only correct to the nearest square metre.

e Afiya measures the distance across a table to be 50 cm, but this is only correct to the nearest centimetre.

14d Using a calculator

example

Use your calculator to evaluate $\frac{2 \times 10^3 + 1000^{\frac{2}{3}}}{(2 \times 10^2)^2}$

Give your answer **i** exactly, and **ii** to 1 significant figure.

i The correct sequence of buttons on your calculator will give the answer 0.0525.

ii 0.0525 is 0.05 to 1 significant figure.

1 Use your calculator to evaluate these.

a $256^{\frac{1}{2}}$ **b** $729^{\frac{2}{3}}$ **c** $64^{\frac{5}{6}}$ **d** $625^{\frac{3}{4}}$

e $32^{\frac{4}{5}}$ **f** $512^{\frac{4}{3}}$ **g** $1024^{\frac{3}{2}}$ **h** $81^{\frac{7}{4}}$

2 Use your calculator to evaluate these. Give your answers **i** exactly, and **ii** to 1 significant figure.

a $\frac{5.5 \times 10^3 + 3.5 \times 10^2}{1.8 \times 10^2}$

b $\frac{(8 \times 10^{-1}) \times (27^{\frac{2}{3}} + 125^{\frac{4}{3}})}{1.585 \times 10^{-2}}$

c $\frac{3.78 \times 10^4}{1000^{\frac{4}{3}} + 125^{\frac{5}{3}}}$

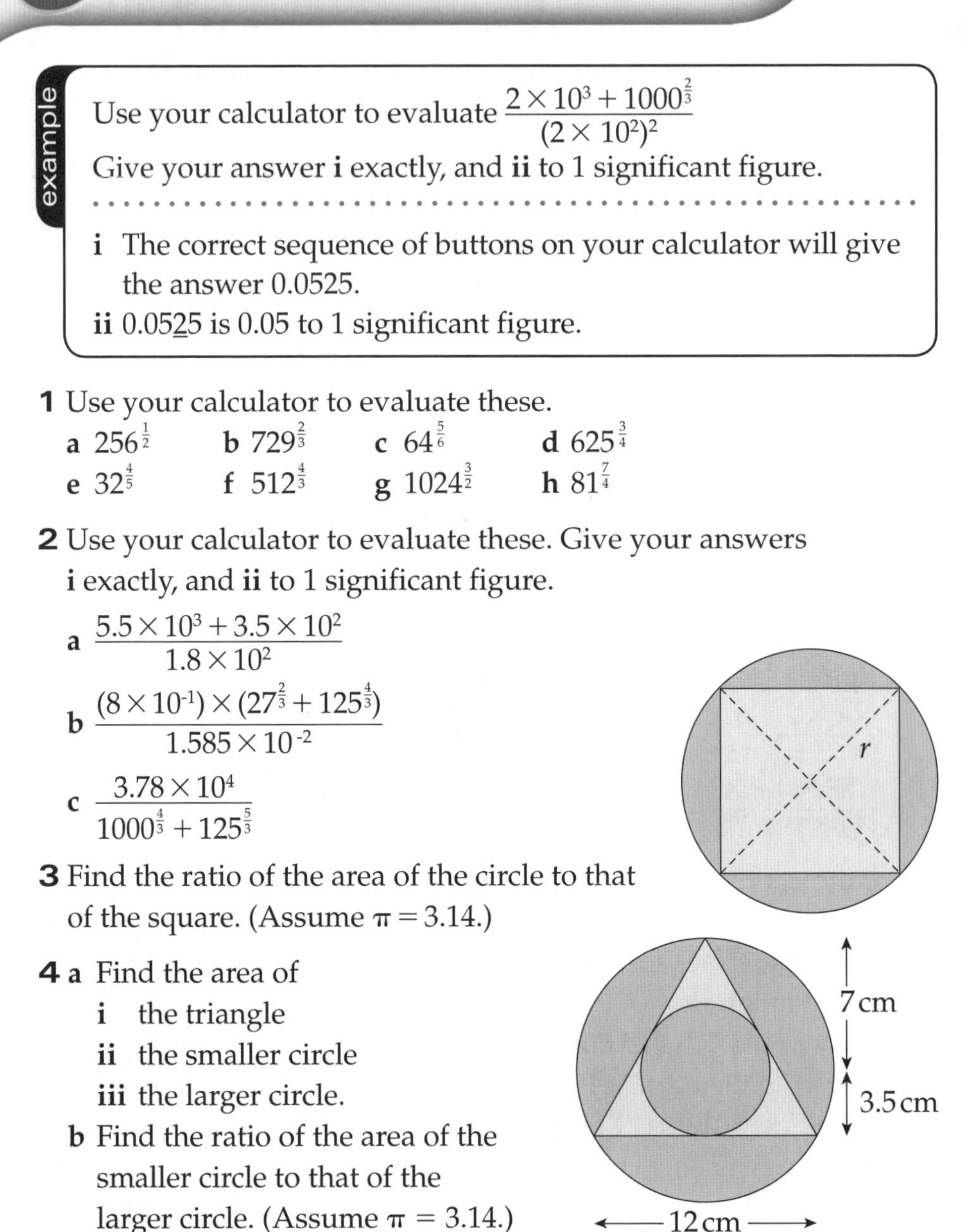

3 Find the ratio of the area of the circle to that of the square. (Assume $\pi = 3.14$.)

4 **a** Find the area of

i the triangle

ii the smaller circle

iii the larger circle.

b Find the ratio of the area of the smaller circle to that of the larger circle. (Assume $\pi = 3.14$.)

5 The Earth is 1.5×10^8 km from the Sun, whereas the planet Pluto is 5.91×10^9 km from the Sun. How many more times further away from the Sun is Pluto than the Earth?

Glossary

accuracy Accuracy describes the degree to which a number is rounded.

adjacent Adjacent means next to.

algebra Algebra is the branch of mathematics where symbols or letters are used to represent numbers.

algebraic expression An algebraic expression is a term, or several terms connected by plus and minus signs.

algebraic fraction A fraction containing letters, for example $\frac{2x}{y}$.

alternate A pair of alternate angles is formed when a straight line crosses a pair of parallel lines. Alternate angles are equal.

$a = b$

angle: acute, obtuse, right, reflex An angle is formed when two straight lines cross or meet each other at a point.
The size of an angle is measured by the amount one line has been turned in relation to the other.

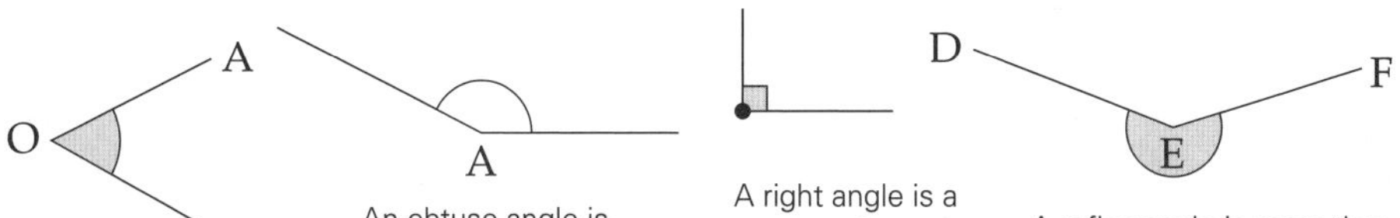

An acute angle is less than 90°.

An obtuse angle is more than 90° but less than 180°.

A right angle is a quarter of a turn, or 90°.

A reflex angle is more than 180° but less than 360°.

angle of elevation/ depression When you look up, the angle between your line of sight and the horizontal is the angle of elevation. When you look down, the angle between your line of sight and the horizontal is the angle of depression.

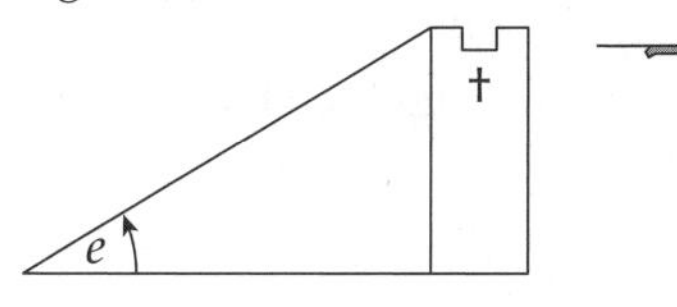

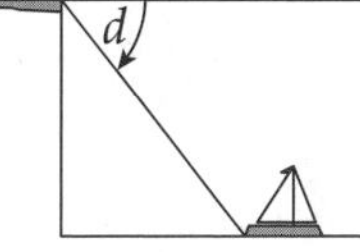

angle bisector An angle bisector cuts an angle in half.

Glossary

angles on a straight line — Angles on a straight line add up to 180°.

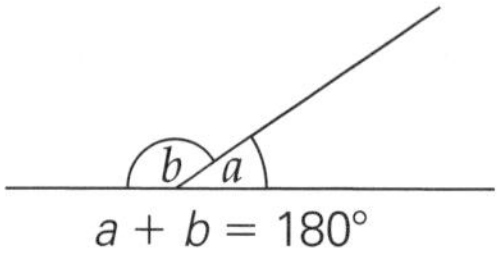

$a + b = 180°$

anomaly — An anomaly is a value that does not fit a pattern.

approximate — To approximate an answer is to work out a rough answer using easier figures. An approximate value is close to the real value.

arc — An arc is part of a curve.

area — The area of a surface is a measure of its size. Square millimetre, square centimetre, square metre, square kilometre are all units of area.

ASA — A triangle given ASA ('angle side angle') is unique. Two triangles are congruent if two angles and the side between them in one triangle are equal to two angles and the corresponding side in the other triangle.

average rate — An average rate is the mean value of a varying quantity, such as speed.

axes — Axes are lines scaled to locate a point by its coordinates.

axis of rotation symmetry — When a shape is rotated about its axis of rotation it has rotation symmetry, that is, it fits onto itself more than once during a full turn.

bar chart — The heights of the bars on a bar chart represent the frequencies of the data.

base (number) — The base is the number which is raised to a power. For example in 2^3, 2 is the base.

bearing, three-figure bearing — A bearing is a clockwise angle measured from the North line giving the direction of a point from a reference point. A bearing should always have three digits.

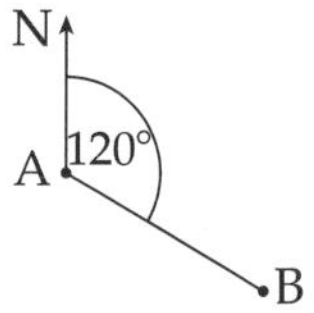

N, A, 120°, B

The bearing of B from A is 120°.

bias — An experiment or selection is biased if not all outcomes are equally likely.

BIDMAS — BIDMAS is a mnemonic to remind you of the correct order of operations: **b**rackets, **i**ndices, **d**ivision or **m**ultiplication, **a**ddition or **s**ubtraction.

bisect, bisector — To bisect is to cut in half.
A bisector is a line that cuts something in half.

box-and-whisker plot — A box-and-whisker plot shows the median and the spread of a set of data.

brackets — Brackets show you what part of a calculation to do first.

cancel — You cancel a fraction by dividing the numerator and denominator by a common factor.

capacity — Capacity is a measure of how much liquid a hollow 3-D shape can hold.

census — In a census, everyone in the group being surveyed is included.

centre — The centre of a circle is the point from which all points on the circumference are equidistant.

centre of enlargement — The centre of enlargement is the point from which an enlargement is measured.

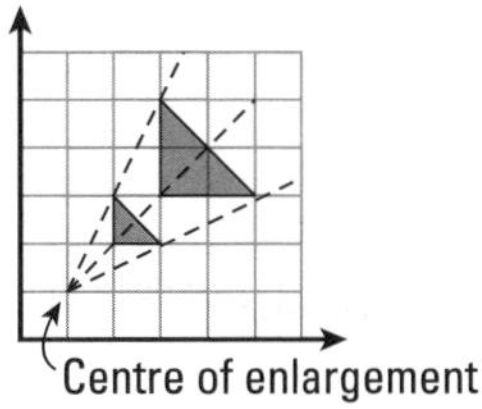

Centre of enlargement

centre of rotation — The centre of rotation is the fixed point about which a rotation takes place.

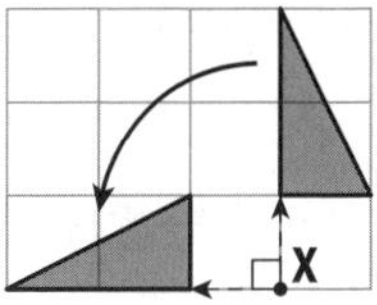

X

Glossary

chord — A chord is a straight line joining two points on a curve, or a circle.

circumcentre — The circumcentre is the centre of a circumcircle.

circumcircle — A circumcircle is a circle drawn around another shape, so that all the vertices of the shape lie on the circle.

circumference — The circumference is the distance around the edge of a circle.

circumscribed — A circumscribed shape is a shape drawn around another shape, for example a circumcircle.

coefficient — The coefficient is the number part of an algebraic term.
For example in $3n^5$ the coefficient of n^5 is 3.

collect like terms — To collect like terms, put together terms with the same letter parts.
For example $5x + 3x = 8x$ and $4y^2 - y^2 = 3y^2$.

common denominator — To add or subtract fractions, change them into equivalent fractions with the same denominator, that is a common denominator.

common factor — A common factor is a factor of two or more numbers or terms.
For example $2p$ is a common factor of $2p^2$ and $6p$.
You factorise an expression by taking out a common factor.
For example $15a^2b + 10bc = 5b(3a^2 + 2c)$

commutative — An operation is commutative if the order of combining two terms does not matter.

compasses — A pair of compasses is a geometrical instrument used to draw circles or arcs.

compensating — The method of compensation is used to make calculations easier.
For example to add 99, add 100 and then compensate by subtracting 1.

compound interest With compound interest you are paid interest on the original amount and the previous years' interest.

conclude, conclusion To conclude is to formulate a result or conclusion based on evidence.

congruent Congruent shapes are exactly the same shape and size.

consecutive Numbers that follow one another, for example 15 and 16, are consecutive numbers.

constant Constant means unchanging. A constant is an algebraic term that remains unchanged.
For example, in the expression $5x + 3$ the constant is 3.

construct, construction To construct is to draw accurately. A construction is an accurate drawing.

construction lines Construction lines are the arcs drawn when making an accurate diagram.

continuous Continuous data can take any value between given limits, for example height.

convention A convention is the accepted way of describing something in maths.

convert, conversion To convert is to change from one unit to another, for example 1 m = 100 cm.

coordinates The coordinates of a point give its position in terms of its distance from the origin along the x and y axes.

correlation Correlation is a measure of the relationship between two variables.

corresponding A pair of corresponding angles is formed when a straight line crosses a pair of parallel lines. Corresponding angles are equal.

$a = b$

Glossary

cosine	In a right-angled triangle, the cosine of an angle is the ratio of the length of the adjacent side to the length of the hypotenuse. $\cos = \frac{\text{adjacent}}{\text{hypotenuse}}$
cost price	Cost price is the price that a retailer pays for an article.
counter-example	A counter-example is an example that shows that a rule does not work.
cross-multiply	Cross-multiplying is a method for removing fractions from equations.
cross-section	The cross-section of a solid is the shape of its transverse section, that is a section cut parallel to the end of the shape.
cube root	The cube root of x is the number that when cubed gives you x. For example $\sqrt[3]{64} = 4$, because $4 \times 4 \times 4 = 64$.
cubic	A cubic expression, equation or function contains a term in x^3 as the highest power.
cumulative frequency	The cumulative frequency is the sum of the frequencies.
curve	Graphs of quadratic, cubic and reciprocal functions are curves.
cylinder	A cylinder is a prism with a circular cross-section.
data	Data are pieces of information.
data collection sheet	A data collection sheet is a form designed for the systematic collection of data.
data logging	Data logging is the automatic collection of data.
decagon	A decagon has ten sides.

decimal A decimal number is a number written using base ten notation.

decimal multiplier A decimal multiplier is used in calculating percentages, for example to increase by $4\frac{1}{2}$% multiply by 1.045.

decimal place Each column after the decimal point is called a decimal place.

definition A definition explains the exact meaning of a word.

degree (°) Angles are measured in degrees. There are 360° in a full turn.

degree of accuracy The degree of accuracy of an answer depends on the accuracy of the figures used in the calculation.

demonstrate You can demonstrate that a statement is true for some values by giving examples.

denominator The denominator is the bottom number in a fraction. It shows how many parts there are in the whole.

density Density is the mass (weight) of a unit volume (for example, per 1 cm^3) of a substance.

derive You can derive a formula from information given in a problem.

derived property In geometry, a derived property arises from the basic properties of a shape.

diagonal A diagonal line is one which is neither horizontal nor vertical.

diameter The diameter is a chord that passes through the centre of a circle.

difference of two squares The identity $(a + b)(a - b) \equiv a^2 - b^2$ is called the difference of two squares.

Glossary

difference pattern — You can find a general rule for a sequence by looking at the pattern of differences between consecutive terms.

digit — A digit is any of the numbers 0, 1, 2, 3, 4, 5, 6, 7, 8, 9.

dimension — A dimension is a length, width or height of a shape or solid.

direct proportion — Two quantities are in direct proportion if one quantity increases at the same rate as the other.

discrete — Discrete data are data that can be counted.

distance–time graph — A distance–time graph is a graph of distance travelled against time taken. Time is plotted on the horizontal axis.

distribution — A distribution is a set of observations of a variable.

divisible, divisibility — A whole number is divisible by another if there is no remainder after division.

divisor — The divisor is the number that does the dividing. For example, in $14 \div 2 = 7$ the divisor is 2.

edge (of solid) — An edge is a line along which two faces of a solid meet.

edge

elevation — An elevation is an accurate drawing of the side or front of a solid.

elimination — A method for solving simultaneous equations by removing (eliminating) one of the variables (letters).

enlargement — An enlargement is a transformation that multiplies all the sides of a shape by the same scale factor.

equation — An equation is a statement showing that two expressions have the same value.

equation (of a graph) — An equation is a statement showing the relationship between the variables on the axes.

equidistant	Equidistant means the same distance apart.
equivalent, equivalence	Two quantities, such as fractions which are equal, but are expressed differently, are equivalent.
estimate	An estimate is an approximate answer. You can estimate a probability by carrying out an experiment.
estimate of the mean/median	The exact mean and median cannot be calculated if the data are grouped. They can be estimated from a cumulative frequency curve.
evaluate	Evaluate means to find the value of an expression.
event	In probability, an event is a trial or experiment.
exhaustive	In probability, two events are exhaustive if they include all possible outcomes.
expand	To expand an expression you remove all the brackets.
expected frequency	In probability, the expected frequency of an event is equal to the number of trials × the probability of the event.
experiment	An experiment is a test or investigation to gather evidence for or against a theory.
experimental probability	You can find the experimental probability of an event by conducting trials.
explain	Explain means to give a reason for your answer.
exponent	The exponent, or index, tells you how many of a number or variable to multiply together. For example, x^4 means $x \times x \times x \times x$.
expression	An expression is a collection of terms linked with operations but with no equals sign.
exterior angle	An exterior angle is made by extending one side of a shape.

Glossary

face	A face is a flat surface of a solid.

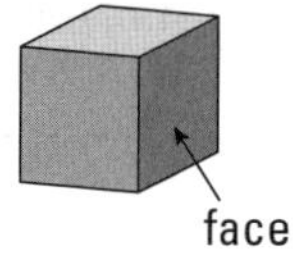

factor	A factor is a number that divides exactly into another number. For example, 3 and 7 are factors of 21.
factorise	You factorise an expression by writing it with a common factor outside brackets.
formula, formulae	A formula is a statement that links variables.
frequency	The frequency is the number of times an event occurs.
frequency diagram	A frequency diagram uses bars to display data. The heights of the bars correspond to the frequencies.
function, linear function	A function is a rule. The graph of a linear function is a straight line.
generalise	Generalise means find a statement or rule that applies to all cases.
general term	The general term in a sequence allows you to evaluate unknown terms. It is sometimes called the *n*th term.
gradient	Gradient is a measure of the steepness of a line.
graph	A graph is a diagram that shows a relationship between variables.
greater than or equal to (≥)	The symbol ≥ means that the term on the left-hand side is greater than or equal to the term on the right-hand side.
hectare	A hectare is a unit of area equal to 10 000 (100 × 100) square metres.
hexagon	A hexagon has six sides.

highest common factor (HCF) The highest common factor is the largest factor that is common to two or more numbers.
For example the HCF of 12 and 8 is 4.

horizontal A horizontal line is parallel to the bottom edge of the page.

hyperbola The graph of a reciprocal function is a hyperbola.

hypotenuse The hypotenuse is the side opposite the right angle in a right-angled triangle.

hypothesis A hypothesis is a statement used as a starting point for a statistical investigation.

identically equal to (≡) One expression is identically equal to another if they are mathematically equivalent.

identity An identity is an equation which is true for all possible values.
For example $3x + 6 \equiv 3(x + 2)$ for all values of x.

identity function $x \rightarrow x$ is called the identity function, because it maps any number on to itself.

image An image is an object after it has been transformed.

implicit An equation in x and y is in implicit form if y is not the subject of the equation.

improper fraction In an improper fraction the numerator is bigger than the denominator.

independent In probability, events are independent if the outcome of one event does not affect the outcome of the other event.

index, indices The index tells you how many of a quantity must be multiplied together.
For example x^3 means $x \times x \times x$.

Glossary

index laws	To multiply powers of the same base add the indices, for example $2^5 \times 2^3 = 2^8$. To divide powers of the same base subtract the indices. For example $5^6 \div 5^3 = 5^2$. To raise a power to a power, multiply the indices. For example $(4^3) = 4^6$.
index notation	A number written as a power of a base number is expressed in index notation, for example $\frac{1}{1000} = 10^{-3}$.
inequality	An inequality is a relationship between two numbers or terms that are comparable but not equal. For example, $7 > 4$.
infer	Infer means to conclude from evidence.
inscribe, inscribed	An inscribed polygon has every vertex lying on the perimeter of a shape, such as a circle. An inscribed circle is drawn inside a polygon so that every side of the polygon is a tangent to the circle.
integer	An integer is a positive or negative whole number (including zero). The integers are: ..., -3, -2, -1, 0, 1, 2, 3, ...
intercept	The intercept is the point at which a graph crosses an axis.
interior angle	An interior angle is inside a shape, between two adjacent sides.
interpret	You interpret data or a problem when you make sense of it.
interquartile range	The interquartile range (IQR) is the difference between the upper and lower quartiles.
intersection, intersecting	The intersection of two lines is the point where they cross.
inverse	Inverse means opposite.

inverse function, operation An inverse function or operation acts in reverse to a specified function or operation.

function
input x → output y
inverse function

inverse mapping The inverse mapping reverses the direction of the mapping.
For example, the inverse of $x \to 3x$ is $x \to \frac{x}{3}$.

investigation A investigation is research carried out to check a hypothesis.

isometric Isometric paper has three axes, ruled in equilateral triangles.

justify You justify a solution of a formula by explaining why it is correct.

less than or equal to (≤) The symbol ≤ means that the term on the left-hand side is less than or equal to the term on the right-hand side.

like terms Like terms are terms with the same letter parts, for example $3x^2$ and $-5x^2$ are like terms.

limit, limiting value If a sequence tends towards a certain value, that value is the limit .4or limiting value.

limitations Limitations are factors that restrict the usefulness of a statistical survey.

line graph On a line graph, points are joined with straight lines.

line of best fit A line of best fit passes through the points on a scatter graph, leaving roughly as many points above the line as below it.

line segment A line segment is the part of a line between two points.

linear equation, linear graph A linear equation contains no squared or higher terms. The graph of a linear equation is a straight line.

Glossary

linear expression	A linear expression contains no square or higher terms, for example $3x + 5$ is a linear expression.
linear sequence	The terms of a linear sequence increase by the same amount each time.
locus, loci	A locus is a set of points (a line, a curve or a region) that satisfies certain conditions. Loci is the plural of locus.
lower bound	The lower bound is the lowest value a rounded figure could have.
lower quartile	The lower quartile is the value $\frac{1}{4}$ of the way along a set of data arranged in ascending order.
lowest common denominator	The lowest common denominator is the lowest number that is a multiple of the denominators of two unlike fractions. For example, 6 is the lowest common denominator of $\frac{1}{2}$ and $\frac{1}{3}$.
lowest common multiple (LCM)	The lowest common multiple is the smallest multiple that is common to two or more numbers, for example the LCM of 4 and 6 is 12.
map	A map is a representation of an area of land.
mapping	A mapping is a rule that can be applied to a set of numbers to give another set of numbers.
mass	The mass of an object is a measure of the quantity of matter in it.
maximum	A maximum is the highest point on a curved graph, where the function has its highest value.
mean	The mean is the average value found by adding the data and dividing by the number of data items.
median	The median is the average which is the middle value when the data are arranged in order of size.

metric system In the metric system, units of measurement are related by powers of 10.

midpoint The midpoint of a line segment is the point that is halfway along.

minimum A minimum is the lowest point on a curved graph, where the function has its lowest value.

mirror line A mirror line is a line or axis of symmetry.

misleading Misleading means false. Statistics can be used to give a false impression.

mixed number A mixed number is a whole number with a fraction, for example $2\frac{1}{2}$.

modal class The modal class is the most commonly occurring class when the data is grouped.
It is the class with the highest frequency.

mode The mode is an average.
It is the value that occurs most often.

multiple A multiple of an integer is the product of that integer and any other.
For example 12, 18 and 30 are multiples of 6.

multiple bar chart A multiple bar chart is a bar chart with two or more sets of bars.
It is used to compare two or more data sets.

Glossary

multiplicative inverse	The multiplicative inverse of 3 is $\frac{1}{3}$. Multiplying by $\frac{1}{3}$ undoes the effect of multiplying by 3.
mutually exclusive	Two events are mutually exclusive if they cannot occur at the same time.
negative	A negative number is a number less than zero.
net	A net is a 2-D shape that can be folded to make a 3-D solid.
***n*th term**	The *n*th term is the general term of a sequence.
numerator	The numerator is the top number in a fraction. It tells you how many parts of the whole you have.
object, image	The object is the original shape before a transformation. An image is the shape after a transformation.
operation	An operation is a rule for processing numbers. The basic operations are addition, subtraction, multiplication and division.
opposite	The opposite side in a triangle is the side opposite the angle being considered.
order of operations	The conventional order of operations is: brackets first, then indices, then division and multiplication, then addition and subtraction (see BIDMAS).
order of rotational symmetry	The order of rotational symmetry is the number of times that a shape will fit on to itself during a full turn.
origin	The origin is the point where the x and y axes cross, that is (0, 0).
outcome	In probability, an outcome is the result of a trial.
outlier	An outlier is an observation that is an exception.
p(*n*)	p(n) stands for the probability of an event n.

parabola The graph of a quadratic equation is a parabola.

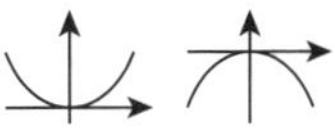

parallel Parallel lines are always the same distance apart.

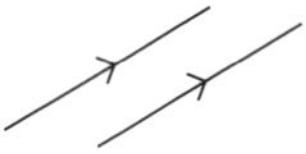

partitioning Partitioning means splitting a number into smaller parts.

pentagon A pentagon is a 5-sided polygon.

percentage change Percentage change is an increase or decrease by a percentage of the original amount.

perimeter The perimeter is the distance round the edge of a shape.

perpendicular A line or plane is perpendicular to another line or plane if they meet at a right angle.

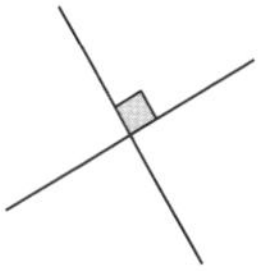

perpendicular bisector The perpendicular bisector of a line is the line that divides it into two equal parts and is at right angles to it.

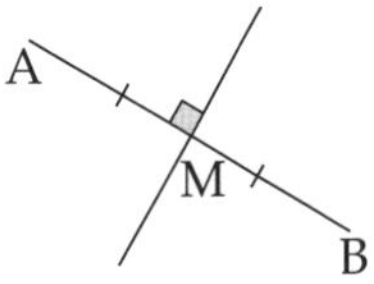

A M B

AM = MB

pi (π) The ratio $\frac{\text{circumference}}{\text{diameter}}$ is the same for all circles.
This ratio is denoted by the Greek letter π.

pie chart A pie chart is a circular diagram used to display data. The angle in each sector is proportional to the frequency.

pilot survey A pilot survey is a small preliminary survey used to help plan an investigation.

place value The place value is the value of a digit in a decimal number.
For example in 3.65 the digit 6 has a value of $\frac{6}{10}$.

Glossary

plan	The plan or plan view of a solid is an accurate drawing of the view from directly above.
plane	A plane is a flat surface.
plane symmetry	A solid has plane symmetry if it can be divided into two identical halves.
plane of symmetry	A plane of symmetry divides a solid into two identical halves.
polygon	A polygon is a shape with three or more straight sides.
population	The population is the complete set of individuals from which a sample is drawn.
position-to-term rule	A position-to-term rule tells you how to calculate the value of a term if you know its position in the sequence.
positive	A positive number is greater than zero.
power	The power (or index) of a number or a term tells you how many of the number must be multiplied together. For example 10 to the power 4 is 10 000.
practical demonstration	A practical demonstration shows that a statement is true for some values.
predict	Predict means to assign a value, such as a time or a length, by comparison with some known data.
pressure	Pressure is weight per unit area (for example, per 1 cm^2).
primary data, primary source	Primary data is data you have collected yourself.
prime	A prime number is a number that has exactly two different factors.

prime factor A prime factor is a factor that is a prime number.

prime factor decomposition Prime factor decomposition means splitting a number into its prime factors.

prism A prism is a solid with a uniform cross-section.

probability Probability is a measure of the likelihood of an event occurring.

problem A problem is a question requiring a solution.

properties The properties of a shape are its characteristic features.

product The product is the result of a multiplication.
For example, the product of 3 and 4 is 12.

projection A projection is a 2-D view of a solid.

proportion A proportion compares the size of a part with the size of the whole.

proportional to ($\propto$) When two quantities are in direct proportion, one quantity is proportional to the other.

proportionality The method of proportionality uses the proportion between quantities to solve problems.

prove, proof You prove a statement is true by arguing from known facts.

Pythagoras' theorem The area of the square drawn on the hypotenuse of a right-angled triangle is equal to the sum of the areas of the squares drawn on the other two sides.

$a^2 = b^2 + c^2$

Glossary

Pythagorean triple A Pythagorean triple is a set of three integers that form the sides of a right-angled triangle.

quadratic A quadratic expression, equation or function contains a square term, for example x^2.

quadratic sequence In a quadratic sequence the second difference is constant.

quadrilateral A quadrilateral is a polygon with four sides.

rectangle

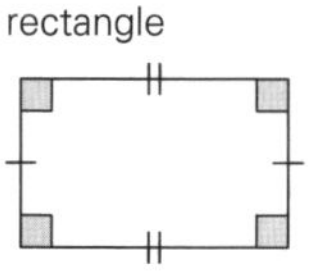

All angles are right angles.Opposite sides equal.

parallelogram

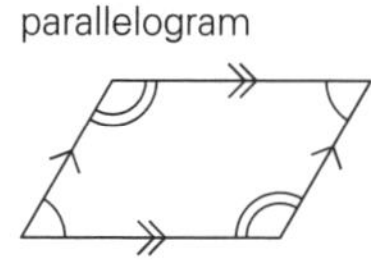

Two pairs of parallel sides.

kite

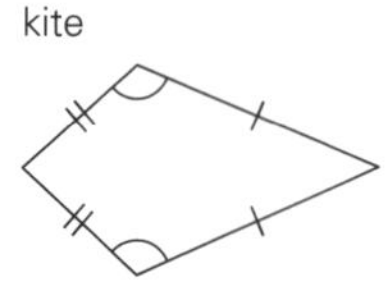

Two pairs of adjacent sides equal. No interior angle greater than 180°.

rhombus

All sides the same length. Opposite angles equal.

square

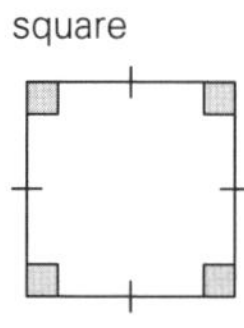

All sides and angles equal.

trapezium

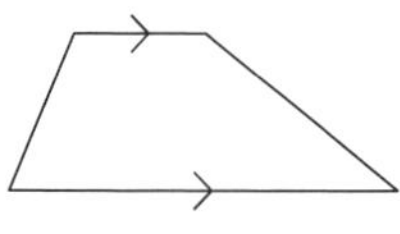

One pair of parallel sides.

quotient A quotient is the result of a division.
For example, the quotient of 12 ÷ 5 is $2\frac{2}{5}$, or 2.4.

radius, radii The radius is the distance from the centre to the circumference of a circle. Radii is the plural of radius.

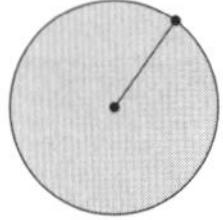

random process The outcome of a random process cannot be predicted.

random sample In a random sample every item has an equal chance of being selected.

range The range is the difference between the largest and smallest values in a set of data.

rate A rate is the change per unit of time, area, volume, and so on.

ratio A ratio compares the size of one part with the size of another part.

raw data Raw data is data before it has been processed.

rearrange You rearrange an equation or formula by moving terms from one side to the other.

reciprocal The reciprocal of a quantity k is $1 \div k$.
For example the reciprocal of 5 is $\frac{1}{5}$ or 0.2; the reciprocal of x^2 is $\frac{1}{x^2}$.

recurring A recurring decimal has a repeating pattern of digits after the decimal point, for example 0.33333 ...
You show the recurring digit with a dot: $0.3333 = 0.\dot{3}$

reflect, reflection A reflection is a transformation in which corresponding points in the object and the image are the same distance from the mirror line.

reflection symmetry A shape has reflection symmetry if it has a line of symmetry.

region A region is an area on a graph or a locus where certain rules hold.

regular A regular polygon has equal sides and equal angles.

RHS Two Right-angled triangles are congruent if their Hypotenuses and one other Side are equal.
A triangle given RHS is unique.

relative frequency Relative frequency is the proportion of successful trials in an experiment.

relative frequency diagram A relative frequency diagram is a graph showing how relative frequency changes as the number of trials increases.

Glossary

repeated subtraction	Repeated subtraction is a method of long division in which multiples of the divisor are subtracted from the dividend (the number being divided).
representative	A representative sample is a selection chosen rom a population to give an accurate indication of the population characteristic being studied.
rotate, rotation	A rotation is a transformation in which every point in the object turns through the same angle relative to a fixed point.
rotation symmetry	A shape has rotation symmetry if it fits onto itself more than once during a full turn.
right prism	Apart from its two end faces, the faces of a right prism are all rectangles.
root	The square root of 9 is 3, because $3 \times 3 = 3^2 = 9$. The cube root of 8 is 2, because $2 \times 2 \times 2 = 2^3 = 8$.
rounding	You round a number by expressing it to a given degree of accuracy.
rule	A fixed procedure for finding a term in a sequence.
sample	A sample is a set of individuals or items drawn from a population.
sampling	Sampling is choosing some items from a set.
sample space, sample space diagram	In probability, the set of all possible outcomes in an experiment is called the sample space. A sample space diagram is a diagram recording all the outcomes.
SAS	Two triangles are congruent if two Sides and the Angle between them in one triangle are equal to two sides and the corresponding angle in the other triangle. A triangle given SAS is unique.

scale
A scale gives the ratio between the size of an object and its diagram.

scale drawing
A scale drawing is an accurate drawing of a shape to a given scale.

scale factor
A scale factor is a multiplier.

scatter diagram
Pairs of variables, for example age and height, can be plotted on a scatter diagram. The diagram shows whether there is a relationship between the two variables.

secondary data, secondary source
Secondary data is data that someone else has collected. Common secondary sources include books, magazines and the internet.

sector
A sector is part of a circle bounded by an arc and two radii.

second difference
The differences between the terms of a sequence are the *first* differences. The differences between the first differences are the *second* differences.

segment
A segment is part of a circle bounded by an arc and a chord.

self-inverse
The inverse of a self-inverse function is the function itself.
For example, $x \to 10 - x$ is the inverse of $x \to 10 - x$.
So $x \to 10 - x$ is self-inverse.

selling price
Selling price is the price an article is sold for. It is usually calculated by increasing the cost price by a percentage.

sequence
A sequence is a set of numbers, objects or terms that follow a rule.

Glossary

significant figures (sf)

The first non-zero figure in a number is its first significant figure.

For example, the first significant figure of 0.0308 is 3.

similar, similarity

Similar shapes have the same shape but are different sizes.

simplify

You simplify a fraction by cancelling. You simplify an algebraic expression by collecting like terms or combining terms.

simulation

A simulation is an experiment designed to model a real-life situation.

simultaneous equations

Simultaneous equations are two or more equations whose unknowns have the same values.

sine

In a right-angled triangle the sine of an angle is the ratio of the length of the opposite side to the length of the hypotenuse. $\sin = \dfrac{\text{opposite}}{\text{hypotenuse}}$

skew

A distribution is skewed if there are more values at either one end or the other.

slope

The slope of a line is measured by the angle it makes with the x-axis.

solid

A solid is a shape formed in three-dimensional space.

cube

six square faces

cuboid

six rectangular faces

prism

the end faces are constant

pyramid

the faces meet at a common vertex

tetrahedron

all the faces are equilateral triangles

square-based pyramid

the base is a square

solution, solve	The solution of an equation is the value that makes it true.
speed	Speed is a measure of the rate at which distance is covered. It is often measured in miles per hour or metres per second.
sphere	A sphere is a 3-D shape in which every point on its surface is equidistant from the centre.
square	To square an expression, you multiply it by itself.
square number	If you multiply an integer by itself you get a square number.
square root	A square root is a number that when multiplied by itself is equal to a given number. For example, $\sqrt{25} = 5$, because $5 \times 5 = 25$.
SSS	Two triangles are congruent if the three sides of one triangle are equal to the three sides in the other triangle. A triangle given SSS is unique.
standard form	A number in standard form is written as a number between 1 and 10 multiplied by a power of 10, for example $731 = 7.31 \times 10^2$.
statement	A statement is a sentence giving a fact.
steepness	The steepness of a line depends on the angle the line makes with the x-axis. Gradient is a measure of steepness.
stem-and-leaf diagram	A stem-and-leaf diagram is used to display raw data in numerical order.

Glossary

straight-line graph A straight-line graph is the graph of a linear equation.

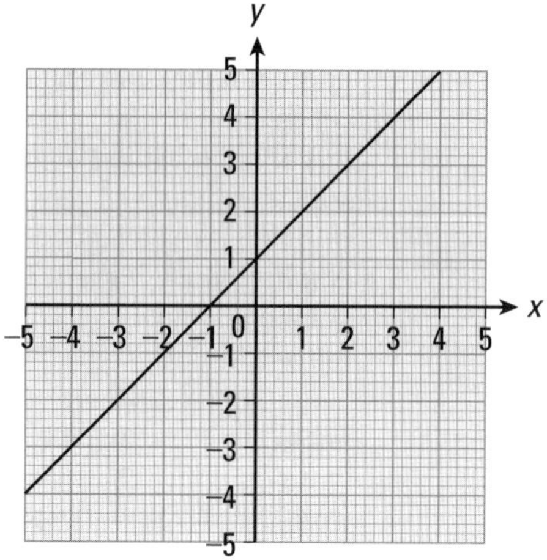

y

5 4 3 2 1 0 −1 −2 −3 −4 −5

−5 −4 −3 −2 −1 1 2 3 4 5 x

strategy A strategy is a plan for solving a problem.

stratified sample In a stratified sample, people are chosen from different groups so that the sample is representative of the population.

subject The subject of an equation or formula is the term on its own in front of the equals sign.
For example, the subject of $v = u + at$ is v.

substitute To substitute is to replace a variable with a numerical value.

sum A sum is the total of an addition.

supplementary Supplementary angles add up to 180°. You can form a pair of supplementary angles on a straight line.

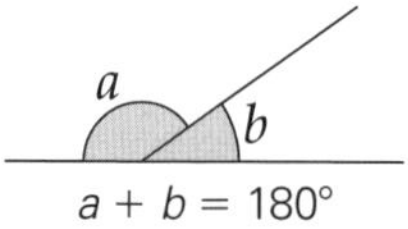

a b

$a + b = 180°$

surd A surd is a square root that cannot be written as a decimal, for example $\sqrt{3} = 1.732\,050\,808\,\ldots$

surface area The surface area of a solid is the total area of its faces.

symmetry, symmetrical — A shape is symmetrical if it is unchanged after a rotation or reflection.

systematic sample — A example of a systematic sample is to choose every tenth vehicle on a motorway.

T(n) — T(n) stands for the general term in a sequence.

tangent — A tangent is a line that touches a circle or a curve at one point.

task — A task can be a calculation that is part of a larger problem.

term — A term is a number or object in a sequence.
It is also part of an expression.

terminating — A terminating decimal has a limited number of digits after the decimal point.

tessellation — A tessellation is a tiling pattern with no gaps.

theoretical probability — The theoretical probability of an event $= \frac{\text{number of favourable outcomes}}{\text{total possible number of uotcomes}}$

tonne — The tonne is a unit of mass, equal to 1000 kg.

transform — You transform an expression by taking out single-term common factors.

transformation — A transformation moves a shape from one place to another.

translate, translation — A translation is a transformation in which every point in an object moves the same distance and direction.
It is a sliding movement.

tree diagram — A tree diagram shows the possible outcomes of a probability experiment on branches.

trend — A trend is a general tendency.

Glossary

trial In probability, a trial is an experiment.

trial and improvement Square roots, cube roots and solutions to equations can be estimated by the method of trial and improvement. An estimated solution is tried and refined by a better estimate until the required degree of accuracy is achieved.

triangle A triangle is a polygon with three sides.

equilateral

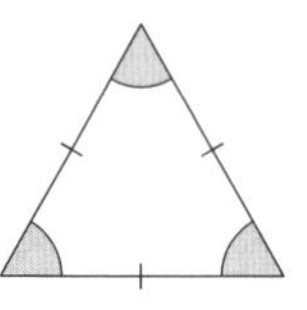

three equal sides

isosceles

scalene

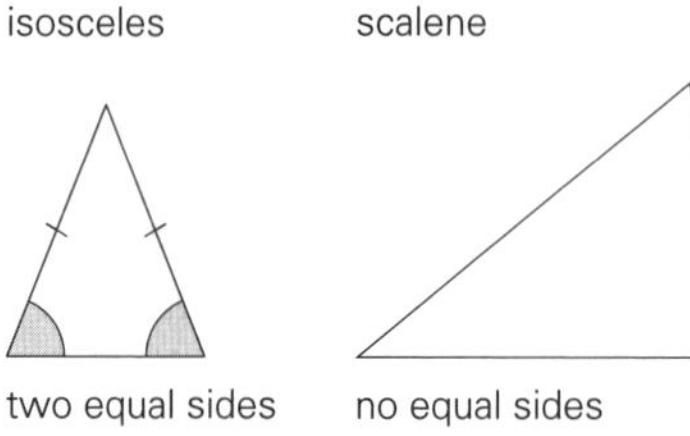

two equal sides

no equal sides

right-angled

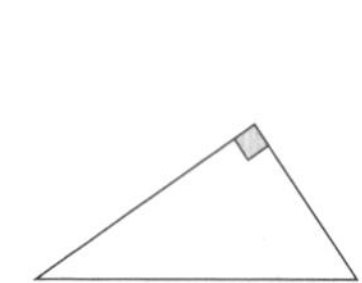

one angle is 90°

triangular number A triangular number is the number of dots in a triangular pattern. The numbers form the sequence 1, 3, 6, 10, 15, 21, 28, ...

triangular prism A triangular prism is a prism with a triangular cross-section.

trigonometry Trigonometry is the relation between the sides and angles of a triangle.

unit fraction A unit fraction has a numerator of 1.
For example, $\frac{1}{3}$ and $\frac{1}{7}$ are unit fractions.

unitary form A ratio is in unitary form when one of the numbers is 1.
For example the ratio 4 : 3 is 1 : 0.75 in unitary form.

unitary method In the unitary method, you calculate the value of one item or 1% first.

unknown In an equation, the unknown is a letter.

upper bound The upper bound is the highest value a rounded figure could have.

upper quartile The upper quartile is the value $\frac{3}{4}$ of the way along a set of data arranged in ascending order.

variable A variable is a quantity that can take a range of values.

vector A vector describes a translation by giving the x- and y-components of the translation.

vertex, vertices A vertex of a shape is a point at which two or more edges meet.

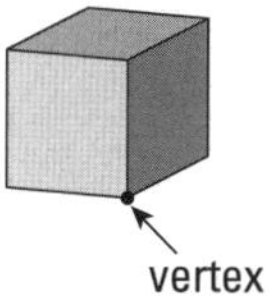

vertex

vertical A vertical line is at right angles to the horizontal.

vertically opposite angles When two straight lines cross they form two pairs of equal angles called vertically opposite angles.

$a = b$
$c = d$

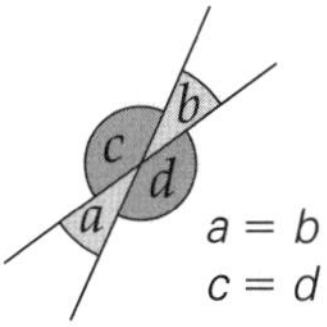

view A view of a solid is an accurate drawing of the appearance of the solid above, in front or from the side.

volume Volume is a measure of the space occupied by a 3-D shape. Cubic millimetres, cubic centimetres and cubic metres are all units of volume.

***x*-axis, *y*-axis** On a coordinate grid, the x-axis is the horizontal axis and the y-axis is the vertical axis.

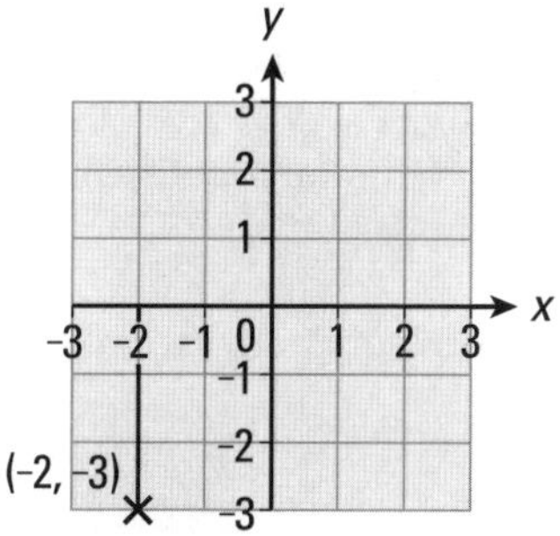

Glossary

x-coordinate, y-coordinate The x-coordinate is the distance along the x-axis. The y-coordinate is the distance along the y-axis.
For example, (-2, -3) is -2 along the x-axis and -3 along the y-axis.

zero Zero is nought or nothing. A zero place holder is used to show the place value of other digits in a number.
For example, in 1056 the 0 allows the 1 to stand for 1 thousand. If it wasn't there the number would be 156 and the 1 would stand for 1 hundred.

Thousands	Hundreds	Tens	Units
1	0	5	6

A GEOGRAPHY OF EURO... ...ON

A GEOGRAPHY OF EUROPEAN INTEGRATION

Andrew H. Dawson

Belhaven Press
London and New York

Co-published in the Americas by Halsted Press
an imprint of John Wiley & Sons, Inc.

Belhaven Press
(a division of Pinter Publishers Ltd)
25 Floral Street, Covent Garden, London, WC2E 9DS, United Kingdom

First published in 1993

Co-published in the Americas by Halsted Press, an imprint of
John Wiley & Sons, Inc., 605 Third Avenue, New York, NY 10158-0012

British Library Cataloguing in Publication Data
A CIP catalogue record for this book is available from the British Library

ISBN 1 85293 244 9 (hb)
1 85293 248 1 (pb)

Library of Congress Cataloging-in-Publication Data
Dawson, Andrew
A Geography of European integration / Andrew Dawson.
p. cm.
Includes bibliographical references and index.
ISBN 1–85293–244–9 — ISBN 1–85293–248–1 (pbk.)
ISBN 0–470–21995–5 (US) — ISBN 0–470–21996–3 (pbk. US)
1. Europe—Economic conditions—1945– 2. Europe, Eastern—Economic conditions—1945– 3. Europe—Economic integration. 4. Economic geography. I. Title
HC240.D335 1993
337.4—dc20 92–43295
CIP

ISBN 0 470 21995 5 (hb) (in the Americas only)
0 470 21996 3 (pb) (in the Americas only)

Typeset by Ewan Smith at 48 Shacklewell Lane, London E8
Printed and bound in Great Britain by Biddles Ltd, Guildford and King's Lynn

CONTENTS

List of boxes		vi
List of figures		vii
List of tables		viii
Acknowledgements		ix
Section I	**The challenge of Europe**	**1**
Section II	**The integrated space economy**	**21**
1	Some models	23
2	Europe in the early 1990s	38
Section III	**Europe in the Fourth Kondratiev**	**67**
3	The Fourth Kondratiev	70
4	The primary industries	80
5	Manufacturing	104
6	The service industries	122
7	The developing space economy	132
Section IV	**The map of economic rents**	**147**
Section V	**Common European home?**	**173**
References		209
Subject index		217
Author index		223

LIST OF BOXES

Box 1	Definitions	2
Box 2	Long Waves	74
Box 3	Long Waves in the space economy	133
Box 4	Germany	176
Box 5	The Russian Federation	188
Box 6	The Ukraine	204

LIST OF FIGURES

Figure I.1	The European space economy	15
Figure I.2	Scandinavia: core and periphery	16
Figure II.1	A Christallan space economy	25
Figure II.2	An Isardian space economy	27
Figure II.3	Trading blocs, 1992	42
Figure II.4	Gross national product per capita in the late 1980s	61
Figure III.1	Changes in economic activity, 1933–87	71
Figure III.2	The changing structure of the largest economies, 1930s to 1980s	81
Figure III.3	Farm size in the 1980s	84
Figure III.4	Wheat yields in the late 1980s	87
Figure III.5	Milk yields in the late 1980s	89
Figure III.6	The production of hard coal, 1932–87	95
Figure III.7	The major energy-producing areas in the 1980s	100
Figure III.8	The supply of, and demand for, energy in 1987	101
Figure III.9	The production of steel, 1933–87	107
Figure III.10	The production of cloth in the late 1980s	115
Figure III.11	The production of television sets in the late 1980s	119
Figure III.12	Centres of decision making in the early 1990s	135
Figure III.13	Convergence and divergence among the countries of Europe,1930s to 1980s	145
Figure IV.1	Crop reliability and the northern limits of cultivation	149
Figure IV.2	Soils	152
Figure IV.3	Areas of oil- and gas-bearing and potentially oil- and gas-bearing rocks	154
Figure IV.4	The distribution of population in the early 1990s	161
Figure IV.5	Motorways in the early 1990s	165
Figure IV.6	Telephones per thousand of the population in the late 1980s	168
Figure IV.7	Minorities and wars in the early 1990s	170

LIST OF TABLES

Table II.1	The chief countries of Europe in 1992	41
Table II.2	Trade in goods, 1985–8	47
Table III.1	Average annual agricultural output in the late 1980s	90
Table III.2	Trade in cereals, 1985–8	91
Table III.3	The manufacturing industries discussed in Chapter 5	105

ACKNOWLEDGEMENTS

I wish to thank Graeme Sandeman, of the Department of Geography and Geology, University of St. Andrews, who drew the figures; Laura Smethurst for commenting upon some sections of the text; Professors Ian Masser and K. J. Thomson for discussing some of the issues in Section V with me; and Dr Iain Stevenson, of Belhaven Press, for his advice and encouragement.

Section I
The challenge of Europe

As the communist governments of eastern Europe collapsed during the autumn of 1989, people spoke of the 'reunification' of the continent. The Soviet President, Gorbachev, wondered in public about a 'common European home'; and new leaders in Czechoslovakia and elsewhere spoke of 'rejoining' Europe. Unfortunately, geographers were ill prepared to respond. One, apparently quick-off-the-mark text in 1990 was entitled *Unfamiliar Territory: the reshaping of European Geography*, though it turned out, on inspection, to have been written before the 1989 events, and gave no indication that they were even a possibility. Indeed, Europe, according to this text, included none of the eastern countries except Yugoslavia. But it has not been alone. At a time when the European Community was also considering its relationships, both between its members and with the rest of the continent – the 'deepening' versus 'widening' debate – geographical writing offered little guidance as to what might or should happen. Rarely has Europe been treated as a whole by geographers; analysis of its economic geography (see Box 1) has frequently been but a superficial reflection of the political structure of the area under study, rather than being independent of it; many writers have failed to set economic change within appropriate time scales; and little attempt has been made to harness either experience or theory to forecast the likely future pattern of economic activities.

This book seeks to remedy those complaints by addressing the economic geography of the whole of the continent from a common viewpoint. More particularly, it aims to describe what has been happening to the spatial arrangement of economic activities within a time scale which is related to the functioning of the economy itself, and to indicate what may happen in the future, setting all this against the background of states and their policies, and of the maps of site and situation, that are Europe. In other words, it essays the interplay between the institutional arrangements made by nations to protect their economic interests, the technology of production – with its overtones of scales of enterprise, thresholds of demand, functional regions and periodicities of change – and the rents of fertility and location. However, it will begin, in this section, with a review of some of the earlier accounts of the economic geography of the continent, by way of establishing what approach might be appropriately adopted now.

Box 1

Definitions

Several terms are used widely in this book. A definition of each is given below.

Economic Geography is both a process and a result. It is the process whereby individuals and groups use space to compete for wealth. It is also the consequential spatial arrangement of those competitors and of the wealth which they generate. The study of economic geography deals, therefore, not only with such matters as:

— decisions by owners about the use of their land;
— decisions by investors as to where their capital is to be used;
— decisions by labour with regard to its place of employment;
— choices of location by producers of goods or services;
— and the way in those decisions interact with each other to create and alter space economies (see below),
— but also with the institutional and legal framework of those economies, and the way in which competitors use that framework as another way of pursuing their aims.

In other words, it examines the way in which conflicts of interest are handled in and through the spatial arrangement of economic activities and associated institutions. It sees these conflicts as continuous but ever-changing according to the particular circumstances of the history, resources and technology of places. The process of economic geography has neither a beginning nor an end.

Similarly, the *space economy* is both a process – that by which sites are allocated among competing users – and a result of that process. The spatial arrangements of land values, land uses and land-use intensities are all aspects of that result, and are being constantly altered as owners of the factors of production, producers and consumers reassess the appropriateness of their locations or the use which they are making of them.

The space economy is usually a continuous area whose boundary, or perimeter, is marked by unused land of no value. That boundary rarely coincides with those of states or other administrative areas, but is often closely related to such physical characteristics as the geology, landforms, climate and soils of a place, and to the distance of that place from centres of population and transport networks – in short, to the place's properties of site and situation.

Areas which are subject to the greatest competition, and which carry the highest values and intensity of use are the 'core' of the space economy. Those, in contrast, which are not in use lie outwith that economy. City centres and conurbations are examples of the first of these, and the uninhabited tundra, taiga and deserts examples of the second. Areas which are subject to little competition, and which often lie close to that boundary, form the 'periphery'.

Kondratiev Cycles or *Long Waves* are oscillations in the level of economic activity which are thought to be about fifty years in length. They were identified first by the Dutch economist van Gelderen, but have been named after the Russian statistician, Kondratiev, who drew attention in the 1920s to cyclical patterns in the prices of commodities in the developed countries. The Austrian economist Schumpeter (1939) later linked these cycles to innovation, suggesting that innovations tend to be bunched, giving rise to new industries and to rapid growth in the economy as a whole, but also eventually to periods of slower growth or decline as demand for the products of the new industries becomes satisfied. Several other explanations have also been offered for these oscillations; there is neither agreement as to the cause nor even the existence of Long Waves.

Economic rent is income which is received by landowners other than that paid to compensate them for any improvements which they may have made to their land. It arises out of the value placed by potential users on the free gifts of nature in any place – the rent of 'fertility' – or from the value which has been created there inadvertently by, for instance, the construction of transport links between the site and others – the rent of situation. It is, therefore, unearned. Land within a space economy, by definition, yields a rent, whereas the income from land outwith the space economy is inadequate to cover the costs of its use. Land which yields a return which is only just sufficient to cover those costs is 'marginal', and the edge of a space economy is marked by such land.

The existence of economic rents at particular sites, and the possibility of appropriating those rents, encourages potential users to compete for sites. Alternatively, those engaged in the game of economic geography may attempt to mould the space economy in such a way as to create rents in the places where they are already operating.

Europe – the area which forms the European space economy, including those parts of it which lie east of the Urals.

Eastern Europe – those countries which form part of the European space economy and which have developed under the communist system of central planning and the public ownership of the means of production during much of the Fourth Kondratiev. Thus, the former East Germany (the so-called German Democratic Republic), Yugoslavia, and those republics of the former Soviet Union which lie within the European space economy are included in it.

Western Europe – those countries which form part of the European space economy and which have developed under what has been called the 'free-market' system – a system in which, despite its name, governments have owned many economic activities, intervened to influence the developmental and locational decisions of many others, and exercised much control over international trade, the movement of capital and labour, and the use of land.

Early economic geographies of Europe

There have been surprisingly few attempts to describe the economic geography of Europe in an advanced manner, given the importance of the continent. Rather, geographers have written about restricted parts of it, or treated it briefly in texts covering the whole world, or have placed their descriptions of its economic activities within the broader frame of the regional approach. Nor do economic geographies of Europe have a long pedigree, for the first to style itself as such was not published until 1925.

The first account of the geography of Europe in a modern idiom was probably that of Carl Ritter, who published *Europa, ein Geographisch-Historisch-Statisches Gemälde* in three volumes between 1804 and 1807. This account appeared at a time when the systematic collection of information about the earth's surface, and its orderly presentation, were being recognised as a necessary aid to the continent's economic and political progress. However, Ritter's contribution went beyond this, for he attempted not so much a gazetteer or cartographical survey as an explanation, in which, building upon the thought of Emmanuel Kant, he drew attention to the connections between the physical environment of an area and the history of its people. Moreover, he presented his study in a regional, rather than a systematic, framework. Ritter's was not an economic geography; and very little was said about economic activities within it; but it laid a foundation upon which the first such geographies were to be constructed almost a century later.

Amongst the first economic geographers to write about Europe, pride of place should probably be accorded to Chisholm, whose *Handbook of Commercial Geography* was published in 1889. As the title suggests, this was intended to be a methodical account of the world-wide pattern of trade; but it was more than that. After a brief introduction, world patterns of production and trade in about sixty commodities were described and explained, while the second half of the book, which was entitled 'Regional Geography', discussed the economic activity of each country individually. The work concluded with a lengthy statistical appendix of the imports and exports of various countries, and of the prices of some products. Thus, within a single book, Chisholm employed three different approaches to economic geography – theoretical, systematic and regional – and also found space for much detailed data.

Some indication of Chisholm's aims may be gained from the preface:

> this book is not to be regarded as a general work of reference on all that may be included under the head of Commercial Geography. ... It is not a mere repertory of the where and whence of commodities of all kinds ...

and, in this, he was as good as his word. Both in the introduction, and through the two main sections of the text, he attempted to indicate the reasons behind the location of activities, and their prosperity or decline; and in his opening sentences, he set out the explanation which he was to offer in more detail throughout the book:

> The great geographical fact on which commerce depends is that different parts of the world yield different products, or furnish the same products under unequally favourable conditions. In the case of cultivated products, soil and climate are considerations of first importance in determining the variety obtaining at different places.

His appeal to the influence of the physical environment was further expressed in his discussion of the impact of technical innovation:

> the full advantage [of these innovations and the disturbances and hardships to which they give rise] is not reaped until every kind of production is carried on in the place that has the greatest *natural advantages* (p. 6)

by which he meant not only climate, minerals and soils, but also accessibility. However, he was not what could be called a strict 'environmental determinist', for he went on to say:

> With natural advantages may be contrasted *historical advantages*, which are ... more temporary. ... Perhaps the most important of all is a strong government based on just and fixed principles not hostile to industry (p. 7).

Nor was he unaware of the working of the political economy, for he noted the tendency of capitalists to seek opportunities for economic development wherever they occur, of states to adopt protectionist policies, and, as a result of trade between one part of the world and another, of developments in one place to affect those in others in a complicated sequence of actions and reactions, all of which remain to this day major topics of interest for economic geographers. Moreover, references to such concepts as the law of diminishing returns indicate some knowledge of the work of such economists as Smith and Marshall.

However, it was in his country-by-country section that Chisholm provided a model for regional economic geographies. In that section, brief descriptions of the natural environment and transport routes in each country preceded accounts of the production and trade of its most important commodities, and explanations for them couched in terms of the natural and historical advantages noted above. The section dealing with Europe covered approximately a hundred pages, or a fifth of the book; but it should be noted that the Asiatic parts of the Russian Empire were described separately. Nor was there any reference to any trading or other economic connections which existed between the European and Asiatic parts of that Empire, which might have affected the patterns of economic activity in either in the late nineteenth century. Europe was discussed strictly as Europe.

The *Handbook of Commercial Geography* went through many editions, and was still in print in the 1980s; but long before that, rivals had appeared which owed more to Darwin than to modern economic theory. In 1914, John McFarlane published *Economic Geography*, the opening sentence of which claimed that:

> Economic Geography may be defined as the study of the influence exerted upon the economic activities of man by his physical environment

and went on to opine that:

> physical factors, it is true, do not determine absolutely the character of economic life, but they exercise a control over it which is more apparent, no doubt, in the earlier stages of history, but which is no less real in advanced civilizations.

The inspiration for McFarlane's book had been the theory of natural regions, which Herbertson, influenced by Darwin, had set out in 1905. In the preface, McFarlane wrote:

> the theory of natural regions implies the treatment of the earth's surface quite independently of the political boundaries which may be traced upon it

going on to claim that:

> the economist and the statesman may both benefit by a method which enables them to distinguish from one another regions in which the nature of geographic control is essentially different.

In the event, he did not follow his own precept, for, after the opening chapters on climate and vegetation, the rest of the book was divided not according to natural regions, but the countries of the world, beginning with those of Europe. However, each of those chapters did begin with an account of the physical geography and some 'general considerations' concerning the relations between the location and physical characteristics of the country and its political and economic history. Furthermore, each included a detailed description of the natural regions within the country, together with their economic activities, before concluding with comments on its communications and foreign trade. Nowhere, however, was there a clear description of the criteria which had been employed in the recognition of natural regions; and examination of those criteria reveals that they had been selected by dichotomous division, and thus were quite arbitrary. Britain, for example, was divided into eighteen areas, such as the 'York, Derby and Nottingham coalfield', 'the Jurassic Region', 'the Basin of London' and 'the North East Coal and Iron Region'. That of the Basin of London was particularly revealing, for it included the eastern half of Norfolk, and was delimited less with reference to the capital city than with regard to the area covered by the post-cretaceous rocks which lie between the Chilterns and the North Downs.

Too much must not, however, be made of the contrasts between the explanatory frameworks which Chisholm and McFarlane claimed to have adopted, for the detailed discussions within their books were very similar. For instance, their explanations for the existence of the Lancashire textile industry were almost identical. Moreover, they tended to be of a determinist and exceptionalist type. Relativist arguments, of the sort which an economic approach such as that set out initially by Chisholm might have led to, explaining why textiles were preferred to other forms of economic enterprise there (as Michael Chisholm did in his *Geography and Economics* in 1966) were absent. Similarly, in neither book were the Asiatic parts of the Russian Empire included with the account of those west of the Urals. Nevertheless, it was McFarlane's approach that was adopted by later writers on the economic geography of Europe, rather than Chisholm's, with the result that, during the inter-war years, texts strongly emphasised the influence of the natural environment on the pattern of economic activities, were couched in terms of natural regions, and paid little attention to the workings of the economy.

The first *Economic Geography of Europe* to be entitled as such may well have been that published in 1925 by Smith. Certainly, the author acknowledged no earlier work on the topic, not even that of McFarlane! However, the approach was clearly derivative:

> The object of this book is to give the student a concise account of the main facts of economic importance in connection with the geography of Europe. ... An attempt has been made to show how the geographer should correlate the information supplied by the geologist, the meteorologist, and other specialists, and weave it into a connected whole which will throw some light on the relationship of Man to his environment.

The book opened with brief accounts of the geology, landforms and climate of the continent, followed by chapters on each of its countries, which described their natural regions, chief cities and associated economic activities. It concluded with a summary of the 'economic resources of some of the more important products of Europe'. Like that of McFarlane, Smith's book suffered from an arbitrary choice of so-called 'natural regions'. Nor was the country-by-country format applied uniformly, for the Rhine and Danube basins were discussed separately from the rest of the countries of which they were a part, on the grounds that:

> Although the Rhine basin is divisible politically into sections belonging to Switzerland, France, Germany, and Holland, its economic interests are sufficiently homogeneous to justify its treatment as a separate economic and geographic unit. It is becoming increasingly obvious that modern trade and industry pay less attention to political boundaries (p. 93).

> The length of the Danube and the area drained by this river and its tributaries would seem to justify the treatment of the Danube basin as a separate geographical unit, apart from the countries of which the basin forms a part (p. 185).

However, the chapter on Russia allowed no such possibility of the integration of the economy, even over the territory of a unitary state, and dealt solely with the European part of the country, ignoring areas east of the Urals. Thus, despite its claim to provide a 'scientific treatment' of the topic, Smith's approach was less rigorous and more deterministic than that of Chisholm, and showed little evidence of any acquaintance with economic theory. Moreover, in spite of its protestations to the contrary, its 250 pages were long on fact, but short on explanation.

Perhaps it was for this reason that the Americans, Blanchard and Visher, felt able to claim in the Preface to their *Economic Geography of Europe* in 1931 that:

> The lack of a textbook on the economic geography of Europe ... is one that has been keenly felt. ... Americans have long hoped that Europeans would supply a suitable textbook [but] no satisfactory textbook on Europe by Europeans has appeared.

Theirs was a much more substantial work than that of Smith; but in many respects it was not different. An introductory section discussed the continent as a whole, while the second part, accounting for about two-thirds of the text, described the individual countries. The book concluded with a short statistical appendix. Moreover, much of the explanation was exceptionalist and was couched in terms of environmental control, including that of the differing accessibility of the various parts of the continent to the oceans, and thus to other parts of the world. Sub-headings such as 'Climate, climatic regions, and health', 'Contrasts in soil, vegetation, and agriculture', 'How mining and minerals have influenced European civilisation', and 'Leadership based on coal and iron' indicate the type of explanation offered for the location of economic activities; and there was frequent reference to the work of one of the leading environmental determinists of the time, Ellsworth Huntington.

Writing since the Second World War

In view of these drawbacks, it is of interest to note that no other advanced economic geography of the whole continent has appeared since that of Blanchard and Visher. However, it is not surprising, for developments in geography have combined with political changes within Europe since 1931 to encourage several, quite different, approaches to the topic. Firstly, regional geographies accorded ever-longer sections to economic activities, but gave up the attempt to cover the whole of Europe. For instance, whereas Newbigin's *Southern Europe: A Regional and Economic Geography of the Mediterranean Lands* of 1932 included minimal economic content, despite its title, Monkhouse's *A regional geography of western Europe*, Mutton's *Central Europe* and Pounds' *Eastern Europe*, which were all published in the late 1950s and 1960s, gave much space to agriculture, industry, transport and trade. There was, however, little or no suggestion in these books that the economies of the chosen groups of countries were functionally linked in any way which might exert a significant influence upon the location or nature of the economic activities within them. Nor was the basis of their explanations different from that of earlier writers. Secondly, during the 1970s several more-specialised texts appeared, each dealing with a limited range of economic activities or regional problems. For instance, Hoffman published *Regional Development Strategy in Southeast Europe: A Comparative Analysis of Albania, Bulgaria, Greece, Romania and Yugoslavia* in 1972; and, in 1975, Clout edited *Regional Development in Western Europe*, and Mellor published *Eastern Europe: A Geography of the Comecon Countries*, while Turnock wrote about the manufacturing and mining industries of eastern Europe in 1978. Meanwhile, Parker's *The Logic of Unity* sought not so much to describe and explain the economic geography of the continent, as to advocate the entry of Britain to the European Economic Community at a time of much debate about whether the country should persist with its application for membership.

More recently, however, several authors have produced economic geographies of a rather different type. In 1978, Minshull published *The New Europe: An Economic Geography of The EEC*. Williams' *The Western European Economy: A Geography of Post-War Development* appeared in 1987, Turnock's *Eastern Europe: An Economic and Political Geography* in 1989, Pinder's *Western Europe: Challenge and Change* in 1990, and Bradshaw's *The Soviet Union: A New Regional Geography?* in 1991. The approach of these is in marked contrast to earlier texts. Gone is the country-by-country format: chapters address such topics as small firms, technological change and uneven regional development, drawing upon the experiences of all the countries within the area of study. Furthermore, no attempt is made to provide a comprehensive account of all the countries or regions, be they 'natural' or otherwise. Rather, it is the concept of the 'space economy' – the competition between producers for the most lucrative sites for their activities (see Box 1) – which underlies the discussion. In so far as regional studies remain, they serve only as examples of areas experiencing the successes or problems of development which are to be found in any space economy. Thus, regions are delimited not so much by geology or climate as by unemployment and emigration, or because they are areas of investment and population growth. Indeed, the emphasis is explicitly upon the factors of production of capital and labour as these are drawn out of backward or depressed areas into regions of 'accumulation', and upon the links which exist between the economic development of one area and others – upon 'core and periphery'. References to the physical environment are very brief, and are not presented as the primary explanation of either the spatial arrangement of economic activities or the level of development.

Some of these texts also reflect an appreciation of the fact that those arrangements are not permanent, nor necessarily very long lasting, and that they are usually altered less by major, catastrophic and external events than by the normal workings of the economy itself. The fact that competition is always in the process of building up new types of economic activity, each with its own locational requirements, while destroying others, that economic change is endogenous and may display temporal regularities, that capital and labour are constantly on the move in response to such changes, and that all these changes have to be negotiated between the various forms of capital and between capital and labour, often through the medium of the state, is accorded a place within the explanation of the economic geography of Europe for the first time. Thus, Williams describes the aim of his book as follows:

> there is a need to review the changing economic geography of post-war Europe in a new light, whereby study of patterns (of firms, coal mines, etc.) is replaced by analysis of the processes which produce these – that is, capital accumulation and the tensions between capital, labour and the state (p. 12).

Three additional points should be made about geographical writing on Europe since the Second World War. Firstly, while the pre-war authors paid little attention to the new form of government in the Soviet Union, and certainly did not see it as a reason to exclude the country from their accounts, those writing after the war have perceived the continent to be divided into discrete blocs, any one of which could be discussed without more than passing reference to the others. Western Europe has been the subject of several studies, as has eastern Europe; but this latter area has rarely, if ever, included any part of the Soviet Union. Indeed, that country has more usually been considered on its own. Only Mutton, in her *Central Europe*, which covered Austria, Czechoslovakia, Germany, both East and West, and Switzerland, has attempted to bridge the political division; but her book would appear to have been more an emulation of Partsch's *Mitteleuropa* of 1904 than an examination of the consequences of the Iron Curtain for the countries on either side of it. Moreover, the definition of the blocs has not been constant. 'Western' Europe has not always include Scandinavia, and sometimes has referred only to the European Economic Community, however that was composed at the time of writing. Similarly, 'Eastern' Europe has sometimes, but not always, included East Germany. The Soviet Union, in contrast, has everywhere been treated as a single country, from the Baltic to the Pacific.

Secondly, this fragmentation of interest has been accompanied by the emergence of contrasting approaches to the various parts of the continent. Those writing about western Europe in the 1970s placed much emphasis upon regional planning. In the 1980s, in contrast, as planning fell from favour, the economic geography of the area was presented largely as the result of the internal workings of capitalism, ameliorated in part by the activities of the state. Meanwhile, those writing on eastern Europe were concerned very largely with the system of central planning, and the blueprints for economic development which it produced. However, their analysis was generally shallow in comparison with those of the capitalist space economy; and the relationship between the internal workings of the system, as revealed by Kornai, and the spatial arrangement of its economic activities, was hardly explored. Books about the Soviet Union, such as those by Cole and Symons, were largely, but not entirely, of the general geography type, paying much attention to the physical environment, and emphasising the possibilities and problems which it offers for economic development, in something of the same way that the land-use and regional planning agencies of the country might have done. In short, there is a suspicion that, in adopting such contrasting approaches, authors have been drawn unwittingly into writing books that are in keeping with the prevailing public view of the area under study, rather than looking at it more disinterestedly. If it is the case that there will always be a need for some state involvement, be it of regional or other forms of planning, within the capitalist economy because of the continuing existence of market failure, and that in consequence there will always be something of relevance for economic geographers to say on the topic, so there is no good reason why such concepts as leading and lagging regions, core and periphery, and economic restructuring, which have traditionally been employed in the study of such economies, should have been eschewed in discussions of eastern Europe. There is, indeed, much evidence to suggest that the economic geography of Europe, both east and west, could have been commonly approached from any one of several, sceptical standpoints, as Bradshaw and his colleagues have demonstrated in their application of some of the concepts of economic restructuring to the Soviet Union.

Thirdly, although Chisholm claimed that:

> One of the chief uses, if not absolutely the most important of all the uses of Commercial or Economic geography, is to enable us to form some reasonable estimate of the future course of commercial development, so far as that is governed by geographical conditions (p. 16)

there is very little discussion about the future pattern of economic activities in any of the most recent texts. Few have followed the bold example of Hall in *Europe 2000*, who essayed the economic and social prospects from 1977 using an eclectic approach, in which extrapolations of present trends were assessed in the light of the wider experience of the probable range of events, as indicated by history. Grenon and Batisse's *Futures for the Mediterranean Basin* (1989) focuses on that area alone, while Masser, Svidén and Wegener's *Geography of Europe's Futures* (1992) is concerned largely with the western half of the continent. The unwillingness of those writing about eastern Europe to hazard an opinion as to how the economic geography of that area might change is especially disappointing when it is remembered that development there until 1989 was undertaken against the background of detailed short-term, medium-term and perspective plans. Indeed, there appears to have been little attempt even to assess the realism, or otherwise, of those plans. However, these authors have not been the only ones who, after describing the development of the present pattern, have left readers to draw their own conclusions about the future economic geography of Europe. In spite of his claim, Chisholm did not provide a 'reasonable estimate of the future course of commercial development'; and neither have most of those who have written about western Europe.

The challenge of Europe

Thus, Europe offers the economic geographer a challenge. No new text dealing with the whole of the continent has been published since 1931, despite the fact that developments in one part of it since then have not been independent of those in others. But the matter is now much more urgent. As what was the Soviet Union disintegrates; as its successor republics and the countries of eastern Europe express their wish for closer economic links with the West; and as barriers to trade and migration are lowered throughout the continent, the economic geography of Europe will inevitably become more interdependent than before. Some form of 'common European home' may be established. Alternatively, it may not. The future is not only uncertain, but disputed between the interested parties; and the purpose of this book is to identify the circumstances of the moment, and indicate what is likely to happen in the future, by way of informing current debate.

But is the task of describing, explaining and predicting the economic geography of the whole continent too great? Those economic geographies which were published before the Second World War tended to be encyclopaedic in both content and size; and even those which have appeared since about more restricted areas have not been slim. However, comprehensiveness in that sense is not the aim. Nor is it necessary, for, if it is the case that the game of economic geography which producers play is to seek out and exploit more lucrative sites for their activities than those of their competitors, taking advantage of both the institutional opportunities and those of the physical environment, it follows that the general nature of that game is at least as interesting as its detail. The abandonment of exceptionalism by geographers relieves the writer of the need to give an account of every industry and region within Europe, after the manner of Chisholm and McFarlane, and allows for detail of that sort to be subsumed within more general discussions of economic development. That is not to say that common processes of change produce identical results in all places, for clearly they do not, but that similar effects occur in different regions, and that it is the recognition and analysis of the types of effect, rather than of the regions, which should be given priority.

Nevertheless, if the purpose is not to describe each region, but to address more general trends; and, if the aim is not to concentrate upon the particular enterprise or industry, but to examine the common relationships between those competing for sites within the space economy, is it justifiable to consider the economic geography of an area which is smaller than that within which that competition occurs? In other words, should this account not be of Europe's place within the global economic system? Earlier books dealing with individual countries or blocs appear to have been written on the assumption that those entities displayed significant degrees of self-sufficiency or local closure, and that external influences upon them were either limited or strictly controlled. But, just as the fact that the blocs within Europe are now dissolving is one of the most important reasons for this book, so it can be argued that Europe is also open to changes from elsewhere; and, in these circumstances, the question might be raised as to what justification there is for considering Europe on its own? The internationalisation of capital since the early nineteenth century, mass migrations in search of work and a better standard of living both into and out of Europe over the same period, and trade between the continent and the rest of the world, have all been as large, if not larger, than the comparable movements within Europe; and the effects of these movements upon the economic geography of the continent have been immense. Nor is there any reason to believe that such situations will not occur again, for there are many individuals, firms and governments in Europe that wish for improved opportunities for trade with areas elsewhere; and many in other parts of the world who are requesting access to the continent. Nevertheless, since the fall of the Berlin Wall, public debate in Europe has focused on the development of new relationships within the continent, rather than upon links with the rest of the world. That focus may be inappropriate, and the assumption behind it – that economic integration will be both possible and beneficial – may be wrong; but, while it exists, the probable effects of such developments should be examined.

However, if Europe is to be the focus of attention – and, if that implies that the half of the continent which lies within what has been the Soviet Union is not to be excluded – should this study also encompass the rest of that huge country, three-quarters of which lies in Asia? Earlier writers have been criticised above for ignoring the influence of one part of, first, Russia, and, then, the Soviet Union, upon the economic geography of the other; and therefore it would seem appropriate that those parts of it which lie outwith Europe, but which are relevant to its economic geography, should be considered here. That does not, however, include the whole country, for much of what was Soviet Asia lies beyond the œcumene, or habitable area. This is not to say that it is uninhabited, for many thousands of native peoples live in the forests and along the rivers of Siberia. But those people have contributed little to the Soviet economy, and are only weakly connected with it. Although they are able to survive in the harsh environments of that area by trapping, fishing and the herding of reindeer, their economy, which in many cases is nomadic, is not one which would support a dense population or a developed economy of the European type. It is also true that the Soviet Union has exploited some of the huge mineral and timber resources of the northern forests; has established ports on the Arctic and Pacific coasts; has built roads, railways and pipelines across Siberia and Central Asia; has banished political prisoners to those outlying areas; and has used the more remote northern islands and the seas around them for nuclear tests and the dumping of toxic waste. Population has been increasing sharply in some of these areas in recent decades, though the absolute numbers have been small (Dewdney 1990). Furthermore, it can be argued that the whole territory of the Soviet Union has been subject to a common system of economic planning and set of policies – that all these areas have been part of the functional region which has been the Soviet economy.

They have not, however, all been part of the Soviet space economy. In the past, economic planners and industrial ministries have not considered all parts of the country when deciding where to produce; nor is it likely that the newly-independent republican authorities and any privatised enterprises will do so, for much of the country is not useful to them. Large parts of what has been Soviet Asia provide no more than a reserve of sites for economic activities, available to be brought into use in the future, but only if some new technology remedies their sub-marginal character, or if the demands on those within the present space economy increase greatly. Some polluted areas may be too dangerous to be used. However, rather than expanding, it would appear that the Soviet space economy may be about to contract. French has drawn attention to the migration of people from Siberia. Shabad has noted the quiet abandonment of major investments there; and Bond and Giroux have commented on the likely intensification of the economy west of the Urals, in preference to further expansion into peripheral areas, under the twelfth five-year plan, which was announced in 1986. In short, much of what was Soviet Asia is of limited relevance to an examination of the economic geography of Europe; and this study will cover only the continuously-settled areas of south-western Siberia and north Kazakhstan which are contiguous with European Russia (Figure I.1). Deserts, both hot and cold, will be excluded, as will those parts of the former Soviet Union, some of which are now independent states, which are separated from the continuously-settled area of Europe by such areas.

It follows from this argument that much of the north-west of Russia and northern Scandinavia should also be omitted. In *Scandinavia: A New Geography*, John identifies four economic zones – the economic heartland, peripheral zone, pioneer fringe and the economically marginal – the third and fourth of which are similar to the northern parts of Siberia. Densities of population do not exceed five per square kilometre; three-quarters of the inhabitants are concentrated in a few ports, mining towns and military bases whose strategic significance has been reduced by the ending of the Cold War; and the rest of the area, much of which is inaccessible to all except the most specialised forms of modern transport, is the preserve of native reindeer herders and trappers, if it is used at all. More than half of Finland, Norway and Sweden fall into these two zones – which are shown in Figure I.2 as 'beyond the periphery' – and those areas of European Russia which lie north of sixty degrees are very similar.

Figure I.1 The European space economy

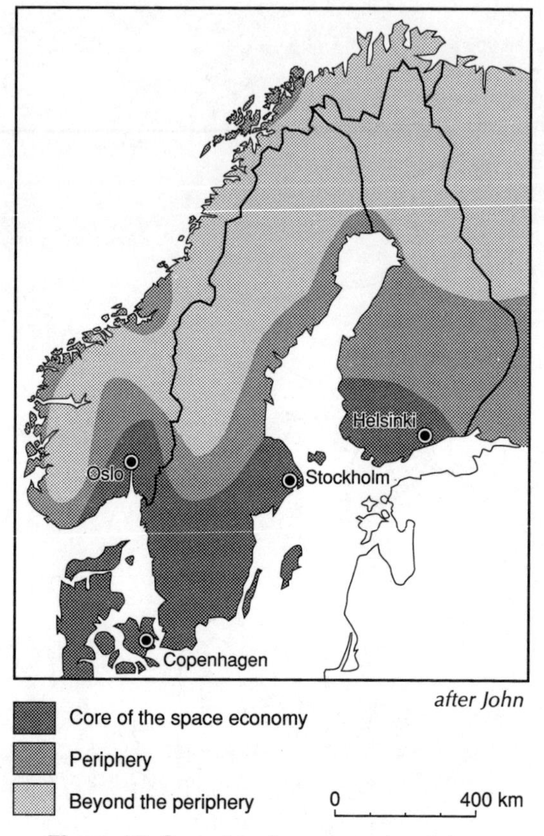

Figure I.2 Scandinavia: core and periphery

The approach of the book

There is also a question as to how the economic geography of Europe should be presented. Blanchard and Visher started their account with a description of the physical environment, Minshull with that of the relationship of the 'nation state' to the EEC, and Williams with the economy. This book will follow none of these approaches. Rather, it will begin with the issue of the moment – the nature of the integrated space economy. What will happen as a result of the establishment of the Single Market within the European Community? What will be the effect of the Association Agreements which have been signed between the Community and Czechoslovakia, Hungary and Poland? What consequences would flow from monetary union within the Community, or the admission of those countries of EFTA and eastern Europe that wish to join it?

These are the questions of the moment; and they are questions about the integration of national and hitherto separate space economies. More particularly, they concern the effects which may follow from the freeing of trade, and from the granting of rights to firms from one country to conduct business in others, and to workers and investors to operate not only at home, but also abroad. Before the First World War, the economic geography of Europe was much affected by the movement of capital and labour, as well as by trade. Western European investors financed much of the textile industry and railways in the Russian Empire. Polish workers were employed in large numbers by Prussian farmers and German mine-owners. Trade flowed between the industrial northwest of the continent and the more agricultural east. Little of this, however, was discussed by the writers mentioned earlier; and imports and exports were relegated to statistical appendices – afterthoughts – in their books, despite their relevance to the growth of production in one part of Europe, rather than another. Nor did the barriers to trade, which governments increasingly erected during the latter part of the nineteenth century, and especially between the world wars, and which sought to protect domestic producers while causing the decline of those located elsewhere, receive much attention. Some progress has been made since the Second World War to free trade in both goods and services, and to permit the movement of capital and labour, between the countries of western Europe, but many obstacles remain; and it is these which are now the subject of public discussion.

The impact of their removal could be considerable. Some economists have considered in theory the effects of the integration of previously-separated space economies, while others have drawn attention to what they see to be disturbing examples of what has resulted. Perhaps the most influential of these has been Myrdal, who published *Economic Theory and Under-Developed Regions* in 1957, while Holland and Seers (1979, 1980) have both written about the effects of integration within the Community. Their work will be reviewed in Chapter 1 by way of indicating what changes may be expected from any further integration within Europe, and as a model against which the degree of integration of its space economy in the early 1990s, which is set out in Chapter 2, may be measured.

Any future economic geography of Europe must also necessarily reflect the present pattern of economic activities, and the trends within it. That pattern is not a recent creation. Rather, it is the result of centuries of technical innovation, and of the new types of production, and associated patterns of settlement and land use, to which those innovations have given rise. No account of the economic geography of the continent would be complete without some acknowledgement of these. But this is not to argue that this book should be an economic history, nor that it is necessary to repeat here the accounts of the origins of the economic geography of Europe by East, W.H. Parker, Pounds (1974, 1979, 1990) and C.T. Smith. Rather, it is to suggest that some attention should be paid to the ways in which economic activities, countries and regions have been developing in the recent past.

The problem is: when to begin? Williams' answer is 1945; but that date, despite its significance for many aspects of European history, is unconnected with the way in which the economy has developed as a result of its own momentum, or with the periodicities which are endogenous to it. Some of the economy's own time scales, such as the business cycle, are well documented, while the existence of others, such as the Kuznets Swing, are more controversial. Even more controversial is the Kondratiev or Long Wave, the fifty-year fluctuation in the international prices of commodities, which was subsequently linked by Schumpeter to innovations and the rise and decline of industries (see Box 1). Nevertheless, it is this time frame which will be used here, precisely because it is the one which has been associated with the creation of new products, methods of production and industries; with the destruction of those thus rendered obsolete; and with all the consequences for the growth of new settlements, the decline of others, and the movement of labour and capital between the two, which is the very stuff of economic geography. This is not to claim that all recent economic change in Europe can be explained by reference to Long Waves – some writers dismiss Long Wave theory as lacking any explanatory power – but that they provide a temporal context for discussions of such change which has been linked, at least by some, to processes which are endogenous to developed economies.

However, the Long Wave may be especially controversial in the context of this book, for it was identified by Kondratiev, a Soviet statistician, during a study of capitalist economies, and thus may be held to be inapplicable to the analysis of an area, half of which has spent the last seventy years under the communist system of central planning. One can only note that it was precisely because those economies which were based upon central planning and public ownership were unable to exchange the phase of 'extensive' economic growth of the 1950s and 1960s for 'intensive' growth thereafter, in part because of their failure to keep up with innovations elsewhere, and thus fell behind in the economic race, that the crisis of 1989 occurred (Kontorovich 1992). Thus it is that Section III will provide an account of the chief developments – technological, sectoral and spatial – in the economic geography of Europe during the last of the four Long Waves, which began with the Great Slump of the 1930s and may have ended in western Europe with the recessions of the 1980s and 1990s, and in eastern Europe and the Soviet Union with the collapse of 1989-91.

The impact of any closer integration of the countries of Europe upon the spatial arrangement of their economic activities will also be influenced by the natural and other resources which they possess. Chisholm drew particular attention to the 'natural advantages' associated with the physical environment to the shaping of the economic geography of any area; and many other, early, writers considered them to be of primary importance. Bradshaw and Williams, in contrast, hardly mention them. Both positions would seem to be mistaken. In the past, climate and soils, landforms and minerals did, indeed, exert a very considerable influence upon which areas were settled, and which ignored. The centres of population which exist today are in part the legacy of such environmental 'controls'. Nor are they irrelevant to future developments in agriculture, extractive industry, tourism and other activities. However, that is not to say that the present pattern of settlement and land use is environmentally determined. Most sites can be used variously. Moreover, the distribution of population, and therefore of labour and markets, is at least as important a consideration in the location decisions of producers as is the physical environment. Put another way, the economy operates against the background of a map of opportunities which reflects the characteristics of both site and situation. The return from some sites is less than the expense involved in using them, and they remain empty. But that from others is greater, not on account of the improvements which some entrepreneur or government has made to them, but because of their inherent characteristics, be they physical or human. In short, there is a map of economic rents (see Box 1) which will affect not only the use to which each piece of land is put, but also with what intensity; and it is that map, rather than the physical environment alone or direct, which is of interest to the economic geographer.

It is also a map which reflects the damage that Europeans have done to their environment. The cutting of timber and extraction of minerals have greatly altered the opportunities for further development in many parts of the continent, as have the erosion of soils and pollution of land, air and water. Some of this damage is capable of repair; but some represents a permanent reduction of productive potential. Either way, the economic rents of some sites have been reduced, and, in the case of the most damaged areas, rendered negative. Moreover, the map is not constant. Many economic geographies in the past began their explanations by describing the physical environment, implying that its influence was unchanging. That cannot be so. Land, like the other factors of production, offers a range of financial returns; but a range which is contingent upon the structure and technology of the economy itself, and which changes as new industries draw people and capital from old to new locations. Therefore, rather than describe the physical environment, it will be the map of opportunities for profit and accumulation, but also of environmental damage, as these exist today, which will be examined in this book. Furthermore, this will be undertaken not by way of introduction, but in Section IV, as a foundation for the assessment as to how it, together with the institutional and economic circumstances described in the two preceding sections, may combine to shape the future economic geography of Europe.

Recent events would seem to suggest that that future will be very different – that the economic geography of Europe will, indeed, be reshaped into some 'unfamiliar territory', to use Hebbert and Hansen's phrase. Following the changes of 1989, it was widely expected that central planning and public ownership would be replaced by the market and privatisation; that the fragmentation of the European economy would give way to its integration; and that, in consequence, the economies of eastern Europe would go into steep decline, that there would be wholesale closures among the primitive, polluting and unproductive factories there, that unemployment would soar, and that thousands, if not millions, of people would stream westwards in search of work. If ever events could be described as epoch-making, these might be they. Will there be a 'common European home'; and, if so, what will it look like? These questions will be essayed in Section V.

Summary

Over the last century, several accounts have been given of the economic geography of Europe. Early ones explained that geography primarily in terms of the influence of the natural environment and of particular historical events; but later studies have argued that geographers should be more interested in the workings of the economy, and in particular in the way in which competition between people and firms leads to product and process innovation, the search for profitable locations, the reassessment of the use to which sites are put, and to migration and settlement change – in short, to the spatial patterns of growth and decline. This section has described how the economic geography of some parts of Europe has, indeed, come to be explained in such terms. But no attempt has yet been made to describe the continent as a whole from such a viewpoint, or to take up the challenge, which the collapse of its communist governments has created, of assessing the likely effects of the closer integration of its economies in the light of that approach. It is that challenge which this book seeks to address.

Further reading

Readers who wish to acquire a more detailed view of the way in which the presentation of the economic geography of Europe has changed are invited to compare Blanchard and Visher's *Economic geography of Europe*, which was published in 1931, with Bradshaw's *The Soviet Union: A new regional geography?* of 1991, and Williams' *The western European economy: A geography of post-war development*, of 1987.

Pounds' *An historical geography of Europe* (1990) provides a good introduction to the development of the economic geography of the continent up to the early twentieth century.

Section II
The integrated space economy

Attention was drawn in Section I to the fact that many early writers of economic geography treated Europe as if it were a series of countries whose economies were but weakly connected. International trade, if it was mentioned at all, was often an afterthought, while movements of capital and labour between states were largely ignored. Only recently have attempts been made to explore the economic links between countries; and many of these have been no more than investigations of common problems or systems of economic management. Few have investigated the way in which developments in one country impact upon the economic geography of others; and no text has attempted this for the whole of Europe. But this is the issue which is now on the public agenda, as political and economic leaders throughout Europe discuss the desirability of strengthening the links between countries, and the case for and against relinquishing national controls over economic management to larger, international groups.

Supporters of European economic integration claim that it will yield economies of scale, and lead to the relocation of activities in low-cost sites; that welfare will be increased; and that the binding together of the states of Europe will prevent the outbreak of further ruinous wars between them. They argue that the market for capital is now largely independent of individual governments; and that the only way to ensure the currency stability which is necessary to encourage investment is to replace Europe's many national currencies by a single one. They point to the fact that the dominant players in the world economy – the multinational companies – are now so powerful that their investment decisions can no longer be controlled by the governments of even medium-sized countries; and they assume that integration will take place within the framework of the free market, after the manner of that already established by the European Community.

Critics, in contrast, fear that this type of integration will give rise to deflationary policies, and worsen the position of the continent's peripheral regions. They point to a continuing need for some sort of economic planning, regional assistance and industrial policy, though not necessarily those which have been going out of fashion in western Europe since the end of the Long Boom, and demand new and swingeing taxes on polluters and private transport. A few even argue for a return to the central planning of the international division of labour which characterised the economic integration of eastern Europe under Comecon. If the gap between rich and poor in Europe continues to widen, and if pollution and social unrest continue to increase, their time may come again.

But, first, we should examine in more detail what might be meant by an integrated space economy, and what the effects of the integration of formerly-separate economies within a free market might be for the spatial arrangement of their activities. We do this in Chapter 1. We should also ask how near Europe is to such integration now; and this will be considered in Chapter 2.

CHAPTER 1

SOME MODELS

An integrated space economy might be defined as one in which the only restraints on the freedom to conduct business would be those imposed by the natural environment. The exchange of goods between one part of it and another might be inhibited by the costs of transporting them, but would not be limited by quotas, tariffs or differences in technical, safety or other standards among the countries within it. Firms offering services in one country would not be impeded from doing so in others. The movement of labour would not be restricted by immigration controls or the non-transferability of insurance and pension rights; and unemployment and social security benefits would be uniform throughout the area. The flow of capital across the boundaries within such a space economy would not be controlled by governments, or made more expensive by the requirement to change currency; and some common means of exchange might be used. Producers in one area would be uniquely advantaged, not by lower taxes, special payments or less stringent employment, health or pollution regulations than in others, or by preferential purchase policies by governments favouring their own citizens, but only by their access to fertile soils, minerals, and other natural resources or to centres of population offering them cheap or skilled labour or markets, and to regional and other aids which would be made available in all parts of the space economy in response to similar levels of need. In such a space economy there would be free trade and fair competition; and capital and labour would be able to move in response to the changing pattern of demand for them. In other words, locational behaviour within an integrated space economy would be similar, though not identical, to that in a single state.

Economists have suggested that the results of the establishment of such a 'level playing field', as it has been called, among a group of countries which had previously been separated by trade and other barriers could be considerable. The extent to which their economies would be affected would probably depend, amongst other things, upon:

— the degree to which one country held a natural advantage over others in the production of goods and services;

— the distance between them;
— the size of their markets;
— the extent to which the structures of their economies were competitive, rather than complementary;
— the severity of the quotas or height of the tariff barriers between them; and
— the stringency of their immigration policies and controls over movements of capital.

Some would benefit, but others might suffer; and much of the debate about integration has been provoked by the possibility that it might lead to diverging standards of living amongst participating countries.

Models of the integrated space economy fall into two broad groups. Some appear to be based upon the assumption that economies adjust fully to changes in their circumstances, and that divergence does not occur. Others take the opposite view. This chapter will outline a selection of the arguments from each group, and will conclude by drawing some of the lessons which arise from this debate for a second and related discussion, namely, that between those who would give preference to the 'deepening' of the links which already exist between countries, and those who argue instead for their extension – 'widening' – to other states.

The integrated space economy at equilibrium

Neo-classical, equilibrium models of the economy assume that, once barriers to trade are removed, markets will function properly; prices of goods and services, and also of capital and labour, among participating countries will converge; and that the 'efficient allocation of resources' between different types of production and location will be achieved. The consequent distribution of economic activities will reflect the comparative advantage of the countries, with each specialising in those in which it can produce more cheaply than others; and the extent of the changes associated with integration will probably be greater for neighbouring, but small, countries which were previously separated by substantial barriers to trade and factor movements and had competitive production structures, than for others. However, while trade may increase between those countries which are linked, exporters from third countries may lose the markets they previously enjoyed: integration may create trade, but it may also divert it. It is also likely that large numbers of small-scale producers, working inefficiently in limited and separated markets, will be replaced by a few large ones, each supplying markets in more than one of the countries which are thus connected (Balassa 1961, Dunning 1972).

Where, exactly, these producers are likely to locate has been indicated by a variety of writers. One of the first was Christaller (1933), writing against the

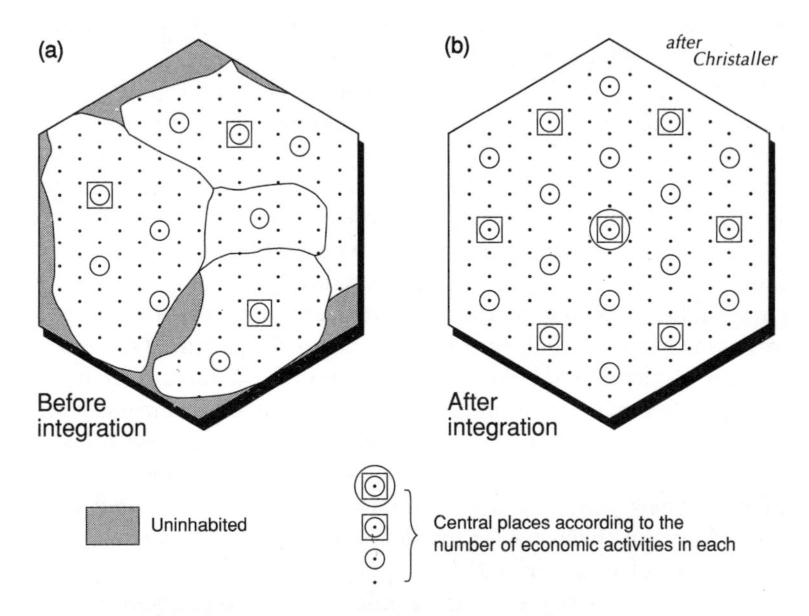

Figure II.1 (a and b) A Christallan space economy

background of the unification of the mass of states and principalities which came together to form Germany during the nineteenth century, but also the break-up of the hitherto integrated Austro-Hungarian Empire in 1918. Although his purpose was not to discuss the question of the integration of the space economy, except in very limited circumstances, he did draw attention to the contrasts which would exist in space economies operating on the 'market', as distinct from the 'separation', principle. Under the latter, which Christaller associated with the early stages of economic development, communities would each focus upon a capital city, in which a range of more specialised activities would be undertaken, and around which there would be a

> wreath of satellite places of lesser importance, and toward the edge of the region a thinning population density – and even uninhabited areas (Christaller 1966, p. 77).

Market areas would be discrete, and would be separated from those around them by borders which would be areas of little or no economic activity (Figure II.1 (a)). Christaller implied that space economies organised around the market principle would, in contrast, be continuous, or at least much larger; that the level of demand within them would be greater; and that this would allow the production of more specialised goods and services within them. Moreover, his theory indicates that the production of those goods and services would be undertaken only at sites which were accessible to a market area offering the necessary threshold level of demand, that is, sites which were central to the integrated market, and which might, therefore, serve an area greater than that of the country in which they lay.

This distinction implies at least three types of change in space economies following integration. Firstly, because the number of locations which would acquire levels of demand in excess of those in individual national markets (and thus be likely to enjoy the greatest benefits of integration) would almost certainly be fewer than the number of those markets, central places in some states would grow faster than those in others. Secondly, one location in particular would benefit. That would be the central place supplying the service which would be peculiar to the integrated economy – the supranational organisation charged with the introduction and management of the process of integration – which would become the pinnacle of the hierarchy of administrative centres, and the economic capital of the group of countries. National capitals, in contrast, would lose those powers and activities which had been ceded to the new authority. Christaller's theory implies, thirdly, that border areas between newly-integrated economies would cease to be isolated, and that settlements within them, whose market areas had hitherto been truncated, would grow until they reached their appropriate level in the central place hierarchy. Thus, the space economy would adjust to integration, and might come to look like that in Figure II.1(b).

There are also implications for the form of the transport network of neighbouring states, and the distribution of economic activities among their settlements, which Christaller did examine. He suggested that, following the removal of barriers between neighbouring countries, traffic would increase, and that this would encourage the improvement of the routes between them. Routes which formerly terminated at frontiers might be linked with those on the opposite side; and a series of direct, high-quality routes would come into existence between the major centres of population (Christaller 1966, pp. 113–14). These ideas would seem to imply that large agglomerations of economic activities would inevitably become the foci of not only national, but also international, transport facilities, while some smaller places would be bypassed. In other words, the separate national transport systems would be replaced by a single one, in which the highest-order central places would become the hubs, and in which the smaller and more peripheral places, including perhaps the capital cities of smaller countries, would be connected only by transport routes of lesser capacity. The increased accessibility of the largest places would increase their markets, and strengthen their ability to attract manufacturing and service industries. Areas which were not connected directly to the new routes would, in contrast, become relatively less attractive.

Thus, Christaller discussed several of the circumstances in which central places would not only be founded and grow, but also those in which they might lose activities; and he acknowledged that such losses might cause substantial problems of downward adjustment, affecting levels of employment, the capital stock, and the value and intensity of land use. However, he assumed that

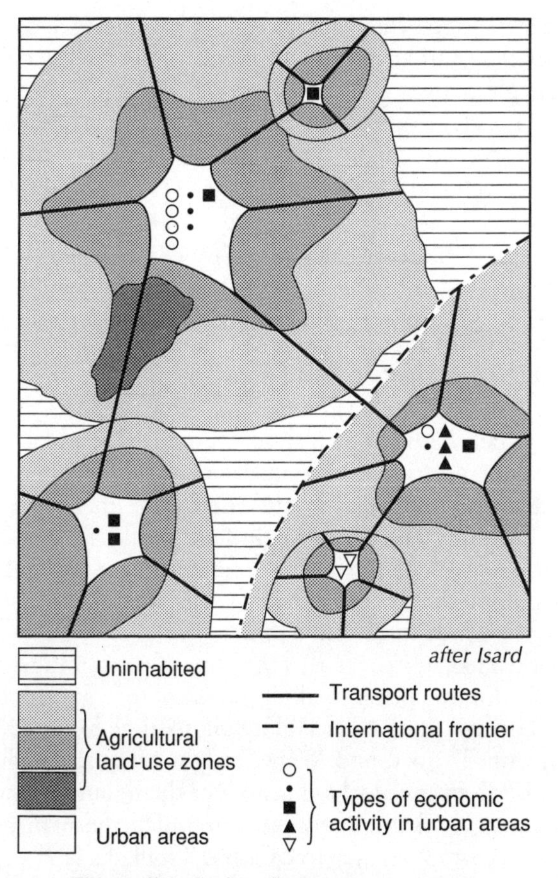

Figure II.2 An Isardian space economy

adjustments of this sort would be made in full, claiming that 'we may conclude that the transition from one rank of importance to another is quickly accomplished' (1966, p. 130).

Another contributor, if only indirectly, to discussion of the form of the integrated space economy was Isard. In 1956, he attempted to bring together the theories of von Thünen, Weber and Lösch, along with that of international trade, to create a general theory of location. He did not discuss the way in which formerly-separated economies might develop as a result of the removal of institutional barriers between them; but he did consider what might happen as economies grow, as their transport links with each other improve, and as, in consequence, the conditions of production in one impact upon others through trade. However, he assumed that neither capital nor labour would be able to move between different countries. The conclusions of *Location and Space-Economy* were that economies of scale, localisation and urbanisation would encourage the formation of large urban agglomerations, each containing many different industries, and that these agglomerations would be separated by extensive areas given over to a much smaller range of production, chiefly agriculture and forestry. Agricultural land lying close to agglomerations might be intensively worked, as might areas with soil of exceptional fertility. Land which was further away would be used more extensively; and some, which was far from markets or suffered from poor soils or harsh climates, might remain unused. The range of industries in each agglomeration would probably differ from those in other agglomerations in the same country, after the manner of Weber's theory of the location of manufacturing, and from those in other countries, according to the principles of comparative advantage. The space economy would be served by a series of transport routes. Some would link rural areas with their markets in the agglomerations. Some would link agglomerations, thus facilitating trade between their different industries; and a third set would join together those countries which traded with each other. The pattern of land use in both urban and rural areas would reflect these lines of improved access; and the space economy as a whole might look similar to that in Figure II.2. However, all this was discussed within the framework of the equilibrium of the firm, and based upon the view, like that of Christaller, that the space economy would converge towards some stable form.

Christaller assumed, moreover, that the game of economic geography would be played on a uniform plane, making no allowance for the impact which variations in fertility or the availability of natural resources, of the sort considered by von Thünen and Weber, might make upon the location of central places. Isard, in contrast, did introduce them; but he ignored both the role of government, and the many ways in which the management of the economy may vary from country to country. Tsoukalis (1991, pp. 82-3) has suggested, however, that:

> Comparative advantage is no longer seen as something determined by the particular factor endowments of a country. Instead, comparative advantage is created through deliberate policies directed at investment, education, and research and development. Countries pursue strategic trade policies in order to capture an ever-increasing share of dynamic sectors where demand is growing and where the benefits of scale economies, advantages of experience, and innovation can be reaped; in economic terms, sectors where there are good prospects for 'rent'. ... Such a world ... is thousands of miles apart from the assumptions made by traditional theories of international trade.

While it would be wrong to ignore the physical environment entirely, as we shall show in Section IV, Tsoukalis has drawn attention to a further, and an important, set of conditions which are likely to affect the location of activities following any integration of hitherto-separated economies.

Siebert (1991) has developed this point. He suggests that, following the establishment of free trade, and the deregulation of capital markets, amongst any group of countries, there will be a competition between their institutional arrangements, in which each country, having its own system of economic management, and thus being distinctive but immobile, will compete with others for the mobile factors of production, and especially capital. Economies with attractive systems will grow, while those which are less favoured will find themselves under pressure to reform. He offers this sketch both as an explanation of the collapse of systems, such as that of central planning, in the past, and as a means of harmonising those which exist amongst groups of countries which wish to integrate their economies in the future. More particularly, he argues that the *ex ante* harmonisation of the institutional arrangements within any group of countries is unworkable, and that the *ex post* route of competition is more in keeping with the free-market ethos. In other words, he claims that market forces will 'level the playing field', and that painstakingly-negotiated, intergovernmental agreements over harmonisation and monetary union, of the type which has excited the derision of opponents of the European Community, are unnecessary. In such a situation, peripheral countries, once inside a single market, will be unable to protect themselves by state aids or taxation regimes favourable to industry, preferential purchasing of domestic products, lower levels of social security provision and environmental protection, or other devices, from the competition of the core, for the costs of these will soon become unsupportable. Meanwhile, any short-term success which they enjoy will provoke core countries to make themselves more attractive to investors, by reducing their expenditure on such items. Thus, conditions within an integrated market will eventually converge, as firms compete away their ability to bargain with individual governments. This is not to say that the systems of economic management will be everywhere the same amongst the countries of an integrated market; but it does imply that the institutional packages in different countries will be such that the marginal costs of the factors of production, and the marginal revenues accruing to them, will be uniform across the integrated economy. However, Siebert does not indicate how long it will take to achieve such a state. Nor does he consider the possibility that institutional adaptation may be inadequate to bring the space economy into balance, following economic integration.

The problem of divergence

Many other writers, however, while accepting that integration may lead to very considerable changes in the space economies of participating countries, and that the extent of these will be closely related to the conditions listed on pages 23–4, reject the assumptions of the neo-classicists as unrealistic, and consider that the free market always contains sufficient elements of monopoly to prevent the achievement of equilibrium. They claim that the growth of employment in some places, and its decline in others, will not be followed by sufficient movement of either labour to growth areas or of capital to declining ones to offset these changes. They suggest that unemployment will rise and stay high in some countries, and that living standards will be lower there than in others. They agree that there will be increased specialisation in the types of activity carried out in the different countries; but they argue that this will not lead to an efficient allocation of resources. Rather, they claim that such specialisation will merely reflect the ability of the more advanced economies to undercut the production of complex goods in the less developed, thereby condemning the latter to be no more than suppliers of primary products (for which the elasticity of demand is low), simple manufactured goods and unsophisticated services. The space economy, they warn, rather than converging upon some equilibrium form, will become unstable.

One of the earliest writers to address the question as to what would happen as a consequence of the integration of previously-separated space economies was Giersch (1949). He suggested that, where many small producers were located widely over an area of uniform conditions for production and consumption, such as that assumed by Christaller, they would be replaced by a smaller number of larger firms, which would prefer locations that were more central to the new, united market. He also suggested that, in a more differentiated environment, firms might concentrate in those areas in which mineral deposits or skilled labour had provided the conditions for the growth of urban and industrial agglomerations; and that, in a newly-integrated space economy, firms would move to the largest of these, whichever country they happened to be in. Producers in peripheral locations, and in locations which were centres of agglomeration only because they lay within what had been protected national markets, would, in contrast, be forced out of production. However, regions which previously were peripheral to their national space economies, but bordered on countries which had been brought within the group, might attract those firms which were anxious to export, but did not wish to move outside their domestic market. He expected that labour would migrate to those places in which economic expansion was occurring, and that the forces of agglomeration in the more favoured locations would be so strong, and the availability of immigrant labour such, that employers would probably not be obliged to consider moving to the regions where the collapse of smaller firms had led to high unemployment. Moreover, he pointed out that, in a free market, those enjoying the external economies created by agglomeration would escape the costs which fall upon peripheral areas as capital and labour withdraw from them, and expressed the view that governments would have a duty to intervene to prevent or remedy such market failures.

But it was Myrdal who was to provide the broad-ranging argument that free markets lead to divergence in the space economy at both national and international scales. He drew attention to the probability that, once a country or region has acquired a competitive advantage, usually as a result of early industrialisation, the free-market movement of capital and labour will lead to a 'circular and cumulative causation' in which the growth of industries there, and of the infrastructure required by their employees and their families, will stimulate yet more growth. External economies will build up, which will be available to any producer who locates in the area; and firms will increasingly be drawn to it. Capital will be invested, and labour attracted. Meanwhile, the converse will be occurring in relatively disadvantaged places. Industries in these areas will find it difficult to compete with those in the core, and may be undercut by imports from them. Jobs and incomes will decline; and, in what he described as the 'backwash' effect, capital and labour will be drawn out of the periphery, thus depressing their economies still further. The growth of demand in the core for the products of the periphery – the 'spread' effect – will not be sufficiently strong to prevent this. The moral which he drew for any integration of economies is plain:

> if there were no exchange controls and if, at the same time, there were no elements in their national development policies securing high profits for capital – i.e. if the forces in the capital market were given unhampered play – capitalists in underdeveloped countries would be exporting their capital. Even with such controls and policies in existence, there is actually a steady flight going on from under-developed countries (Myrdal 1957, p. 53).

He considered that colonies and other poor countries, amongst which he included Italy and Spain, would be especially prone to divergence, both within their space economies and between themselves and the richer, metropolitan nations; and he drew attention to the way in which the integration of peripheral countries with more developed ones has led to an increasing dependence of the former upon the production of primary goods. He elaborated the problems which follow from such specialisation, namely, that the income of peripheral states is likely to grow more slowly than that of the core; that, in recession, the low elasticities of demand for their goods will further reduce their earnings; that, even where the products of peripheral areas are complementary to those of the core, and thus growth in the core is likely to 'trickle down' (Hirschman 1958) most fully, the periphery is likely to be denied any outlet during times of recession for its surplus labour; and that this situation will be made worse in so far as peripheral regions often have faster rates of population growth than the core. It is of interest, in view of what has happened subsequently in Europe, to note that, writing in the mid-1950s, Myrdal considered that the likelihood of large movements of labour from peripheral to core countries was small; and that his conclusion about peripheral countries was that:

> Internationally, for the reasons just given, the spread effects are much weaker and the cumulative process will more easily go in the direction of inequality, if the forces in the market are given their free play (1957, pp. 55–6).

Many subsequent writers have elaborated these arguments. Vernon (1966) did not discuss the consequences of integration explicitly, but he outlined the relationship between the location of manufacturing industry, the product life cycle and the multinational firm. He suggests that innovations are likely to occur in areas with special labour skills, close interaction between research and production, strong market potential and close contact with existing customers; in other words, in developed countries. As the output of any good becomes standardised, however, cost cutting will become imperative; and production will be moved to branch plants or licensees in countries with lower wages, while the more advanced economies change to new products which are in an earlier stage of development. Meanwhile, says Friedman (1972), interaction between firms in core regions is likely to stimulate a permanent increase in the rate of innovation there, and thus of economic growth, and sustain levels of pay which will be far higher than those in the periphery.

What is more, says Klodt (1992), some of the industries which are most important for economic growth may never move to peripheral countries. If a distinction is made between mobile and immobile 'Schumpeterian industries' – research-intensive forms of production in which it is, respectively, easy to carry out research and production in different countries, and those in which the two are so closely connected that it would be inefficient to separate them, even when some of the costs of production are much lower in peripheral locations – it follows that the latter may not be transferred to such places. Thus, the computer and micro-electronic industries would seem to be mobile, for, while their research and development are carried out largely in advanced economies, the manufacture and assembly of their products are often sited in low-wage countries. Conversely, most elements of aerospace production would seem to be located in advanced economies, and would appear, therefore, to be immobile; and biotechnology and pharmaceuticals, in which highly-skilled workers of a type not readily available in many less-developed economies are required in the production process, would seem to be similar.

The multinational structure of firms raises a further point concerning divergence. Giersch assumed that firms conduct no business beyond the boundaries of the integrated economy, but, by the late 1980s, intra-company movements within multinational firms accounted for almost a third of world trade, much transmission of technological progress, and also much overseas investment (Welfens 1992). Such firms, wishing to move standardised forms of production to lower-cost locations, but finding that wage levels within an integrated economy are everywhere higher than those in other parts of the world, may leapfrog the poorer regions of the integrated economy altogether (Molle 1990, pp. 136–143). In other words, the authorities in any integrated economy are unlikely to be able to control its regional development unless they are prepared to raise very high barriers between it and the rest of the world, or expand it to include a very large portion of the œcumene. Otherwise, they are likely to find themselves in the role of supplicants to the major companies, offering them subsidies of one sort or another, or preferential access to markets, in order to persuade them to invest in their lagging regions.

We may summarise the foregoing arguments by concluding that there would seem to be many reasons why, following the integration of economies, standards of living amongst them may diverge; and, agreeing with Seers (1980, p. 12), that 'markets would have to work very hard indeed to inhibit unequal development'.

Divergence – some counter-arguments

However, the process of divergence among advanced economies should not be exaggerated. Just as trade does not flow only in one direction between countries, movements of capital and labour are not usually one way either. Rather, there are usually very many different types of transaction occurring between places, reflecting the complementary nature of their activities and needs. It was Myrdal's view that:

> Nationally, once a country has reached a higher average level of economic development, this tendency [to divergence] will be offset by the spread effects of expansionary momentum and by national integration policies (p. 55),

and that:

> the higher the level of economic development that a country has attained, the stronger the spread effects will usually be (p. 34).

In other words, advanced economies enjoy rapid growth, which enables high labour productivity to be achieved throughout them, and makes the relationships between one region and another more equal and less exploitative than in less developed countries; and similar situations may exist among groups of countries, all of which have advanced economies. Furthermore, developed economies are not based solely upon free market transactions. For instance, all European countries have adopted very substantial public service programmes connected with income redistribution, education and health, which provide high levels of public expenditure and common minimum standards of support throughout their space economies. Thus, convergence or divergence is the result of the net, rather than the aggregate, of all the transactions which make up the external economic relations of an area; and, in the advanced economy, that net flow will often be small in relation to the aggregate.

Nor may the peripheral members of an integrated space economy be perpetual losers. Eventually, growth may lead to significant external diseconomies in the core. Urban agglomerations may become congested, and rich countries may suffer from high labour costs. Businesses may be driven to cheaper locations. Secondly, technical change is constantly altering the locational requirements of existing industries and creating new forms of production – changes which may not only undermine existing cores, but lead to the emergence of new ones. Thirdly, firms based in one integrated space economy, but wishing to establish branch plants within the tariff walls or other barriers surrounding another, will tend to search for sites at which production costs are low; and these are likely to be in the periphery (Vaitsos 1979).

It may also be the case that, whatever the risks of divergence following integration, isolation may be even more potent in fostering unequal development. Murrell (1992), noting that the rise in international trade since the Second World War has been closely connected with the growth of multinational firms and the movements of high-technology components which occur between branch plants within such organisations, has suggested that the low level of trade between eastern and western Europe in the recent past has largely been the result of communist governments shunning such companies. He draws attention to the fact that eastern European trade in advanced goods has been at a significantly lower level than that of the capitalist economies; and he concludes that:

> The absence of cross-border internal organization – multinational corporations – means that the socialist countries have simply been unable to absorb new products as fast as those countries that embrace foreign direct investment

with dire consequences for innovation, productivity and the standard of living in those countries.

The conclusion might be that, although it is probable that few, if any, regions within the space economy at whatever scale are in overall balance with the rest of the world at any moment, such a situation should not be either unexpected or unacceptable, unless it is associated with clear differences in the standard of living between one area and another, and differences which are not declining. Nor should the risk that divergence may occur be used to resist moves towards the integration of isolated economies.

'Deepening' and 'widening'

The discussion about divergence throws light upon recent debates in Europe between those advocating the 'deepening' of integration among the countries which are already linked, and those who prefer to 'widen' those links to include others.

Integration is unlikely to be a single act. Nor is it likely to proceed in the same manner in all cases. Rather, it will probably proceed by steps, in which weak links between countries lead on to stronger ones; and in which the steps adopted in some cases are not necessarily the same, and do not always occur in the same order, as those in others. The following account indicates broadly the sequence which has been adopted in western Europe, and which bids fair to become the model for the whole of the continent.

That sequence may begin with the establishment of a free-trade area. It may proceed thereafter through a customs union and common market to economic and monetary union, carrying with it at this last stage the creation of federal political institutions and the progressive surrender of national sovereignty to them. In a free-trade area, all restrictions and duties upon the movement of goods between member states are removed; but controls remain over those which have been imported from third countries, under the trade arrangements established by individual members. The second stage – that of the customs union – is one in which common external controls over imports of goods allow the removal of internal checks; and in the third – the common market – any restraints on the movement of capital and labour are also removed. Progress in the first three stages will probably depend upon the harmonisation of any national regulations, either by intergovernmental agreement or the sort of institutional competition envisaged by Siebert, which would otherwise give an advantage to producers in particular member countries. It will probably also depend upon the reconciliation of their systems of economic management and convergence of their levels of development, where these are very different; and such a reconciliation will certainly be necessary before the later stages of integration – the adoption of common economic policies and a common currency – become possible. Alternatively, in the absence of convergence through the workings of the market, it will be necessary to set up a central fund, from which some of the gains made by the more successful, core economies can be redistributed to those on the periphery.

Molle (1990) argues that integration develops its own momentum, and that progress at one stage often increases the need to move to a higher one. Thus, customs unions are easier to operate than free-trade areas; fair trade within such a union requires the harmonisation of national regulations and levels of taxation, and the removal of subsidies; the subsequent adjustment of levels and types of production is more likely to be achieved if capital and labour are also allowed to move; and capital movements are likely to be less speculative and capricious, that is, more helpful to stable, long-term development, if the economic policies of the member countries are closely coordinated, and if there is monetary union.

Where, however, divergence is perceived to be occurring, it is probable that such integration as has already been achieved will be undermined, and that any further attempts to 'deepen' that integration will be jeopardised. 'Deepening' is likely to involve a progressive transfer of powers from the individual state to such central organisations as have been established to manage common currency, taxation and trade arrangements. It is also likely to require that a majority of the states involved should be able to impose new arrangements upon all, even where they may not be in the short-term interest of individual members. Furthermore, countries which have developed their own systems and priorities of economic management, including regional policies, over long periods of independence will probably be required to 'harmonise' them, giving up some of their practices, and adopting those preferred by others, with consequential gains for some of their industries and regions, but losses for others. It is argued by supporters of integration that, in the long term, all those involved will benefit from it. But it is clear that the degree to which integration is achieved amongst any group of states will depend in large part upon their perception of the likely balance of advantage between the loss of sovereignty and any such gains. Even those with the most favourable prospects may be reluctant to cross the Rubicon of replacing their individual currencies by a common one, and thus finally surrendering their economic sovereignty.

Divergence may also restrict any 'widening' of an integrated space economy. Myrdal's conclusions about the development of space economies would seem to suggest that, even if the individual space economies of a group of countries were not diverging, the removal of the barriers designed to protect the activities of the peripheral countries would probably initiate the forces of polarisation. His conclusions would also seem to indicate that the success of any integration depends upon raising the level of labour productivity in the peripheral countries to something akin to that in the core, and extending the national systems of education, health and social security payments of the core countries to cover the peripheral ones as well. It follows that the cost of such a transfer from the wealthy to the poorer members of an integrated economy will probably limit the rate at which the 'widening' of such an economy can be achieved.

Pollard (1981), noting how economic cooperation between the states of Europe in the mid-nineteenth century increasingly gave way to protectionism thereafter, has warned that it is all too easy for the governments of those countries which might lose out to respond positively to pressure groups within their electorates that are seeking protection, especially in times of recession. In other words, any failure to act against the decline of industries and the creation of unemployment in some countries, but not in others, following the removal of the economic barriers between them, is likely to undermine the will for integration amongst the losers, and put a brake on further moves to 'deepen' or 'widen' such integration as has already been achieved. But, to the extent that the processes of adjustment within the enlarged economy are restricted, the benefits from it will also be limited.

It is time to examine the extent to which the European space economy has already become integrated, and what barriers remain; and this we shall do in the next chapter.

Further reading

Readers wishing to follow the debate about integration more fully are advised to read Isard's *Location and Space-Economy: A General Theory Relating to Industrial*

Location, Market Areas, Land Use, Trade, and Urban Structure (1956), for an introduction to the form of the space economy at equilibrium in a free market under perfect competition; Balassa's *The Theory of Economic Integration* (1961), or Robson's *The Economics of International Integration* (1987), for a balanced introduction to the economic theory of integration; and Myrdal's *Economic Theory and Under-Developed Regions* (1957), for a warning as to the problems which integration is likely to produce in the real, as distinct from the theoretical, world.

CHAPTER 2
EUROPE IN THE EARLY 1990s

Aspirations with regard to European integration are not new. Some go back over many centuries; and a succession of European leaders and writers have advocated closer cooperation amongst the countries of the continent. But progress towards such integration has frequently been interrupted, and some of the most formidable barriers to trade and movement have been erected during the twentieth century. The fall of the Berlin Wall and the collapse of the Soviet Union appear, therefore, to offer the most promising opportunity for many years to bind the economies of the continent more closely together. This chapter will sketch the historical background to the present situation, and examine the type of integration which is now being advocated. It will describe the arrangements which govern the trade in goods in Europe in the early 1990s, and in services; and it will outline the conditions which currently surround the movement of labour, expertise and capital between one part of the continent and another, before considering how far Europe has progressed towards economic and monetary union. Finally, the chapter will sketch the tasks, risks and opportunities for integration which lie ahead.

The historical background

The desire to avoid war between the states of Europe, and the idea that trade might have a role to play in achieving that aim, are not new. In 1300, Pierre Dubois, a Norman French lawyer who served the kings of both England and France, published *De Abbreviatione* (*A Treatise on the Way to Shorten Wars*), in which he advocated a confederal Europe with power to impose economic sanctions against states which did not accept its arbitration in disputes. Later, Emeric Crucé, another Frenchman, published *Le nouveau Cynée* in 1623, in which he expounded 'his belief in the symbiotic relationship between peace and free trade' (Heater 1992, p. 17); and his ideas were quickly taken up by the Duc de Sully in his Grand Design. Sully argued that the peace of Europe could best be achieved through a reorganisation of the continent, from Portugal to the Urals, into fifteen states, each of which should be of approximately equal strength and be homogeneous in people and language, and between which there would be free trade. He proposed that the Tsar of Russia should be obliged to concur with this western-inspired reorganisation, on pain of losing his lands west of the Urals! A further work, *The Reorganisation of the European Community*, was published in 1814 by the Comte de Saint-Simon, who, observing the introduction of large-scale factory industry in Britain, concluded that the economies of Europe could only progress if they were allowed to operate within larger units than those of the nation state, and that states would dissolve into such units as a result of this economic pressure. Even if, as seems probable, Dubois, Sully and Saint-Simon were as much concerned with ensuring that France should be in control of, and benefit from, any European system which was adopted, their writings, and those of many others, reveal that many of the late-twentieth century's concerns about European integration have long been anticipated.

During the nineteenth century, free trade was, indeed, widely, though not uniformly, established in Europe; the movement of labour was eased; and that of capital was aided by the existence of a common standard of value, gold. The Prussian-led customs union, *Zollverein*, assisted in the creation and economic development of a united Germany; and the economic integration of the Swiss cantons in 1848, replacing thirty-eight currencies with one, proved to be an enduring success, despite the fact that four different language groups were involved. The Mezzogiorno of southern Italy, in contrast, suffered sharply from its union with the more industrialised north of that country in 1861. Gradually, however, in the latter part of the century, governments abandoned free trade; and, after the First World War, orderly economic relations were increasingly replaced by the beggar-my-neighbour autarky of quotas, tariffs and competing devaluations.

The response to those problems after the Second World War was multi-faceted. The Bretton Woods conference agreed arrangements for linking the world's major currencies to the dollar at fixed exchange rates; and the General Agreement on Tariffs and Trade (GATT) was established with a view to reducing tariffs, and applying uniform conditions to world trade. Meanwhile, Belgium, Luxembourg and the Netherlands established the Benelux common market, and initiated a programme to lead to economic union; trade between the countries of western Europe was facilitated by the establishment, first, of the European Payments Union in 1950, and second, by a return to currency convertibility in the late 1950s; Stalin grouped the communist countries into the Council for Mutual Economic Assistance (Comecon); France, West Germany, Italy and the Benelux countries formed the European Coal and Steel Community, which led on to the Treaty of Rome in 1957 and to Euratom; and seven other countries formed the European Free Trade Association (EFTA). After being rebuffed by the Community in 1963, Britain, Denmark and

Ireland left EFTA to join it ten years later. However, the Bretton Woods exchange rate system broke down in 1971; a period of 'Eurosclerosis' occurred as the countries of western Europe struggled with the oil price rises of 1973 and 1979, and the recession of the early 1980s; and, just as renewed growth in the mid- and late 1980s seemed to encourage a new wave of initiatives regarding integration in western Europe, Comecon collapsed, and the Soviet Union and Yugoslavia disintegrated into their constituent republics, leaving the Community as the dominant economic grouping in Europe.

Thus, by 1992, there were almost forty countries in Europe with populations of one million or more. Of these, by far the largest in both area and population was the Russian Federation, followed by France, Germany, Italy, the Ukraine and the United Kingdom (Table II.1). At the other extreme, there were many states with very small populations, including some which had only recently regained their independence – Estonia, Latvia and Lithuania – some which had never enjoyed independence during peace in modern times – Armenia, Azerbaijan, Croatia and Slovenia – and some which were subject to considerable dispute – Bosnia and Macedonia. More than a dozen had spent almost all of their recent history as part of the highly-integrated economies of two federations – the USSR and Yugoslavia. All, however, seemed to be seeking new links with at least some of the other states of Europe; and, the Soviet model of integration having collapsed, the Community had become the leader, model and focus of aspiration for the rest of the continent. Twelve of the countries of Europe were already members of that Community; the EFTA countries had agreed to bind themselves more closely to it in a European Economic Space; and three of the eastern countries – Czechoslovakia, Hungary and Poland – had signed Association Agreements with it (Figure II.3).

European integration – the preferred approach

But the Community was offering a very particular model of integration. Thus, it has indicated from the start that its aim is to achieve real freedom in the movement of goods, services, capital and labour among its members. It has argued that much harmonisation will be necessary, if the competition between states is to be fair; and it has sought to standardise many of the definitions and regulations employed by member countries in economic matters, and guard against the creation of monopolies and the unfair provision of state aids to producers. It has treated publicly-owned industries with suspicion, requiring governments to demonstrate that such industries are not in receipt of covert subsidies which would give them an advantage over those in other member countries; and its transport policy aims to control freight rates, thus ensuring that transport costs are not used as a form of tariff against foreign goods; all of which has led Holland (1980, p. 4) to claim that the post-war movement to integration in

Table II.1 The chief countries of Europe in 1992

Country	Area (1,000 km²)	Population (millions in 1990)	GNP ($US in 1988 per capita)
Albania	29	3	
Armenia	30	3	(5)
Austria	84	8	15,470
Azerbaijan	87	7	(10)
Belarus	208	10	(6)
Belgium	31	10	14,490
Bosnia	51	4	(D)
Bulgaria	111	9	2,550
Croatia	57	5	(B)
Czechoslovakia	128	16	4,250
Denmark	43	5	18,450
Eire	70	4	7,750
Estonia	45	2	(1)
Finland	337	5	18,590
France	547	56	16,090
Georgia	70	5	(8)
Germany*	357	77	18,480
Greece	132	10	4,800
Hungary	93	11	2,660
Italy	301	58	13,330
Latvia	65	3	(2)
Lithuania	65	4	(3)
Macedonia	26	2	(E)
Moldova	34	4	(9)
Netherlands	42	15	14,520
Norway	324	4	19,990
Poland	313	38	1,860
Portugal	92	10	3,650
Romania	238	23	1,750
Russia	17,075	148	(4)
Slovenia	20	2	(A)
Spain	505	39	7,740
Sweden	450	8	19,300
Switzerland	41	7	27,500
Ukraine	604	52	(7)
U K	244	57	12,810
Yugoslavia**	102	11	(C)

Source: World Bank, *National Statistical Yearbooks*

Notes

* GNP for West Germany only
** Serbia and Montenegro only
Figures in parentheses for republics of the former Soviet Union and letters for the parts of what was Yugoslavia indicate their rank order within each of those countries in personal income in 1988.

Figure II.3 Trading blocs, 1992

western Europe has been based on an unquestioning acceptance of Adam Smith's case for free trade. The Community intended that the last barriers to such trade should have been abolished by the end of 1992, when the Single Market, as it is called, should have been established.

It has not, however, been concerned with the establishment of a free market, irrespective of the consequences; and it has increasingly accepted that the costs of integration may not be equally spread, and that it may be necessary to cushion those who are most vulnerable. Thus, the Regional and Social Funds provide assistance to areas or groups within the Community whose living standards are considered to be too low, or in danger of falling significantly as a result of the changes brought about by integration; and the Funds' proportion of the Community's budget has been increased with each enlargement of its membership. This expenditure is not made in order to support declining manufacturing or mining industries, or to encourage new ones, after the manner of the industrial and regional policies adopted in most member states in the 1950s and 1960s. Rather, it is intended to improve the general infrastructure and amenities of less fortunate areas, and the skills of their populations, with a view to equalising the conditions for production between one part of the Community and another, and thus ensuring that large-scale movements of labour do not become a major means of adjustment. Thus, assistance has been available for:

— less developed regions;
— areas of industrial decline;
— rural areas;
— the long-term unemployed;
— the employment of young people; and
— the adjustment of agricultural structure,

in those areas in which per capita income is less than three-quarters of the Community average. More particularly, three types of rural area were identified in 1988 as being in need of assistance, namely, those

— 'suffering from the pressures of rural life', which were largely in the rural fringe, and required assistance for environmental protection;
— in which agriculture was still important, but in which few jobs existed outwith farming, and in which, in the view of the Commission, jobs should be created to replace those being lost in agriculture; and
— those which are very remote, with declining populations. The Commission took the view that agriculture in these areas should be supported, that the infrastructure should be improved and that new activities, such as tourism, should be promoted (Commission 1988).

The Community has also had regard to the difficulties of many frontier regions.

There have, nevertheless, been important exceptions to the policy of helping areas, rather than industries. For instance, the Common Agricultural Policy was designed to safeguard the standard of living of less efficient farmers by supporting the prices of the chief farm products, but has done so irrespective of whether those producing them have low incomes or not. Secondly, the Community's technology programmes have sought to assist selected industries to improve their competitiveness in relation to those of the United States and Japan. Moreover, the priorities of the Community should be noted. While the Regional and Social Funds were taking about a quarter of the Community budget in the early 1990s, the Agricultural and Industrial Policies were absorbing more than three-fifths. In other words, while the Community has set its face against national subsidies, its *raison d'être* is based in large part upon the protection of some of the most fundamental of its economic activities from external competition; and it has not hesitated to use generous subsidies to achieve their survival. Community Europe has, to a considerable degree, been 'fortress Europe'.

Lastly, the Community has made clear that the form of integration which it has adopted is not negotiable, and must be accepted by any new members.

But conditions within the European space economy in the early 1990s were far from those which the Community has set as its targets. Whether it be the harmonisation of the role of the state, free trade, factor mobility or economic union, the rules and practices of the countries of Europe, including those within the Community itself, fell far short of those necessary for the achievement of integration. We shall examine the position with regard to each of the following, in turn:

— harmonisation of the role of national governments;
— trade in goods;
— trade in services;
— the movement of labour;
— the transfer of expertise;
— the movement of capital; and
— economic and monetary union

before assessing the tasks, risks and opportunities which the greater integration of the European space economy may entail.

Harmonisation of the role of national governments

The harmonisation of the role of the state, which many consider to be necessary to the establishment of a free and fair market for goods, services, capital and labour, was patchy and nowhere complete, even within the Community, in the early 1990s. Governments in all western European countries owned large, though somewhat differently composed, sectors of their economies, and subsidised or otherwise protected a range of domestic activities from foreign competition. For example, all governments had some form of energy policy, related to the domestic availability of fuels, were deeply involved with transport and communications, and supplied many of the educational and medical services. The most extreme case was probably Italy, where about half the economy was under government control, provoking one commentator to claim that:

> The state-owned companies ... are strongly politicised. They provide employment for party appointees and permit loss-making operations to continue in order to retain regional support (Wilkinson 1992).

But it was by no means the only one (Williams 1991, pp. 90–111). The Community's Competition Policy was being brought to bear upon many of these cases in the early 1990s, in pursuit of the goal of a Single Market; but there was still much variation in the level and nature of state intervention, and therefore fragmentation of markets in western Europe.

Western European governments have also intervened very substantially in the economy through their procurement policies, spending an average of fifteen per cent of GDP on purchases of goods and services from the private sector. Preference has generally been given to domestic producers; and some governments have used their position as monopsonists to influence the structure of the companies which supply them. This has been particularly true of the defence industries, which are not subject to the Competition Policy of the Community. For example, France, Britain and West Germany have all spent large proportions of their research and development budgets on the aircraft industry, and intervened frequently and decisively to ensure the survival of domestic producers (Klepper 1991b). But, other industries have also been affected. Nguyen (1985) has drawn attention to the unfortunate consequences of such policies for the users of telecommunications, and Charles *et al.* (1989) to the limited progress which has been made in opening up the markets of individual members for telecommunication equipment to competition from elsewhere in the Community. Mayes (1991) has indicated the scope for increased competition and economies of scale in the manufacture of railway rolling stock and equipment in western Europe, which the abandonment of such practices would allow. Here, as in other matters, the Community was attempting to unify its market in the early 1990s by instituting a system of open tendering for public contracts; however, cross-border transactions were few.

There have also been several cases in which, notwithstanding the adoption of uniform policies across the Community, crucial elements of their execution have been retained or modified by individual governments, leading to variations between one country and another in the conditions facing economic activities. For instance, the Regional Fund is distributed, not according to constant criteria of need across the Community, but to those areas designated by each state as requiring assistance. Similarly, although it has been agreed that social security payments by employers should be harmonised across the Community in the interests of fair competition, member countries have not harmonised their unemployment and social benefits. Lastly, several members of the Community have negotiated special arrangements, under which a number of agricultural products are more heavily subsidised in some countries than others.

In short, the Community's so-called Single Market of 1992 was a fiction; the playing field was anything but level; and very similar circumstances existed among the other grouping of 'market' economies in western Europe, EFTA. It is an irony, but perhaps also a lesson, that the sector of the Community's economy within which the greatest degree of harmonisation of the role of governments had been achieved was the one which it subsidised most generously, namely, agriculture.

It is also, perhaps, ironic, but also instructive, in view of the failure of governments in the Community to harmonise their roles, that the rival system of economic development on the continent, until its collapse in 1989–91 – that of Soviet communism – should have established a largely undifferentiated system of economic management among the countries of eastern Europe. That system was based upon the public ownership of the means of production, and the planning of all output with a view to achieving self-sufficiency in the production of strategically-important fuels and industrial goods. Prices were fixed, and enterprises were not bound by considerations of profit and loss. Investment was decided by governments; and economic transactions were regulated not by price, but by the availability of resources. It is probably true to say that economic relations among the countries of the region were facilitated to some degree by the fact that all the governments knew what rules they were operating to, even if those rules had been imposed by the Soviet Union. However, that uniformity proved to be unsustainable: individual governments in eastern Europe are now developing their own systems of economic management; and what has been a united area, if one with a system of management which was anathema to the Community, is becoming a highly variegated one.

Hungary was the first country to introduce some minor economic reforms in 1968, but radical change only began there and elsewhere in eastern Europe in the early 1990s. Rapid progress has been made in some countries in the freeing of prices; but many enterprises continue to receive subsidies; and governments have only embarked upon the privatisation of small businesses, with a view to progressing to the larger enterprises later. The Hungarian authorities have announced that they do not intend to relinquish ownership of the country's energy, transport and telecommunications industries. Few of the financial, legal and other institutions necessary to the smooth organisation of free markets have been created; and the number of people with appropriate professional training and experience to staff them is small. Little progress has been made in Bulgaria, Romania or the Ukraine in modifying the communist system; and the role of governments everywhere in eastern Europe in the early 1990s was still very different from that which the Community has adopted as its model.

Trade in goods

The European space economy was also fragmented in the early 1990s by many barriers between countries with respect to trade.

Before the Second World War, three countries dominated European foreign trade. About a quarter was conducted by Britain, a sixth by Germany and an eighth by France. No other country contributed more than 5 per cent; and the Soviet Union conducted less foreign trade than Czechoslovakia or Switzerland, as a matter of policy. Britain was linked primarily with its empire, and only secondarily with Europe. Germany, in contrast, traded very largely with Europe, and especially the industrial nations of northwest Europe, though also with eastern Europe, while France occupied a position between these extremes.

However, the pattern had become very different by the 1980s (Table II.2). Four groups of countries may be recognised for the purposes of this analysis: the Community, EFTA, the countries of eastern Europe other than the Soviet Union, and the USSR. Trade between these groups had been severely disrupted

Table II.2 Trade in goods 1985–8 ($US billion)

To:	EC	EFTA	Eastern Europe*	USSR	Europe as % of total
From:					
EC	1,958	368	42	41	71
EFTA	316	84	14	19	74
Eastern Europe*	50	23	78	154	82
USSR	61	19	200	–	69
Europe as % of total	73	83	85	71	–

Source: UN (1990), Vol. 1, Special table B
*Eastern Europe other than the USSR

by the Second World War, and, in particular, by the Soviet takeover of eastern Europe thereafter, and the subsequent decline of all types of link between eastern and western Europe. It had, however, been increasing again from the 1950s onwards; and that between members of the Community had increased faster than the rise in their gross national products, thus indicating an increasing integration of their economies. West German trade in the 1980s amounted to about a quarter of its GDP, British to about a fifth, and French and Italian to about a sixth, at least half of which in each case was with the rest of the Community; and the smaller members' degree of integration with the Community was much greater. Furthermore, trade between the members of the Community had increased faster than that between them and the rest of the world. Intensive trade links also existed between the Community and EFTA; and not less than two-thirds of the trade of each of the four groups of countries in Europe was with the rest of the continent. It would appear, however, that the level of trade within eastern Europe, and between eastern and western Europe, was very much lower than that within the western half of the continent.

Three points should be made about that situation. Firstly, the figures in Table II.2 should be treated with some care, not least because a great deal of specialisation is known to have occurred within Comecon and the USSR; statistics for rail freight indicate that there have been very large flows of goods between both the countries of the region and the constituent republics of the Soviet Union; and estimates of the dollar value of the gross domestic products of the eastern countries may have been low. In other words, trade may have played a rather more important role in the economies of these countries than would appear to have been the case at first sight. Secondly, trade in eastern Europe has been composed rather differently from that in the west. Primary and semi-finished products accounted for between a quarter and a third of it by value, as compared with about a tenth of that in western Europe; the exchange of durable-use consumer goods was small; and the producer goods which were traded in eastern Europe were generally simpler and cruder than those in the west. Thus, Welfens (1992) has contrasted what he calls the 'Schumpeterian trade' in technology-intensive goods of western countries with that of the 'monopolistic division of labour' in eastern Europe; both of which are different from what he terms the 'Heckscher–Ohlin trade' – in which 'countries export goods that use their abundant factors intensively' – of the newly-industrialising countries in Asia. However, notwithstanding these points, it should be admitted, thirdly, that the policies and system of economic management under communism were highly unfavourable to trade. The Stalinist system of economic development was autarkic; and trade was conducted through bilateral, barter agreements between governments or other state agencies, and was set in the framework of central planning and non-convertible currencies. The market in each country was, in effect, closed to all save a limited range of goods, imports of which were subject to implicit quotas. Furthermore, after the collapse of Comecon in 1990, trade slumped; and the dissolution of the Soviet Union severely disrupted what had been domestic links within its highly-integrated economy.

Nor was trade in western Europe free. The most liberal arrangements were those concerning manufactures. EFTA was a free-trade area for manufactured goods; the Community was a customs union; and trade between the Community and EFTA was almost entirely free. Much trade in manufactures between western Europe and the developing countries, including eastern Europe, was also free; but there were important exceptions. Imports of textiles, clothing, cars, ships, steel and televisions from these countries, but also from Japan, were subject to quotas and voluntary export restraints; and many Community members retained non-tariff controls over imports from non-Community countries, which had been imposed before they had entered the Community. Furthermore, anti-dumping duties, local content rules, technical standards and rules of origin were also used, both by individual governments and the Community, to protect their markets from competitors in the rest of Europe and further afield. Trade in temperate farm products was very strictly regulated. Imports into the Community were controlled by a detailed system of variable levies, *ad valorem* and customs duties, and by seasonal barriers and quantitative restrictions; and similar measures were used by EFTA countries. The movement of fuel was also controlled in accordance with the various energy policies of the countries of western Europe.

Thus, despite the efforts under the GATT to free world trade in goods, much of that in Europe continued to be closely controlled by individual governments; and barriers to trade remained high. The conclusion must be that the pattern of trade and the map of agricultural, extractive and manufacturing industry within the continent would have been very different if free trade had been allowed. There would have been more trade, especially between eastern and western Europe; consumers in the Community and EFTA would probably have enjoyed cheaper goods of many types from eastern Europe; and this would have been at the expense of industries in the west. We shall return to a more detailed discussion of the potential for trade in selected goods between the various parts of Europe in Section V. Moreover, great, and perhaps greater, changes in the exchange of goods, and the consequent spatial arrangement of production, would probably have resulted in both eastern and western Europe, if there had been free trade between Europe and the rest of the world.

Trade in services

It is more difficult to quantify the trade between countries in 'invisibles' than in goods, but Molle (1990, p. 472) has shown that such trade between Community countries has been rising, and had reached about nine per cent of their GDP by 1985. France, the United Kingdom, West Germany and Italy were the chief exporters and importers of services in Europe at that time, and were followed by Spain, Switzerland and Sweden (GATT 1990). Elsewhere, in contrast, service trade was at a much lower level, though it accounted for a relatively large proportion of both the GDP and exports of Austria, Greece and Norway. However, the service sector contributed only about a fifth to western Europe's total international trade, or much less than its proportion of the GDP in any European country; it would seem, therefore, that in this, as in the trade in goods, considerable opportunities existed for the further integration of the continent.

The Community established free trade in services in the Treaty of Rome, but many barriers have remained. There was little effective competition between member states in the early 1990s in the provision of many of the services which are usually supplied by governments; services such as banking and insurance were subject to strict regulation by governments in the interests of customer protection; and others were often organised by the professional associations, many of whose controls over entry were supported by national legislation. Regulations governing the private service sector differed between countries, and it was difficult to obtain recognition for qualifications which had been gained elsewhere. It is not surprising, therefore, that the prices of such services as banking and insurance should have differed markedly among the countries of western Europe in the 1980s (Cecchini 1988, pp. 38-9). Some of these obstacles were being tackled by the Community in the early 1990s, as part of its Single Market programme, but they had not all been removed.

Opportunities for trade in the transport and communications industries have also been very limited. No direct competition has been allowed between the railways of western Europe, and the availability and price of air travel has been strictly controlled by governments. Priority has usually been given to the national airline or other domestic carriers, which thereafter have enjoyed the use of landing 'slots' at airports irrespective of whether others could have made better use of them. Cabotage – the offer of services by foreign carriers in other countries – has not been allowed, and most air fares within Europe have been much higher than those within the deregulated and integrated United States market (Button and Swann 1991). Meanwhile, the telecommunications market has been largely controlled by state-owned monopolies, and characterised by inefficiency and high prices (Cecchini 1988, pp. 43–6). The Germans have operated a particularly restrictive system of road haulage licensing.

Construction, retailing, personal and business services, other than banking and insurance, in contrast, have been subject to few controls; and some multinational companies have developed in these industries in western Europe since the 1970s. Mergers have produced a small number of very large companies operating world wide in accountancy and related activities; and tour companies have for long been operating across the continent, buying services in many different countries on behalf of their clients, though usually catering chiefly to their own nationals. Nevertheless, the quantity of cross-border trade has been small.

The problem has been even greater, however, in eastern Europe. Services have formed a much smaller part of the centrally planned economies than in the west; those offered by state agencies in one country have not been made available to people in others; there has been almost no trade in services between eastern and western Europe; and only in the case of tourism have there been substantial movements of customers across borders, and that very largely amongst the countries of the region.

The movement of labour

It is also the aim of the Community that labour and capital should be able to move freely within its borders.

There is a long history of the movement of labour between the countries of Europe, with much migration from the rural areas of eastern Europe and Ireland to the industries and cities of the northwest during the nineteenth century, and movements from the Mediterranean countries to Austria, Belgium, France, Switzerland and West Germany since the Second World War. The peak of the post-war movements was reached in the early 1970s, when about one in twelve of the labour forces of Italy and Yugoslavia were employed elsewhere in Europe, and even more of those of Ireland and Portugal. Between 1968 and 1973, there was a gross inflow of almost five million foreigners into West Germany, and a net inflow of 1,500,000 workers (Federal Republic of Germany, various years), which meant that the West German labour force was augmented by twelve per cent. That of France rose by a similar proportion, while in Switzerland the increase was thirty per cent. Most of the migrants were willing to work in low-paid, unskilled or semi-skilled jobs, and in dirty or otherwise unsocial conditions, which indigenous labour found unattractive. Many of those working in Switzerland and West Germany did so temporarily, but elsewhere in western Europe most immigrants have enjoyed rights to settle. However, migration has shown a marked correlation with changes in employment prospects in northwest Europe since the Second World War, and the numbers of both permanent settlers and *gastarbeiter* fell sharply once the Long Boom of the 1950s and 1960s was over (Molle and van Mourik 1988).

Controls over the movement of labour in western Europe have been exercised chiefly by individual governments, which have decided general levels of immigration, especially amongst the unskilled, and the professions. The influx of *gastarbeiter* into West Germany, for instance, was closely organised by the government under agreements signed with the Italian, Greek, Spanish, Turkish, Portuguese and Yugoslav authorities between 1955 and 1968. A recruitment agency was established to select workers for particular jobs, and each migrant was given a work permit for one year at a time. The object was quite explicitly to secure additional labour for industrial sectors which would otherwise have faced inflationary pressures; and recruitment was halted abruptly in 1973, when the labour shortage in those sectors disappeared. Similarly,

Britain, France, and Switzerland have all curtailed immigration in the 1970s and 1980s, though clandestine immigration, providing workers who are cheaper and easier to employ than Community citizens, may have increased since then (Straubhaar 1988; Tsoukalis 1991, p. 139). Movements of the most highly trained labour in western Europe have been subject to the regulations concerning the right to practice which have been drawn up by professional associations. Almost all of those associations have operated nationally, according to their own rules; and the Community has been attempting to overcome this fragmentation of the market by adopting the principle of 'mutual recognition', as part of the progress towards the Single Market.

The Community operates officially as a common market for labour; and so, for example, West Germany's treatment of its Greek, Portuguese and Spanish workers had to be brought into line with those of its own nationals as each of these countries was admitted. It also aims to achieve the mutual recognition of all professional qualifications within its boundaries as part of the Single Market. But it has yet to establish common external controls over immigration from third countries, and is therefore more akin to a free-trade area in this matter than a customs union. Strong concern was expressed in the early 1990s about the scale of clandestine immigration to the Community, especially from Turkey, north Africa and eastern Europe, and the way in which this may have been facilitated by the differences in immigration practice among its members.

Neo-classical economic theory would suggest that the large post-war migrations in western Europe should have resulted in a marked convergence of wage rates and standards of living between the sending and receiving areas; and several studies have been made with a view to establishing the extent to which this has been the case. These show that wage rates and, more importantly, unit labour costs, did, indeed, converge in western Europe to some extent between 1950 and 1970, but largely as a result of rapid increases within Italy, as workers moved out of farming in the Mezzogiorno and into manufacturing and service industries in the north of the country. They also reveal that many of the Yugoslavs who worked in West Germany remitted money; and that, at the peak, those remittances were three times as great as Yugoslavia's income from tourism. Returning *gastarbeiter* also took with them the skills which they had acquired in German factories, though it is not clear that this made a very significant contribution to the immigrants' home economy. It has also been claimed that the large movements of workers into Switzerland and West Germany benefited the economies of those countries by filling the growing gaps in their labour markets during a period of full employment, thus helping them to avoid wage inflation; though this may merely have allowed employers to postpone investment which would otherwise have been necessary to improve labour productivity (Herbert 1990, pp. 236–7). In other words, the evidence is mixed and difficult to interpret (Molle and van Mourik 1989, pp. 14–15, 101, 190); but, by the late 1980s, members of the Community in northwest Europe had almost identical average unit labour costs, while those in Italy,

Portugal and Spain were about twenty per cent lower, and those in Greece almost thirty per cent less (Tsoukalis 1991, p. 145). On the other hand, wide differences persisted between wage rates, and probably unit costs, in eastern and western Europe; and there were even greater differences between Europe and some other parts of the world. An early-1980s comparison of labour costs in the textile industry indicated a ratio of about 1:5:14 between southeast Asia, Portugal and northwest Europe, respectively (Hardill 1987, p. 60).

The situation in the former communist countries has been very different. Before the First World War, many immigrants and seasonal workers came from the Russian Empire to western Europe; but, after the establishment of communism, emigration almost ceased. There has been some movement by 'experts', and by groups of workers involved in joint projects, such as the oil pipeline from the Soviet Union to eastern Europe, between the Comecon countries; but, in general, labour was very immobile under communism. As shortages developed during the 1970s, immigration was arranged on a government-to-government basis from Third World countries with communist or socialist credentials, such as Mozambique and Vietnam; but these movements were intended to be temporary, and the fall of the communist authorities in Europe was quickly followed by the repatriation of most of those involved (Roesler 1991).

Much more important, however, have been two other movements of labour in eastern Europe, which, because of changed political circumstances, may now give rise to unrest and new migrations. Firstly, movements of Russians into the industrial cities of the eastern Ukraine, which began in the nineteenth century, have been followed since 1945 by large-scale settlement in the Baltic republics and Moldova. But internal migration within the former Soviet Union has created what, since 1991, have become large foreign minorities in newly-independent states. Many were already returning to the Russian Federation in the aftermath of the collapse of the Soviet Union. Secondly, there is the legacy of centuries of German settlement in eastern Europe. Ethnic Germans have been leaving Poland, Romania and the Soviet Union for some time, under agreements with the West German government; and, in the 1980s, about 800,000 *ausseidler*, who are considered to be German citizens with a right to settle, arrived from those countries (Ronge 1991). However, most of the remaining restrictions over the emigration of eastern European and Soviet citizens were also lifted in the early 1990s; and the two to three million ethnic Germans who still live in southwest Siberia, northern Kazakhstan and other central Asian republics are therefore free to leave. Few speak German, but all are eligible to enter Germany, and thus, the Community.

We shall return to the question of the future availability of labour in Europe in Section IV.

The transfer of expertise

The Treaty of Rome makes no reference to expertise as such, and the exchange of expertise is not listed as one of the four freedoms which must be achieved before the Single Market can come into existence. Yet the freedom to exchange information, as well as 'expert' labour, between countries is fundamental to the integration of the space economy; and reference was made in Chapter 1 to the consequences for eastern Europe of its recent isolation in this matter. We shall now outline some of the ways by which expertise is transferred, and, in particular, their operation as between the advanced economies of western Europe and those of the east in the recent past.

One of the most important ways in which expertise is passed from one country to another is through the multinational company. Such firms move managerial and technical information amongst their branches according to need, irrespective of their addresses, and acquire other companies, which possess patents or other information which they want, at home, but also abroad. Many transfers of this type have taken place within western Europe in the recent past, whether the countries involved have belonged to the same trading group or not, as well as between western Europe and the United States and Japan (Klein and Welfens 1992). Such transfers have not, however, occurred frequently between western and eastern Europe, where communist governments were unwilling to allow most of the world's multinational companies to set up branches. Nor did the communist governments attempt to import such expertise by acquiring firms in western Europe.

Joint ventures between independent firms provide another, though weaker, means of transfer. The Community has encouraged firms in the advanced-technology industries in member countries to collaborate in research, and, to this end, has launched more than a dozen programmes covering advanced materials, aerospace, biotechnology, information technology and communications, neuro-computing, and nuclear fusion (EURAM, ESA, BAP, ESPRIT and RACE, BRAIN, and JET, respectively), and also the application of new technology to traditional industries (BRITE). This has been done, in spite of disappointing results from earlier Community programmes to encourage collaboration in the development of nuclear energy and large computers, in an attempt to wrest the initiative in some of these fields from the Americans and Japanese (Sharp 1991, Williams 1991, pp. 85–90). Some governments in western Europe have also initiated and supported joint projects between companies in different countries, several of which have been in aerospace. The communist governments of eastern Europe, in contrast, were generally unwilling to let western companies set up effective joint ventures with state-owned enterprises, and only a few such ventures were established, chiefly in the 1970s and 1980s.

Expertise is also transferred between countries when the production of goods, which hitherto was restricted to advanced economies, is undertaken in countries with poorer educational backgrounds by independent firms, operating under licence or through interfirm cooperation agreements. There have been several examples of this type of movement from western to eastern Europe since the 1960s, most of which were in manufacturing (Nello 1991, pp. 226–41). Poland, for instance, has acquired a few licences and patents from the other countries of eastern Europe since the 1950s, and a larger number from the advanced industrial countries of western Europe; but the absolute numbers have been tiny in comparison with those of the pre-war period and among the countries of western Europe (Poland 1939, p. 154; 1987, pp. 459–60). Moreover, during the period of communist rule, only the manufacture of 'old' products was transferred, and therefore the technical and organisational benefits for the importing countries were limited. It has also been suggested that the export of technology by this means is relatively slow (Mansfield *et al.* 1982); and that the spillover of improvements into the economy at large is limited where that economy is not subject to competitive market conditions, and thus is not challenged by the enterprises which are operating under licence. The influence of the newly-established, Japanese-owned, motor-car factories in western Europe in the early 1990s was without parallel in the east.

Nor has the system of state-owned monopolies, inter-industry (rather than intra-industry) trade, and specialisation at the national scale in eastern Europe fostered the interchange of expertise between the countries there. In a situation in which, for example, Hungary built all the buses for eastern Europe, other countries had no opportunity to acquire similar or related skills, or to attempt to improve on what was available. Not surprisingly, Hungarian buses were crude and uncomfortable in comparison with those from western Europe. More ominously, all nuclear power stations in eastern Europe were built to Soviet designs, similar to that of the station which exploded at Chernobyl; and many were found to be unsafe when examined by western experts after the fall of the communist governments.

It should also be noted that the export of technical knowledge of strategic importance from western to eastern Europe has been deliberately restricted since 1949 under the COCOM arrangements. The Coodinating Committee for Multilateral Export Controls in Paris policed bans, or more limited restrictions, on trade in about 600 products between western and Warsaw Pact countries, thus contributing to the isolation and relative backwardness of the latter. Controls were exercised, in particular, over advanced computers and telecommunications systems, items connected with atomic energy, machine tools and novel materials, all of which might have been used not only for industry and commerce, but also for military purposes (Nello 1991, pp. 63–6).

However, the end of the Warsaw Pact and collapse of the Soviet Union in 1991 put an end to the need for these arrangements, thus opening the way for the advanced manufacturing industries of western Europe to extend their markets to the east. These changes have also meant that much advice about privatisation, the establishment of financial institutions, and other aspects of economic reform – advice which would never have been sought by communist governments – can now be provided by western firms and governments. In other words, an important barrier to the economic integration of Europe has been largely removed.

The movement of capital

Changes have also been occurring in the conditions governing the movement of capital in Europe. Prior to 1914, capital moved freely between countries. For example, there was much development of French- and German-owned industry in eastern Europe; and all the industrialised countries of northwest Europe, but especially Britain, were important exporters of capital. However, the breakdown of the Gold Standard between the two world wars disrupted such movements very considerably.

After the Second World War, most financial markets were national, and movements of capital between European countries, which are necessary if trade between them is to be free, were subject to strict government control. The currencies of eastern Europe were not convertible. However, much has changed since then. Initially, restrictions were circumvented by the development of the so-called Euromarkets, which permitted large firms, but also governments, to obtain money whether or not the government whose currency was being used approved of the transaction. One of the initiators of eurocurrencies was the Soviet government, which wanted to hold dollars, though not in the United States; and the use of such currencies developed rapidly after the Bretton Woods system of fixed exchange rates was replaced by floating currencies in 1971, and in response to the need to recycle the money received by OPEC countries following the oil price increases of 1973. Of course, Euromarkets do not only apply to European firms or to economic activities in Europe; but they apply to them no less than those elsewhere in the world; and, following their success, most countries have eventually removed the restrictions on international dealings in their financial markets. The result of this, and of the introduction of 24-hour, world-wide, computer-based trading, is that the governments of all except the very largest economies in the world can no longer exercise effective control over the market for their currencies. Currency stability is necessary, however, if long-term foreign investment and trade are to be encouraged; and many governments in western Europe have sought new forms of stability by linking their currencies with those of their neighbours in, first, the Snake, and, since 1979, the European Monetary System (O'Brien 1992). Nevertheless, some obstacles to the movement of capital remain. For example, the Swiss, who have long been very willing to look after other people's bank accounts, generally prevent the purchase of their companies by foreigners; and foreign penetration of the Swedish economy has also been resisted. Nevertheless, the capital market in western Europe, and between there and the rest of the world, was probably as free, if not more so, in the early 1990s as any of those for goods, services or labour.

Movements of capital take several forms. Money may be raised on the stock market in one country by companies based in another. Direct investments may be made by companies that wish to enlarge their market by expanding into other countries, either by creating or acquiring businesses there; and governments and international financial agencies, such as the International Monetary Fund and World Bank, may make loans, usually to other governments, either for currency stabilisation or development purposes. All, however, facilitate the integration of economies, either by moving funds from countries in which they have been accumulated to others in which they may provide higher yields, or by smoothing the path of international commerce.

Western Europe has been the recipient of three major waves of investment since the Second World War. The first, under the Marshall Plan, helped to rebuild the infrastructure and economies of the area after that conflict. The second, which also came chiefly from the United States, in the 1950s and 1960s, and was described as the 'American challenge' by Servan-Schreiber, followed the establishment of the Common Market, and was designed to pre-empt any protectionist measures it might have adopted. Several major companies set up branch plants, largely in Britain and West Germany, as a substitute for exporting to the Market (Thomsen and Nicolaides 1991, p. 10). The third has been largely, but not entirely, a by-product of the huge Japanese trade surplus of the 1980s (Panic and Schioppa 1989). Japanese companies have established factories within the Community, many of which have been in Britain and Spain, in response to fears that the continuing growth of their exports would lead to the imposition of more than the existing 'voluntary restraints' (Gittelman and Dunning 1992). Most, however, have been concerned only with the production of fairly standardised, low-value goods; and the manufacture of the newest, most complex and most advanced components and capital goods has generally remained in Japan (Ozawa 1992). In other words, western Europe has been becoming the periphery to Japan's core. The Japanese have also invested heavily in banking, insurance and other financial services in the Community, especially in Britain, the Netherlands and Luxembourg (Thomsen and Nicolaides 1991).

There has also been much movement of capital within western Europe; and the rate of international mergers and take-overs amongst the region's major firms increased sharply during the 1980s (Welfens 1992). West Germany has been the chief source of foreign direct investment in recent years, and more than half of its foreign investments have been in other Community and EFTA countries. Much of this has been in manufacturing – in chemicals, vehicles and engineering – but increasingly in services (Heiduk and Hodges 1992). Spain, on the other hand, has been one of the major recipients, and a third of all investment in Spanish manufacturing in the late 1980s came from abroad (Tsoukalis 1991, pp. 91–4, 231).

It has been calculated that, by the late 1980s, foreign investment accounted for seven per cent of the GDP of the Community. Belgium was the chief recipient, with investment equivalent to about a fifth of its GDP, followed by Britain, Greece, Portugal and the Netherlands. About a third of that in Britain was in manufacturing, and almost as much in the production of energy. A fifth was in financial services. Investment in France, Italy and Germany, in contrast, though large, was small in relation to the size of their economies (Thomsen and Nicolaides 1991, pp. 26–30, 47–68).

Capital movements also occurred in eastern Europe under the communist governments, but in very different circumstances. Some major industrial developments were funded jointly by groups of governments (Mellor 1987); but it is probable that the chief movements of capital between countries were hidden, rather than overt, and occurred as a result of the system of arbitrary pricing and trade by barter which characterised central planning. Many were the complaints that the Soviet Union had exploited the other communist countries by the terms which it set for its trade with them, though the opposite appears to have been the case, at least after the mid-1950s (Robson 1987, pp. 227–31); and several of the republics of the former USSR complained after independence that they had been subsidising others within that Union. It is very difficult to know where the balance of advantage might have lain. There have also been substantial movements of capital into eastern Europe in the form of grants and loans from western governments and banks. Some were made to the communist authorities in the 1970s to finance industrial development and imports, many of which have had to be written off; and, more recently, West Germany has made further large grants to the Soviet Union and its successor states. It has also made massive payments to the former German Democratic Republic since reunification to support living standards there, pending the accomplishment of economic reform. The communist authorities allowed very little foreign direct investment by western companies, and ignored the opportunities for producing in the west; and their currencies were never convertible. Their successors, in contrast, are hoping to attract foreign investment on a large scale to help modernise their industries, though debate continues in some countries about the size of stake which overseas capital should be allowed in any enterprise.

Economic and monetary union

Economic and monetary union are usually presented as being one of the later stages in the progress towards integration, but experience has shown that they are also likely to be closely bound up with the earlier ones. For instance, it is extremely unlikely that such integration as has occurred within the Community could have been achieved without the establishment of a common budget, with contributions from the richer countries and payments to the poorer, and the introduction of the Agricultural Policy and Regional and Social Funds. Similarly, both the Community, with its 'green' currency for the trade in farm goods, and its Exchange Rate Mechanism, and Comecon, with its 'transferable rouble', have found it desirable to establish common instruments to facilitate trade in advance of any more ambitious plans for monetary union. Nevertheless, the Community of the early 1990s was far from achieving any of the essential elements of economic unity, namely, a single currency, a common system of taxation, and a budget of a size which would be capable of dealing with the wide differences in the standard of living among its members.

During the 1980s, most of the currencies of the Community were linked through the Exchange Rate Mechanism; and the Community committed itself in the Maastricht Treaty to build upon this to establish a common currency by the late 1990s. However, it has been obliged to acknowledge that this will only be possible when the inflation rates and budget deficits of the member states have converged. It is not expected that, even if the currency is established, all of the twelve member countries will fulfil the conditions for adopting it before the next century. On the other hand, some EFTA countries have already aligned their currencies and interest rates with those of the Deutschmark; and, by the 1980s, this currency had come to dominate the economic policies of most of western Europe. The Community has also agreed, in the interests of fair trade, to a common framework for value-added taxes and excise duties, but not to identical rates; and here, too, differences are likely to persist between its members for some years (Schwok 1991, p. 16).

But it is arguable that the greatest weakness of the Community, as an integrated space economy, was the insignificant and distorted nature of its budget. By the late 1980s, it had risen to only 1.4 per cent of the GDP of its members. In other words, almost all expenditure remained in the hands of either the private sector or national governments; and therefore the Community's scope for redressing any divergence caused by integration, or otherwise reducing contrasts in the standards of living between one region and another within it, remained very small. It is true that the Community transferred resources from most, but not all, of the richer countries to the poorer. Belgium, West Germany, the United Kingdom, France and Italy were all net contributors, with Belgium giving the most as a proportion of its GDP, and Italy the least, while Ireland, Greece and Portugal were the chief recipients. But, even so, no country was contributing more than one per cent of its GDP each year, though Greece and Ireland were receiving sums equivalent to between three and five per cent of theirs (Tsoukalis 1991, pp. 242–3). The effectiveness of the budget as a mechanism for the redistribution of income must also be questioned in view of the fact that Denmark and the Netherlands – two of the richest members of the Community – have been net recipients; a fairer distribution might be accomplished if resources were to be switched from the Common Agricultural Policy to the Regional and Social Funds. However, Tsoukalis (1991, p.247) is of the opinion that the opportunities for effective redistribution through those Funds may be 'slowly approaching the limits of the absorptive capacity of some regions and even countries'. He suggests, therefore, that convergence might be speeded by the introduction of more uniform levels of unemployment and other social security assistance, and by the more equal provision of educational and health services, paid for by the enlargement of the Community's budget, or by increasing the scale of direct monetary transfers between member states.

The communist countries, in contrast, adopted almost identical economic policies and systems of economic management in the late 1940s, largely at the insistence of Soviet leaders, and undertook complementary patterns of production in several industries (Mellor 1987). All have now turned their backs, at least in public, on the policies of the past, and expressed the wish for closer links with the Community. Some aspire to full membership; but if they are to achieve economic and monetary union with western Europe, they must not only reduce substantially the role of government subsidy in their economies, and restructure or replace the trade which existed among the republics of the Soviet Union and within Comecon (and has now collapsed), but also bring their high levels of unemployment, inflation and government borrowing down to the targets set by the Community. They were far from accomplishing any of these in the early 1990s.

Tasks, risks and opportunities

Thus, while enthusiasm has been expressed from time to time about the possibility of European economic integration, accomplishments have been much more modest. Trade in both goods and services has increased both in total, and as a proportion of all trade and of GNP, in western Europe since the 1930s; and the movement of capital and labour there, though more difficult than before the First World War, has become easier. The countries of eastern Europe, having spent most of the period in almost complete economic isolation from western Europe, and with only limited contacts with each other, ended it by rejecting that situation. However, the most closely integrated group of countries – the Community – had yet to establish comprehensive free trade in either goods or services among its members; and the links between it and the rest of the continent were limited. Close links existed with the EFTA countries; and these were strengthened in 1992 when the Community and EFTA agreed to extend the Single Market to include both groups in what was to be called the European Economic Space. Association Agreements were also signed between the Community and Czechoslovakia, Hungary and Poland, which included commitments on the part of those countries to reform their economies to bring them into line with those of the Community in matters to do with competition, and on the part of the Community to admit them to its free-trade area. They also made provision for the free movement of capital, and for the right to establish businesses. But free trade was to be introduced only gradually over a ten-year period; and restrictions over the movement of labour were to continue. Some of the likely effects of these developments will be examined in Section V. Meanwhile, other countries in eastern Europe were only beginning to build the institutions which are essential if free trade is to be established. In other words, the space economy of Europe continued to be very fragmented.

At the same time, expectations concerning the benefits from closer integration were high. Many of the poorer peoples of Europe, and particularly those

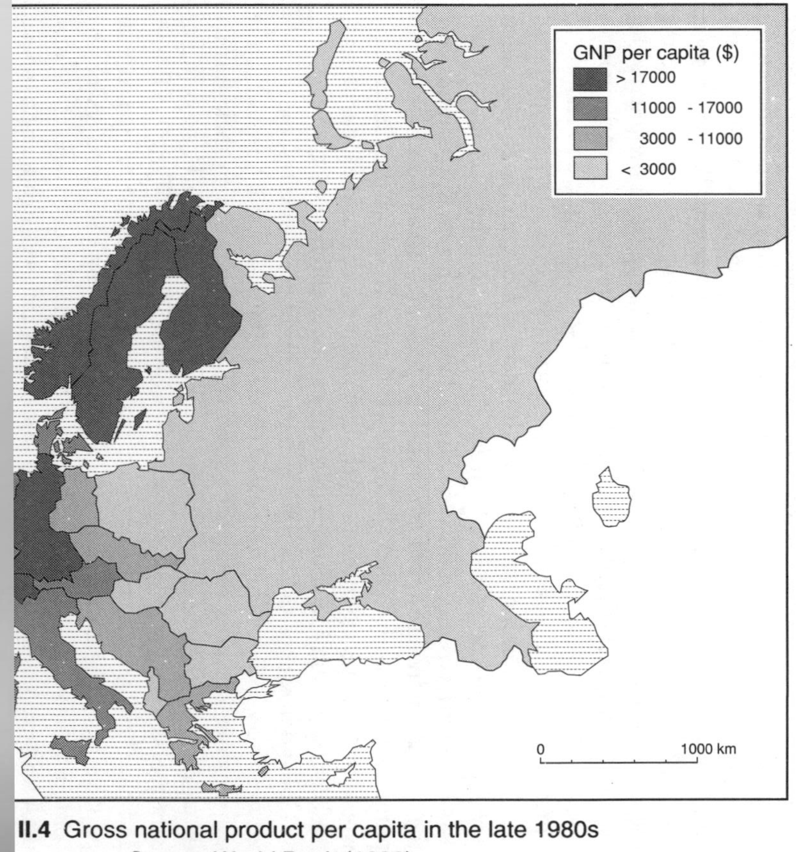

II.4 Gross national product per capita in the late 1980s
Source: World Bank (1992)

in eastern Europe, appeared to believe that new links with the prosperous countries of northwest Europe would admit them to the club of the wealthy. But, the gulf was wide. Table II.1 illustrates something of the range of GNP per capita in the late 1980s, from the richest – Switzerland – to the poorest – Albania – while Figure II.4 indicates how these contrasts form a pattern of core and periphery across the continent. Thus, if West Germany and Denmark form the core of the Community, Greece, Ireland, Portugal and Spain are the periphery; and, if the core of the Community, together with Britain, France, Italy and the Low Countries, Scandinavia and the alpine countries, are the centre of the continent's space economy, eastern Europe is its periphery. Nor should it be forgotten that western Europe is one of the three cores of the world's space economy, competing against Japan and North America, and relating to a periphery in Africa, Asia and Latin America which is even less developed than that of eastern Europe. In other words, there is a range of scales at which development in the past has been very unequal; and the Community has acknowledged its responsibility to assist all these peripheries. But it cannot raise the standard of living everywhere; and, if the poorer countries of Europe cannot point unambiguously to the benefits which any new links with the Community would bring them, any attempt by the Community to act as the focus of some wider integration of the European space economy will fail.

Holland has suggested that this is, indeed, likely, for, he claims, the form of integration which is being advocated by the Community will lead not to the convergence of living standards within the continent, but to their further divergence. In 1980, he drew attention to what he considered to be a significant contrast between the Spaak Report of 1956, which led to the Treaty of Rome, and the Treaty itself. He suggested that whilst the Report envisaged that positive and collective action would be necessary by the members of any common market to stimulate and develop the economies of its weaker regions, the Treaty emphasised that members would not be allowed to offer help to such areas outwith agreed Community levels and procedures. This he regarded as backsliding, arguing that – to the extent that the Community persists in its attempt to run a free-market economy without effective industrial and regional policies – while multinational capital operates at the world scale, divergence within it will continue. He also foresaw the dominance of the Bundesbank in the economic and monetary affairs of the Community, and the fact that it would lead to the imposition of deflationary policies on countries which, though not as economically strong as Germany, would be obliged to set interest rates above those for the Deutschmark.

However, these risks may be avoided. The Rome Treaty, that of 1987 establishing the Single Market, and that of Maastricht in 1992 on monetary union, all lay upon the Community the responsibility to achieve the harmonious development of its various parts, and to reduce the regional disparities within it. Indeed, the Maastricht agreement made provision for the establishment of a 'cohesion fund', whose purpose would be to transfer even more money to the poorer members of the

Community – Greece, Ireland, Portugal and Spain – than had hitherto been the case. Furthermore, if economic integration carries with it the risk of divergence, it also offers the prospect of a general increase in welfare. Those who argue in favour of both deepening and widening such integration as has been achieved in western Europe point to the fact that standards of living have been rising rapidly in the poorer countries of the area since the 1950s, and that there has been a marked, though by no means complete or continuous, convergence between them and the richer ones. They note that, during the Long Boom, GDP per capita rose rapidly in Greece, Portugal and Spain in comparison with the average of the twelve Community countries, but that, once the Boom came to an end, divergence set in, regional unemployment rates rose sharply in the least developed economies, and convergence only began again once a general upturn occurred in the economies of western Europe in the mid-1980s (Pinder 1983 pp. 90, 103–4; Tsoukalis 1991, pp. 206, 221–232). In other words, they claim that it is economic growth, rather than regional policy, that achieves convergence, and go on to assert that it is integration which, by establishing free markets in which the efficient allocation of resources may be more thoroughly pursued, is likely to stimulate that growth. Whatever the validity of these assertions, many countries in eastern Europe were seeking closer economic links with the west in the early 1990s, in the belief that by so doing they would open the door to the economic growth and increased welfare which central planning had failed to provide, and so buttress their newly-established pluralist democracies against any resurgence of dictatorship. Even the EFTA countries, including some of the richest in Europe, appeared to prefer the tasks and risks associated with closer economic integration than to forego the opportunities which it may offer.

Summary

contrast, are likely to experience slower growth, and an outflow of capital and labour. Moreover, as integration proceeds from its simplest form of free trade to monetary union, and as national controls give way to the policies of the integrated economy's central bank, these processes of divergence may be strengthened.

However, notwithstanding these risks, by the early 1990s European aspirations with regard to integration had become focused on the Community and the particular form of economic management which it had adopted. But major reforms, and the removal of many barriers, will be required if those aspirations are to be realised; and the further east in Europe, the greater does the task appear to be. While the structure and management of the EFTA economies, and the trade policies which they have adopted, are very similar to those of the Community; and, while the former German Democratic Republic has been absorbed within the Federal Republic, albeit at very great cost, much reform will be required in eastern Europe, and many of the institutions which are necessary to the running of a market economy will have to be built, before the countries there can be fully integrated with western Europe.

Whether eastern European interest in such integration will be maintained, and how those countries which are presently asserting their national identity will resolve the implicit conflict with their wish for closer economic links with the Community, will depend, in part, upon their experience of the changing spatial arrangement of economic activities which integration will bring. Debate between the protagonists of integration and its opponents would seem to have concluded that while in periods of rapid economic growth even peripheral areas may benefit – especially where their economies are somewhat backward and therefore have scope for restructuring – they are the most vulnerable in any period of recession. However, that conclusion does not indicate what will happen in any particular case. It does not identify which countries and regions are likely to find, after integration, that they are burdened with a surplus of labour. Nor does it show which areas are likely to experience the growth of new industries, and which the decline of the old. Moreover, it leaves unanswered the question as to which of the several national cores in Europe will benefit from closer links with the rest of the continent, and which will not. Yet it is these effects which will be discussed in Section V, which will determine who will benefit, and who suffer, from any closer integration that may be achieved.

That assessment cannot, however, be made yet, for it must be informed not only by the models of the integrated space economy which have been outlined in this section, but also by the recent development of that economy in Europe; and it is to that that we must progress in Section III.

Further reading

Tsoukalis (1991), *The New European Economy: The Politics and Economics of Integration*, and Vickerman (1992), *The Single European Market: Prospects for economic integration*, provide two of the more readable overviews of the aims and achievements of the Community to date, but readers may wish to consider the case against the Community and its approach to integration which is set out by Holland in *Uncommon Market: Capital, Class and Power in the European Community*.

An assessment of the effects of the Community upon each of its members is given in the *EC Membership Evaluated Series*, edited by C. C. Schweitzer, and published by Pinter between 1990 and 1992. Each country is considered in a separate volume.

Nello (1991), *The new Europe: Changing economic relations between East and West*, describes the recent history of trade between the centrally-planned and market economies of Europe and the reforms which will be necessary to facilitate it, and gives some indication of what is likely to happen in the immediate future.

Dawson (1987a) gives a brief outline of the system of management of the space economy under communism.

Section III
Europe in the Fourth Kondratiev

Some indication was given in Section II of the likely effects of the integration of previously separated economies, and of the limited extent to which such integration had progressed in Europe by the early 1990s. The section concluded by noting the strong desire in many countries at that time for closer links with others, and the fact that that desire was based, in part, upon the belief that greater integration would bring significant and, it was hoped, beneficial economic changes.

That belief is almost certainly correct. But it is also naive, for economies are in a constant state of flux. Industries grow, while others decline. Land is put to new uses, and people move in search of a better life. The economic geography of an area at any moment is no more than a snapshot of a constantly changing scene, the understanding of which requires an appreciation of the processes and trends which have been frozen in the picture. Thus, any economic geography [illegible] environmental determinism and exceptionalism were characteristic of the explanations offered in early accounts of the economic geography of Europe. But it argued that geographers should be interested less in occasional and adventitious events than in the everyday and regular way in which people earn their livings, seeking out profitable locations for their activities or making appropriate use of the sites which they occupy. Furthermore, it noted that such behaviour forms a continuous process, in which changes by one player in the game of economic geography encourage complementary ones by others, thus causing the space economy to be continually restructured.

The European space economy has experienced much restructuring in recent centuries. Agricultural improvements in Britain in the eighteenth century were followed by the Industrial Revolution, both of which were copied elsewhere. Labour moved off the land into factories and mines; improved productivity allowed both an increase in population and in the standard of living; and better means of transport integrated what had formerly been largely independent regional and local economies, undermining their craft industries. Indeed, so great was the change in the scale of the space economy that, by the late nineteenth century, the most heavily industrialised European powers were scrambling to secure markets for their new industries throughout the world, and embarking upon an arms race to protect their newly acquired empires. Much of the rest of Europe, however, had yet to experience the economic changes which had occurred in the northwest of the continent, and did not do so to any great extent until the second half of the twentieth century. Rather, it displayed some of the same characteristics as northwest Europe's colonial periphery in Africa and Asia. Meanwhile, the most developed countries of the continent began to move into a post-industrial and service-based phase of development.

Such restructuring is not, however, smooth. Businesses often miscalculate the demand for their products, and bankruptcies occur. Unexpected variations in supply follow, and there are consequential changes in price. Consumers react, as do other producers, rushing to flood the market in response to price rises, and cutting back output in the face of falls. More efficient methods of production are introduced, while new products take the place of old. Labour is rendered redundant in some places, but finds itself in short supply elsewhere; plant and equipment are abandoned in some locations, while investment occurs in others. Even if, given time, the space economy should tend towards equilibrium, the form of that equilibrium is constantly being altered. It has been noted, however, that such fluctuations may show some regularity; and reference was made in Section I to several of the periodicities which have been recognised in economies, and to the particular significance for economic geography of the Kondratiev Cycle, or Long Wave. This is not to say that all recent change in the economic geography of Europe can be explained by Long Wave theory (see Boxes 2 and 3), or that such waves are entirely endogenous events within the economy. Indeed, some writers have argued that not only did some of the Long Waves which have been recognised in the past not occur, but that the periods of faster and slower growth which can be recognised were the result of unique historical events.

Nevertheless, we shall outline the recent economic history of Europe against the background of Long Wave theory in Chapter 3, by way of setting the scene for the description of the changing technology, scale and location of each of the primary, manufacturing and service sectors of the economy over that period in Chapters 4 to 6, respectively; and Chapter 7 will consider some aspects of the European space economy as a whole.

CHAPTER 3

THE FOURTH KONDRATIEV

The economic history of Europe in the twentieth century may be divided into three distinct periods.

Industrial activity, which had reached a peak immediately before the First World War, declined thereafter. A sharp recession in 1920–21, hyperinflation in central Europe in the middle of the decade, and misguided American interest-rate policy in the late 1920s led a number of countries to leave the Gold Standard and to threaten default on their loans, and to the Wall Street crash. The US Congress passed the Hawley-Smoot tariff in 1930, which set off a wave of protectionist legislation elsewhere, and trade collapsed. Unemployment rose to unprecedented levels in the winter of 1932–3; and the Great Slump was the worst depression that the world economy had known, affecting all the countries of Europe. Only the Soviet Union, which had cut itself off, and was embarking upon Stalin's own, brutal experiment in economic restructuring, was unaffected.

However, things were never as bad again. Although the renewal of economic growth was somewhat later in some countries, such as France, than in Britain and Germany, patchy recovery began in the mid-1930s; and this gathered momentum throughout the continent after the Second World War. Output, though not necessarily employment, rose in all the three major sectors of the economy in every European country; and such was the strength of economic growth in the market economies in the 1950s and early 1960s that 'recessions' were periods of slower growth, rather than decline. Some commentators wondered whether Keynesian planning had done away with the business cycle and ushered in permanent growth. But, it was not so. Some of western Europe's long-established industries began to decline in the late 1950s; and some of its regions experienced marked emigrations of labour. Furthermore, the rate of economic growth as a whole began to decline in the late 1960s; the dollar went off the Gold Standard, and the Bretton Woods system of fixed exchange rates gave way, in the early 1970s; the price of commodities appeared to become more volatile; unemployment rose; and the OPEC cartel raised the price of petroleum four-fold in 1973–4. The Long Boom was over.

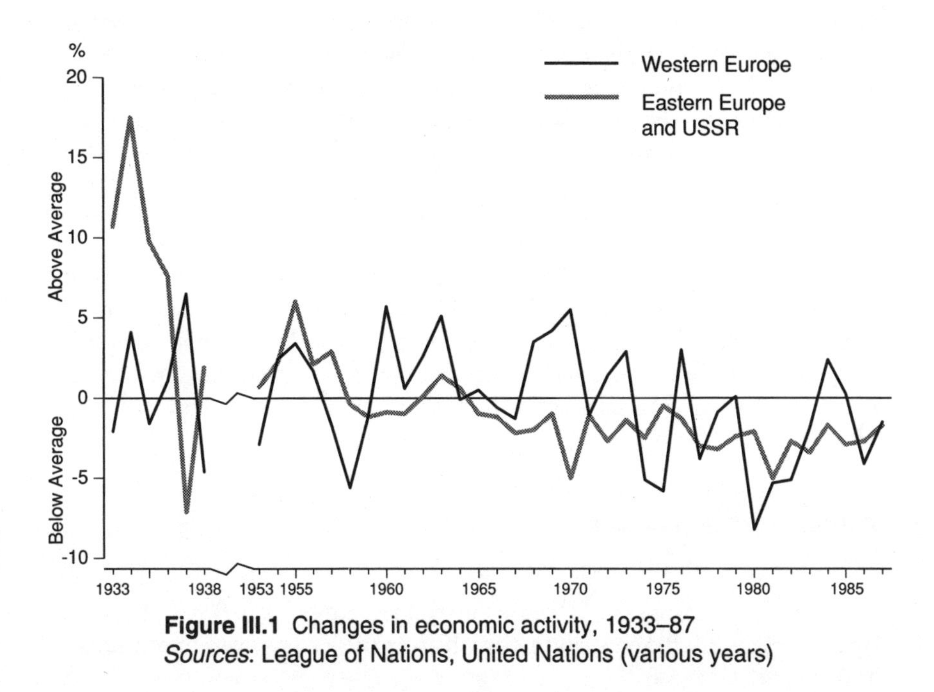

Figure III.1 Changes in economic activity, 1933–87
Sources: League of Nations, United Nations (various years)

This did not mean that economic growth had ceased. Although the mid-1970s were a period of recession in western Europe, growth resumed there later in the decade. But it was short-lived; and there was a sharp recession in the early 1980s. Moreover, it was threatened thereafter by a stock market crash in 1987; and efforts by the world's major market economies to prevent a depression served only to stoke the fires of inflation, leading to persistent recession in the early 1990s. Several of western Europe's long-established industries continued [illegible]

measure in a period of changing economic structures. Nevertheless, some of this sequence of events is represented in Figure III.1, which shows the year-on-year change in the level of economic activity, as measured by the consumption of energy, in relation to the average annual change over the period between 1933 and 1987. Changes for eastern and western Europe are shown separately in relation to their own averages, which were about six per cent for eastern Europe and half that for the west. The figure indicates the volatility of change in the Soviet Union in the 1930s – a period of rapid economic growth, but also social upheaval – and in western Europe, where the pattern of business cycles, each lasting about five years, can be identified. However, it also demonstrates a longer-term trend of above-average growth in eastern Europe until the mid-1960s, and in western Europe until the early 1970s, and below-average performance since then, with the hint of an upturn in western Europe in the mid-1980s.

However, if it is the case that the main events of Europe's economic history during the twentieth century can be quickly sketched, it does not follow that they can be as easily explained. Put briefly, has that economic history been composed of three, unique episodes, or of one and a half Kondratiev Cycles, with turning points in the 1930s and 1970s? We shall examine these different interpretations in more detail below.

Waves versus shocks

Several explanations of Long Waves in the economy are set out in Box 2, all of which are concerned with the mechanisms by which expansion gives way to contraction, or vice versa.

Each of them gives some support to the suggestion that the 1930s marked a major turning point in the economic history of Europe; and one which can be represented as that between the third Long Wave, which is thought to have begun in the late nineteenth century, and the fourth, which has dominated recent times. The fact that productive capacity in several of the major economic activities in the world, including agriculture, mining and heavy industries, had been expanded in the previous decade until it was far too large; that prices for the products of those industries had been falling for some time; and that investment was turning away from production and into the purchase of property and stocks, would seem to accord with those explanations which are based upon lags in the production of primary and capital goods. Only when the surplus capacity in these activities had been scrapped, and when the real price of capital had fallen from its peak in the 1920s (Tylecote 1992, pp. 96–100), did investment and employment in them pick up again in the mid-1930s.

However, a Schumpeterian explanation would also seem to be appropriate. For instance, Court (1954, p. 222) noted that, even before the First World War, three of the most important industries in Britain – coal-mining, iron-making and textiles – were

> ceasing to be the theatres of innovation in technique and organisation which they had once been, and ... to produce the increasing returns to human labour on which their great start in the world had depended

while Schumpeter (1939, p. 963) himself drew attention to the fact that innovation was simultaneously creating new and vigorous growth which eventually lifted the developed economies out of depression. Writing about the United Kingdom, he noted that:

> electric power ... electric manufacture (wire, cables, installations, lamps, apparatus, and machinery), motorcars, nonferrous metals, chemicals including rayon, aeroplanes and so on continued without much interruption even in the worst year [of the Slump]

while Youngson (1967, p. 111) has indicated that:

> The manufacture of rayon ... was greatly affected by technical progress, so that an increase in employment between 1930 and 1935 of only 18 per cent (12,000 people) caused output to double. Prices fell, quality and variety were improved, and a mass market for quasi-luxury textiles rapidly became established.

Writing more recently, Freeman, Clark and Soete (1982) have suggested that a new 'constellation of technically and economically interrelated radical innovations' – oil, petrochemicals and synthetic materials, consumer durables, electronics and vehicles – provided the engine for the sustained economic growth which occurred in Europe after the Second World War. In other words, the decline of the major industries of earlier waves carried the whole economy down; but from the mid-1930s onwards, it was more than offset in the chief industrial countries of Europe, though not in every region within them, by the growth of new forms of production.

The period since the 1930s can, however, be interpreted very differently. Solomou (1987), for instance, points out that strong and sustained economic recovery did not begin until 1950; and he argues that, rather than being the result of endogenous processes within the economy, that growth had historically-specific causes. These were that a technological gap had opened up between the European economies and that of the United States, which the

[illegible] Europe, leading to increased demand in those countries.

There is also conflict concerning the reason for the end of the Long Boom in the late 1960s and early 1970s. Schumpeterian explanations point to the increasing saturation of markets for the products of the growth industries of the Long Boom, and to the associated downturn in the rate of profit and investment. Others, in contrast, draw attention to the growth of labour-related

BOX 2

Long Waves

Several explanations have been offered for the Long Waves which were identified by Kondratiev. These have been concerned to show why an economy which has enjoyed rapid growth for twenty to thirty years, with only minor downturns, should decelerate into short periods of weak expansion, interspersed with longer slumps of some severity; and why, after such a phase of slower growth of about the same length, it should accelerate again. In short, the explanations are concerned with the upper and lower turning points of the wave.

The explanations by Rostow and Kennedy (1979) and by Forrester (1976) are based upon the lags which occur between investment decisions and their impact upon output. Rostow and Kennedy, building on the ideas of one of the first Long Wave theorists, van Gelderen, suggest that the prices of agricultural and other primary commodities will rise as population and wealth grow, but that the impact of that message upon output will be delayed by three types of lag:

— Initially, producers must be convinced that the increase is likely to be sufficiently sustained to justify new investment.
— Secondly, time will elapse while the new infrastructure for the expansion of agriculture or mining is constructed.
— Lastly, there will be an interval between the completion of that plant and its operation at full capacity.

Nevertheless, investment eventually occurs, and employment and output rise. However, because many producers act simultaneously, but without full knowledge of the plans of others, the expansion of capacity tends to overshoot the increase in demand, and this, in turn, causes the price of commodities to fall, and leads to a decline in investment. Thereafter, investment remains below the rate of depreciation, until the surplus plant has been scrapped; and it is only when the long-run graph of rising demand crosses that of falling capacity that shortages appear and prices begin to rise again. Thus, both the upper and lower turning points are explained. Forrester's explanation is similar, except that it suggests that the fluctuations originate in the capital goods industries, and that they are exacerbated by the need for that sector to equip itself before it can increase output. These theories indicate why the level of activity tends to vary in the primary and capital-goods industries, and assume that those oscillations spread out into the wider economy. They also imply that the space economy will expand as price rises make what were sub-marginal sites profitable locations for economic activity, and contract as falls in price return them to their sub-marginal status. However, neither of these explanations makes reference to the creation of new industries or the destruction of old ones, and therefore they appear to be structurally neutral over the Long Wave as a whole. It is obvious that economies do not behave like this.

A third explanation by Mensch (1979), building upon that of Schumpeter (1939), concentrates upon the impact of innovation, and is not restricted to any particular sector of the economy. Mensch distinguishes between primary innovations, which lead to new products, secondary ones which yield improvements to products or changes in methods of production, and what he calls 'pseudo-innovations', which are merely diversifications of the product range. He also argues, with Schumpeter, that product innovations, from which new industries arise, occur in clusters, creating economic growth, but that the markets for those products eventually become saturated. Secondary innovations, which improve the methods of production, may extend that growth somewhat. In time, however, the potential for growth from any bunch of innovations is exhausted, and the economy stagnates. New products and processes are being invented all the time; but it is only when investors see no scope for further development in existing activities that they will risk supporting a new round of product innovations, and only at that moment that the economy will begin to grow again. New products start to replace old ones, and increases in employment in the new industries offset the losses in existing ones until the market for the new goods is saturated. Geographers might add that the new industries which are thus created are very likely to have different locational requirements from those which they are superseding, and that, while capital and labour are being attracted to their sites, areas which are dependent upon the old industries will be declining (see Box 3).

The economy does not, of course, behave as simply as these theories suggest. Indeed, there is evidence to suggest that all the three sequences of events described above exist simultaneously in developed economies. Furthermore, the explanations do not produce waves of the same length: Rostow and Kennedy identified a forty-year cycle in the primary-goods sector, and Forrester a fifty-year oscillation for capital-goods industries. Nor do all economic activities have life cycles of similar length or amplitude. Some grow and decline rapidly, while others appear to be lasting elements in the economic structure. Some behave in sympathy with the overall level of economic activity, while others appear to behave in a counter-cyclical manner. It has also been suggested that, because firms have been devoting increasing attention to research and development in recent times, the product cycle has become shorter. Moreover, the economy does not exist in a political vacuum. The profits which are made by innovating industries may become the subject of dispute between capital and labour; and these disputes may inhibit further investment or lead to retaliation, such as the substitution of capital for labour or the transfer of production to locations where labour is more docile. Meanwhile, declining industries may seek protection from foreign competitors; and governments

[illegible]

the Fourth Kondratiev did not begin until then. But, what is of more importance than the individual year in which any Long Wave is thought to have begun – and 1932–3 has been taken as the starting point for the Fourth Wave in this study – is the recognition of the fact that there are long-term processes at work in economies, some of which may have a cyclical character, which strongly influence their geographical form.

expenditure by firms facing strong trade unions in the context of full employment, and by governments which had been imposing ever-higher taxes to finance increasing levels of social security, health and other transfer payments. They point to the consequent restructuring of economic activities and flight of less-skilled operations to cheaper locations, and to the ensuing disturbance of the balance between the levels of production, employment and social security expenditure in many European countries. Such an explanation would seem to imply that, if the expansionary phase of the Fourth Wave owed something to the efforts of government in both eastern and western Europe to ensure that labour was fully employed and that certain structural and social changes were accomplished, the declining phase might be explained, at least in part, by the misallocations and rigidities which such an approach had built into the economy. It might also suggest that one of the prerequisites for any new period of prolonged growth may be some refocusing of investment by the market, and a compensating decline in the role of the state. Meanwhile, those who place emphasis upon the historical specificity of events may still be able to recall the sudden and substantial oil price rises of 1973, and the reduction in economic expectations in western Europe which accompanied the threats of the OPEC cartel to impose yet more increases. Lastly, Tylecote (1992, pp. 288–9) argues that it was high spending on advanced technology in the developed countries, especially that associated with armaments, in the 1970s and 1980s, which led to the re-emergence of greater inequalities in western countries, a growing gap between the rich North and poor South, depressed demand and the recent slowdown in the world economy. But, whatever the reason, the onset in the early 1970s of a period of slower and discontinuous growth in Europe, both east and west, is not in dispute.

The significance of the present moment, however, is less clear. Those who recognise the existence of Long Waves might suggest that the trough at the end of the Fourth was reached in the recession of the early 1980s, despite the fact that it was much less severe than the Great Slump; arguing that the long-term rate of growth in western Europe and other OECD countries appears to have begun to increase again in the mid-1980s, and that the recession of the early 1990s was less sharp, though more prolonged, than that which had preceded it. They might explain such an upturn by suggesting that the microprocessor has spawned a variety of new products and associated methods of production in a wide range of industries. They might argue with Piore and Sabel (1984) that the application of computer-based technology to design and manufacture, which has been encouraging the growth of networks of small and medium-sized firms involved in the production of high-value goods, but endowing them with a flexibility which was not available to large-scale, mass-production factories of the Fordist style, heralds a return from the mass-production technology of earlier waves to the more customised form of the craft industries. Martinelli and Schoenberger (1991) and Schamp (1991), in taking up the argument that 'economies of scope' are replacing those of scale, have drawn attention to the fact that not only small firms, but also large producers, and not only manufacturers of such goods as textiles and clothes, but also of cars, are equipping themselves to manufacture many variations of the basic product, rather than huge quantities of a single good. Meanwhile, Hall and Preston (1988, pp. 268–74) have drawn attention to the revolution which computing, microelectronics, aerospace and fibre optics are creating in the communications industry. They do not, however, agree that this is already producing the upturn at the start of a fifth wave. Rather, they claim that the Fourth Wave will not end until 2003, and that it will only be at that time that the new bunch of innovations which have been occurring since the early 1970s, and huge investment in the widespread installation of what they term 'Convergent Information Technology', will provide sufficient stimulus to carry the economy into another period of long-term growth.

Alternatively, the upturn in the mid-1980s may have been caused in western Europe by investment in anticipation of the establishment of the Community's Single Market – investment which appears to have occurred not only within the Community, but elsewhere in western Europe (Camagni *et al.* 1991). Or, it may have been stimulated by the rapid growth in the American budget deficit – a Keynesian explanation – or by the supply-side reforms of the Reagan and Thatcher governments, of which deregulation, the reduction in the power of trade unions, and cuts in the levels of direct taxes on earnings and profits were some of the most relevant to potential investors.

However, if it is true, as Solomou argues, that the economy does not accelerate or slow by itself, but is 'shocked' into such change by exogenous events, sustained and rapid growth may not be triggered until there is some much larger conjuncture in the economic environment. Continuing depression in world markets for primary commodities, including fuels, in the early 1990s, high and rising levels of interest rates and unemployment in western Europe, and falling property prices in Britain and elsewhere all suggest that there has been no event, as yet, of sufficient power to produce an upturn

renewed long-term growth can best be accomplished by the greater involvement of the state at the expense of the market; by curtailing the freedom to trade and move capital between countries; and through heavy taxation of those who cause congestion and pollution, but do not pay the full price for it. Private transport, especially in busy areas, should, he avers, be a particular target of such taxes; and he indicates that this would cause the spatial extent of many markets to 'shrink'. Siebert, in contrast, was of the opinion in 1991 that the further integration of the European Community, and closer links between the Community and EFTA, could provide the positive supply-side shock which would usher in a new Long Boom in the mid- and late 1990s.

The centrally-planned economies

All the explanations which have been referred to above for variations in the rate of long-term economic growth relate to the market economies of western Europe; but Figure III.1 illustrates how the centrally-planned economies of eastern Europe also experienced a long period of rapid development, followed by one of slower growth. Various reasons can be offered for this, but those of Long Wave theory do not seem to be appropriate. The explanation may lie, rather, in a quite specific set of weaknesses in the Stalinist model of development.

Ellman and Kontorovich (1992b, pp.1–39) indicate that rapid economic growth in the Soviet Union up to the late 1950s can be explained by the increases in productivity, which were achieved through the transfer of labour from agriculture to manufacturing and mining, high levels of investment and increases in the scale of production, all of which were achieved under conditions of ruthless social discipline and a clear and consistent policy of economic development. They suggest that the decline thereafter was caused by the reduction of both the penalties and rewards on offer to the population, the lack of incentive to innovate, the growing difficulty of running an increasingly complex economy by central planning, and the rising expenditure on defence. They also suggest that, although the system was not capable of sustaining rates of growth comparable with the west in the long run, one of the later Soviet leaders, Andropov, did demonstrate that some of the failings could have been corrected, and that economic growth could have accelerated again; but that a difficult situation in the mid-1980s was turned into a crisis by the Gorbachev reforms. *Perestroika* reduced the ability of the central planning machine to operate, confused its aims, and undermined the currency, thus leading to the dramatic economic collapse of the country in the late 1980s, and the release of the eastern European satellites from its control in 1989. Whether this collapse can be classified as a shock or not, it has been a singular event, brought about by particular circumstances which are unlikely to be repeated. It is not, therefore, a wave-like phenomenon. However, in so far as it has revealed a need for massive restructuring, and to the extent that the economies of eastern and western Europe may now become more integrated, its consequences for future economic development may be of Schumpeterian proportions (Siebert 1991).

Conclusion

Whether the sequence of faster and slower growth since the 1930s forms a Long Wave or not is of less significance than the fact that it is this temporal framework within which the economic geography of Europe has been developing in the recent past. Furthermore, it is a framework in which the importance of the present moment is highlighted. Europe in the early 1990s faces economic turmoil comparable to that of sixty years earlier. But the dangers and opportunities are not everywhere the same; and, in the following chapters in this section, we shall examine the recent development and current state of each of the major sectors of the economy in turn, giving particular attention to the relationships between their changing technologies of production, patterns of trade, and growth or decline.

Further reading

Much has been written about Long Waves in the economy, though rather little about their impact upon the space economy. Schumpeter's *Business Cycles* (1939) is the most important of the early discussions, while Freeman's *Long Waves in the World Economy* (1983) and Freeman, Clark and Soete's *Unemployment and technical innovation: A study of Long Waves and Economic Development* (1982) provide shorter and more recent accounts. Tylecote's *The Long Wave and the World Economy* (1992) provides a more broadly-based historical explanation. Readers are also recommended to read Solomou's *Phases of Economic Growth, 1850-1973: Kondratieff Waves and Kuznets Swings* (1987) for a critical examination of the evidence for Long Waves. An introduction to some of the aspects of the relationship [illegible]

CHAPTER 4

THE PRIMARY INDUSTRIES

The production of food and energy has been fundamental to the form of the European space economy in the past. It has used much land; and, at the start of the Fourth Kondratiev, accounted for more than half the employment in almost all countries, and more than three-quarters in the Soviet Union and many of the other states in eastern and southern Europe. It has deeply influenced the distribution of the continent's other economic activities and population, and the development of its transport network. But the role, character and location of the primary sector have changed markedly since the 1930s, and seem likely to change again, following any closer integration of the continent and associated reform of the various systems of state intervention under which they have been developing in the recent past.

Agriculture

Farming experienced both boom and slump during the Fourth Kondratiev. In the early 1930s it was deeply depressed, but since that time it has been subject to revolutionary changes in its technology, structure and marketing arrangements, and output has risen sharply. However, by the 1990s it was again under pressure in much of Europe.

The inter-war depression was caused chiefly by the overproduction of the major crops worldwide, by the large stocks which accumulated, and by the consequentially low prices, which held down farm incomes and discouraged investment. Even before the Great Slump, several European countries had imposed tariffs, quotas and other devices, designed to protect their farmers, and most of these were strengthened in the early 1930s. Farmers in some countries, notably Germany, were shielded from the full effects of international competition; and those in the countries of eastern and southern Europe which entered into trade agreements with the Germans also benefited to some extent. The British and Danish industries, in contrast, received little help from their governments (Tracy 1982). Agriculture also suffered from the wider economic

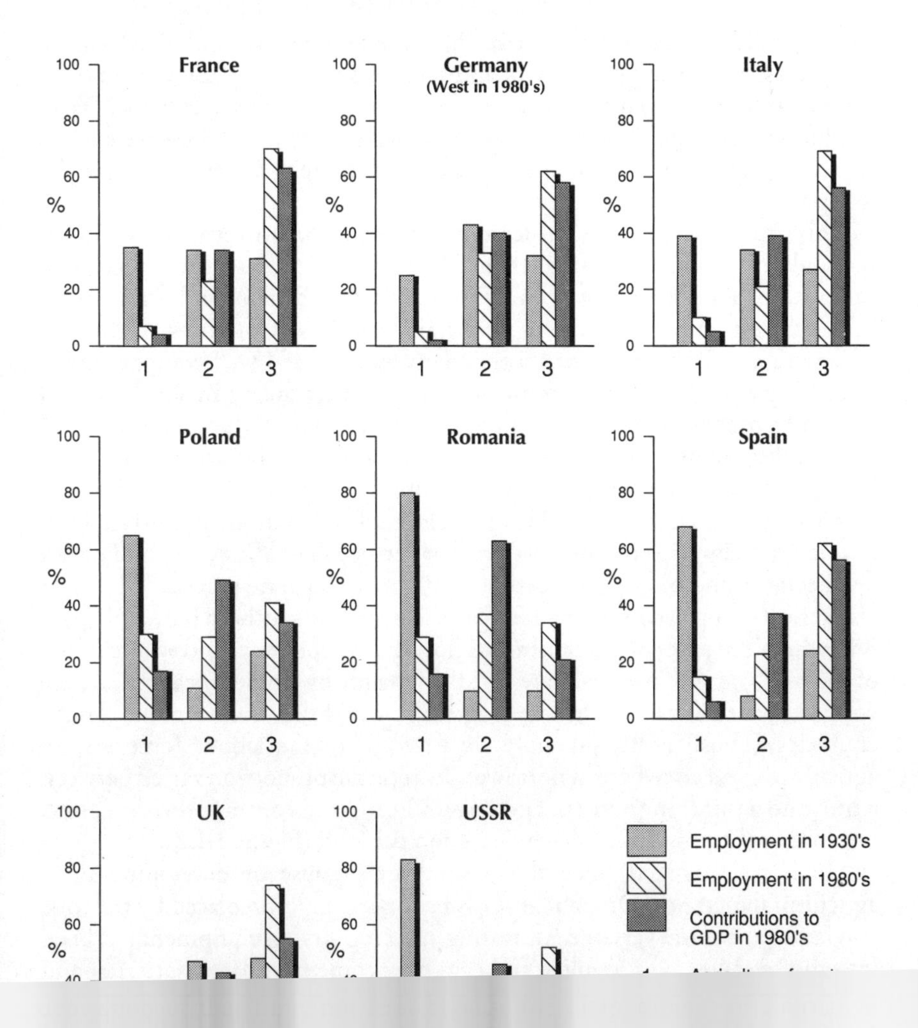

depression of that time, not least because the disappearance of alternative opportunities for employment off the land and for emigration – which had been particularly important in eastern and southern Europe before the First World War – impeded structural change (Warriner 1964). Meanwhile, in the USSR, the full rigour of Stalin's collectivisation drive was subjecting farmers to worse conditions than anywhere else; the more commercially-minded farmers, the kulaks, were being persecuted; and resources were being transferred from rural areas to towns by means of low prices and the compulsory delivery of farm products to the state. Peasants who slaughtered their livestock in preference to surrendering them to the new collectives merely contributed to the decapitalisation of the industry.

This situation was, to say the least, unfortunate, for farm structures and the methods of production in much of Europe had failed to keep pace with innovations in the industry in North America, Britain and some parts of northwest Europe. Whereas in Britain, the Low Countries, Germany, Denmark and Bohemia, farms were relatively large and well equipped, produced high yields, and sold most of their products, many in southern and eastern Europe possessed little land or machinery, and produced low yields of poor quality goods, some, if not most, of which were eaten by farm families. The largest farms, on average, were in the United Kingdom. Bulgaria, Poland, northern Spain, Yugoslavia and Russia before collectivisation, in contrast, were characterised by large numbers of small or very small holdings, often of only a few hectares, and often composed of a number of separate parcels. There was also a third group of countries – Hungary, Prussia, and southern Italy and Spain – in which the relics of feudalism had not been swept away, and where much of the land was still in large estates, worked mainly by landless peasants. These contrasts were reflected in the role of agriculture in the economies of the various countries. Thus, in Britain, only six per cent of the labour force was in agriculture, and elsewhere in northwest Europe the proportion varied between a fifth and a third. In southern and eastern Europe, in contrast, three-quarters or more of the population depended upon the land (Figure III.2).

Much has changed since then, not least because of developments in agricultural methods. Draught animals have been largely replaced by tractors, and larger and more versatile cultivating and crop-drying equipment has been introduced. Most pigs, poultry and eggs now come from large batteries; and improved strains of seed and breeds of livestock, and new chemical fertilisers and pesticides, have greatly increased yields. In other words, technical change has been encouraging increases in scale, the intensification of land use, the replacement of labour with machinery, and the production of goods of more uniform quality. Moreover, improvements in preservation and transport have meant that, whereas in the 1930s diets in much of the continent were restricted to those foods which were in season or were produced locally, the opportunities for those areas whose specialities have come to be more widely marketed have increased greatly. The demand for food, in contrast, has been growing only slowly. Since the 1930s, the population of Europe has increased by less than one per cent per annum, or much less than agricultural productivity; and the income elasticity of demand for agricultural products in a continent in which nutritional levels were already adequate in the 1930s has been low. Farmers, armed with the technology to produce much more food, have faced stagnant markets, especially in western Europe.

The impact of these developments has been marked. Yields of wheat and barley have more than doubled in most parts of the continent since the 1930s, and milk output per cow has increased even more. Supplies of food per capita – as measured in both calories and protein – have been raised. At the same time, farm amalgamations have occurred widely in western Europe; and the collectivisation of peasant holdings and establishment of state farms in much of eastern Europe created huge enterprises, many of which covered a thousand hectares or more initially, but were subsequently enlarged even further (Figure III.3). On the other hand, employment in farming has declined everywhere as farmers and their labourers have responded to the pressures on them, and the relatively better opportunities in other sectors of the economy, by leaving the industry in large numbers. The proportion of the population engaged in agriculture had become very small in most of western Europe and the Soviet Union by the 1980s, and, even in much of the rest of eastern Europe, it had fallen to less than a quarter (Figure III.2). The area of farmland has also declined in most countries as towns and cities have expanded and holdings in mountainous or other harsh environments have been abandoned. In Italy and West Germany it has fallen by almost a fifth, in France by about a tenth, and in Poland, Spain, the United Kingdom and Yugoslavia by more than five per cent. The Soviet authorities, in contrast, attempted to raise output by ploughing up the virgin lands of southwest Siberia and northern Kazakhstan, as well as by other means; and between 1956 and 1960, 42,000,000 hectares, or almost a fifth, were added to the country's sown area (USSR, various years).

Regional patterns of agricultural change

ing, and milking equipment. The production of salad crops, flowers, pigs, poultry and dairy goods, in particular, had become so intensive, being carried out largely in purpose-built glasshouses or other accommodation, that it was more industrial than agricultural. Heavy use was also made of artificial fertilisers and pesticides, and farmers relied on specialist suppliers of seed, and made use of artificial insemination. Products tended to be sold on contract,

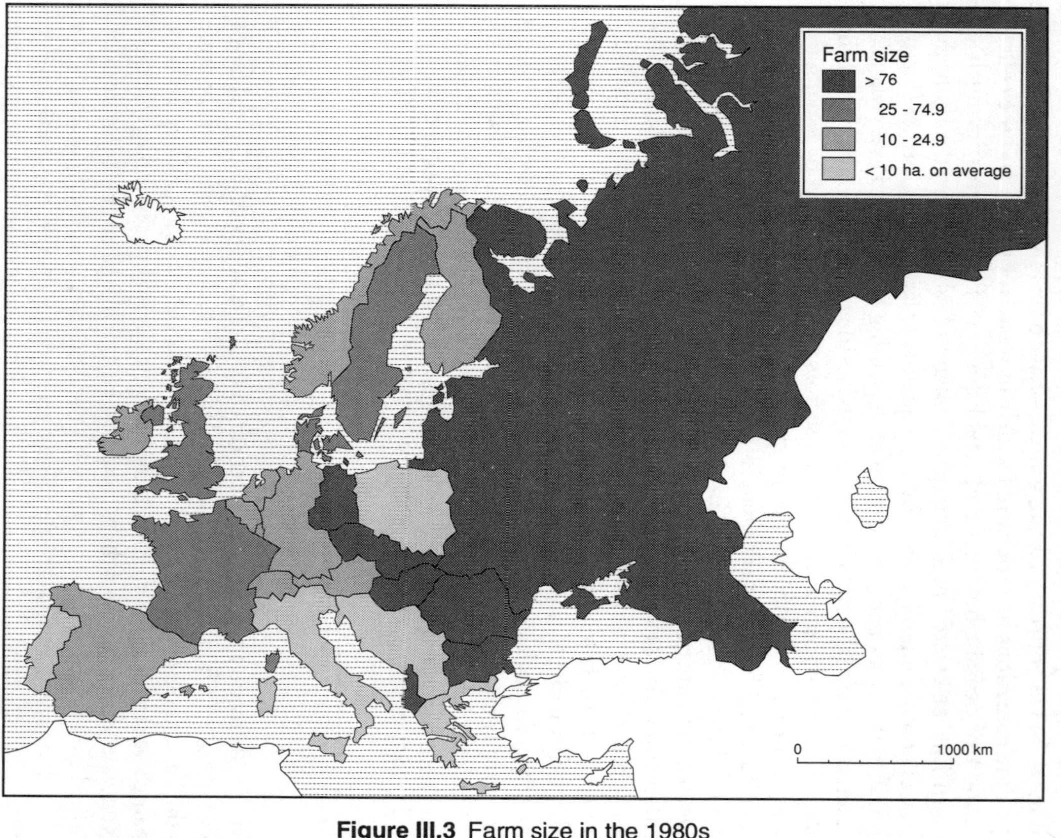

Figure III.3 Farm size in the 1980s
Source: FAO (1989a)

often in advance, to one of a small number of large-scale processors, who required a high and uniform quality of output. Many of these farms had increased their scale of operations since the 1930s, enlarging their land holdings as others had gone out of business, and greatly increasing their yields. The scale of enterprise had also been increased where farmers had grouped together to pursue cooperative ventures in the production or processing of particular crops. Much of this change had come about in response to the high and protected levels of income provided by the European Community or similar government action elsewhere; and, although crop surpluses had occurred, and levels of subsidy had been threatened with decline, the incomes of farmers in this group were higher than anywhere else on the continent. Those in Denmark were twice the Community average, as were those in the Low Countries, where holdings were somewhat smaller than in the rest of northwest Europe, but shared the other characteristics of the large commercial farm outlined above (Commission 1991; Williams 1987, pp. 112–144).

The large farms in southern Italy, Portugal and Spain, in contrast, were not so productive. The traditional holding in these areas had been the *latifundium* – a large estate, often belonging to the nobility, and farmed extensively by landless peasants until the middle of this century. Many of these had become more efficient as the growth of manufacturing and service industries had drawn labour into the towns, and more productive as price supports, and regional and other structural assistance from both national governments and the Community, had encouraged the improvement of equipment and the introduction of better methods, especially in irrigation. However, intensification had not proceeded as far as in northwest Europe by the 1980s, and the return to labour was below the average for the Community (Commission 1991; Harrison 1985).

About 10,000,000 farms in Europe in the 1980s were of less than ten hectares. Some of these, especially in the horticultural sector in the Netherlands and elsewhere, were highly capitalised. Others in northwest Europe, in contrast, were only worked part-time, and were of little significance, either to

sought to help farmers who still operate in what it has recognised to be the 'least-favoured regions' – that is, those with such permanent handicaps as high altitude, steep slopes, long winters or lack of rainfall – by paying for improvements to drainage, irrigation and other infrastructure. Smallholdings throughout the Community have also been less severely penalised than larger farms for the production of goods which are in surplus. Nevertheless, in Greece, parts of

Italy, Portugal, northern Spain and western Ireland, there were still too many small farms and people on the land in the late 1980s, with the result that capital and other inputs remained low, as did yields; and farm incomes were well below the average for the Community (Commission 1987b, 1991).

About half of Europe's small farms were in Poland and Yugoslavia. Although collectivisation was attempted in both countries after the Second World War, it was abandoned in the 1950s in the face of peasant opposition and other difficulties. However, strict limits were placed on the size of privately-owned farms, and the enlargement of even the smallest was discouraged by the communist authorities. Since 1970, Polish farmers have no longer been obliged to make compulsory deliveries of farm products to the state at low prices, and some specialist producers of fruit and flowers have flourished, selling their products largely on the free market. Nevertheless, the communist government never gave up its efforts to increase the socialist sector by persuading elderly farmers to relinquish their land in return for pensions; and the private sector never enjoyed subsidies similar to those lavished on the state farms in those countries, let alone the price supports available to farmers in the European Community. Indeed, they complained that the prices charged by the monopoly state suppliers of fertiliser and other materials were artificially high, and that the processors, which were in state ownership or cooperatives, operated as monopsonists against them. Farms in both countries, in consequence, continued to be very small, with little working capital or incentive to improve the quality of their products. As in western Europe in the 1980s, many provided no more than part-time employment for their owners, who often held factory or office jobs, while others were run by the elderly or widows. Methods of production were backward, and yields tended to be low. Such surpluses as were generated on Polish farms after 1970 were used as much to build large new farmhouses as to intensify production (World Bank 1990, pp. 1–5).

Lastly, there were about 70,000 collective and state farms in eastern Europe in the 1980s, including 50,000 in the Soviet Union, the majority of which were in the European part of the country. In Albania, Bulgaria, Czechoslovakia, East Germany, Hungary, Romania and the Soviet Union, they accounted for more than ninety per cent of the farmland; and there were also a few such farms in Poland and Yugoslavia. These were the largest farms in Europe, usually covering between 3,000 and 6,000 hectares, with machinery and buildings suited to very large-scale cultivation and livestock operations. However, it should be noted that, although the proportion of the labour force in agriculture in the area had fallen substantially since the 1930s, it was still rather higher than in northwest Europe. Moreover, while collectivisation in the Soviet Union aimed to replicate the large scale and productivity of North American farms, and to industrialise agricultural production, Stalin's fundamental goals were to impose control over the Russian peasants, and to transfer resources from agriculture to industry and the towns – goals which created severe problems throughout the period of communist rule. The removal of the more

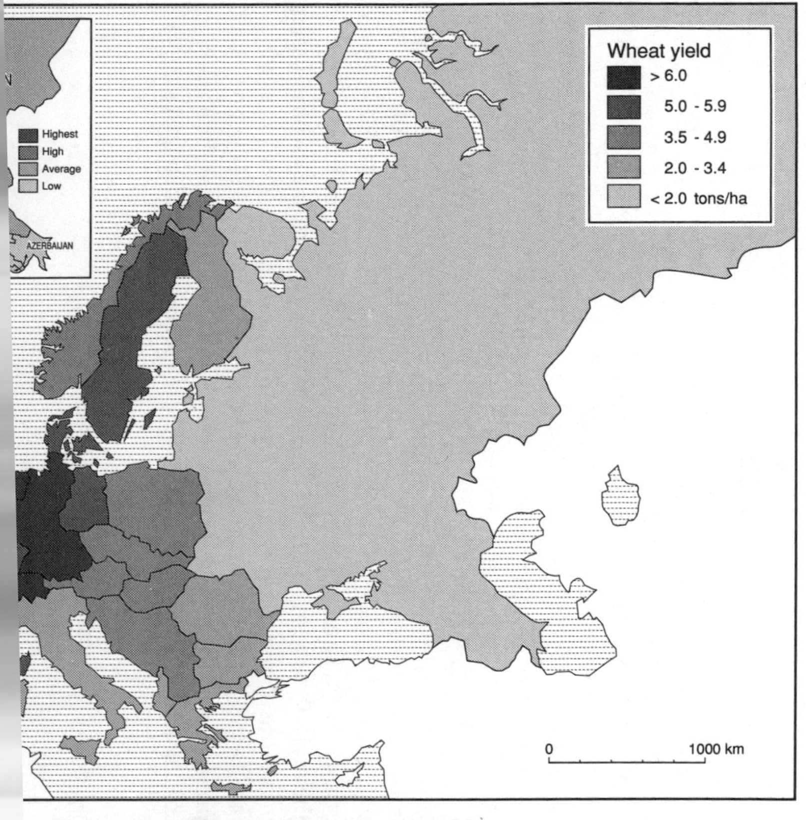

Figure III.4 Wheat yields in the late 1980s
Sources: FAO (1989a), USSR

commercially-minded kulaks from the population, and low agricultural prices, were compounded by unenterprising management and insufficient and poorly-directed investment. A system of massive food subsidies meant that there were few accurate signals as to what to grow where, or how best to proceed in agricultural development; and quantity of output was pursued without much thought about the best mix of products, either on the individual farm or in general. Consequently, yields and the quality of products, both in the Soviet Union and Eastern Europe, were generally inferior to those in the rest of the continent. Moreover, difficulties in the collection, processing and distribution of farm products under central planning led to large-scale waste, which greatly exacerbated these problems; and both the range and quantity of food in the shops of eastern Europe were small (Cook 1992).

Much of the effort of collective farmers has been put into their private plots, of not more than a hectare, on which they have been allowed to grow fruit and vegetables and rear small numbers of livestock. Some of this was eaten by the rural population; the rest was sold on local, free markets, where the contrast between the productivity of the private and socialised parts of the collective farms has become clear. Pallot (1991) reports that, in the Soviet Union, private plots accounted for only 0.7 per cent of agricultural land, but produced about thirty per cent of farm output, while each hectare of private gardens in Hungary in the mid-1980s was producing about four times as much as the collectivised land in terms of value (Hungary 1987, p. 143). However, in a situation in which it was cheaper for farmers to give bread bought in shops to their livestock than to purchase feed from the state, the contribution of their plots to the economy, though crucial to the feeding of the people of the region, is difficult to calculate.

Output and trade

In the 1980s, the Soviet Union was by far the largest producer of most crops, meat and dairy produce, followed by France, Italy, Poland, Spain, the United Kingdom and West Germany. However, absolute levels of output hid wide variations in yields between one part of the continent and another. Yields in the northwest of Europe, in Denmark, the Netherlands, Sweden, the United Kingdom and West Germany, but also in northern France, were the highest, while the lowest were in the Mediterranean countries, especially Albania, Greece, Portugal, Spain and Yugoslavia. Yields were also low in Romania and the north and east of the Soviet Union (Figures III.4 and III.5). Such contrasts are not surprising, especially in the case of field crops, whose yields inevitably reflect climate and soils. The output of milk per cow, in contrast, is less directly affected by such conditions; in the late 1980s, it ranged from as little as 2,500 kilograms in the USSR, through an average of about 3,400 in Eastern Europe, to 3,800 in the Community and 4,800 in the EFTA countries. Albania,

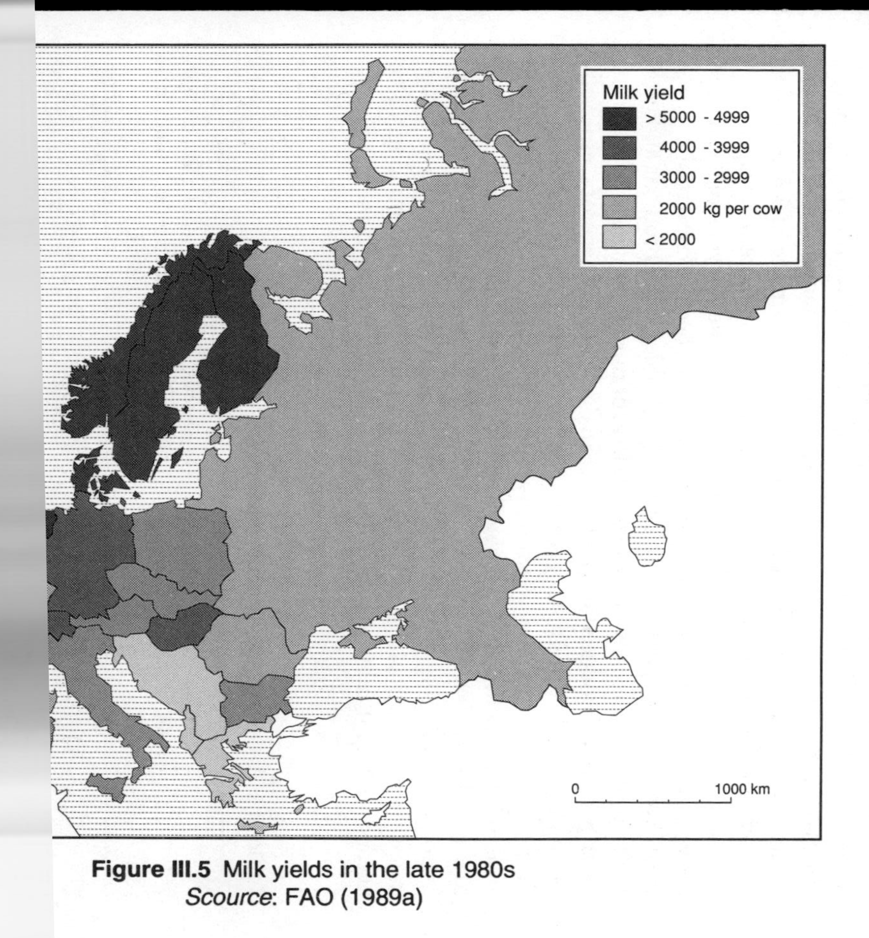

Figure III.5 Milk yields in the late 1980s
Scource: FAO (1989a)

Romania and Yugoslavia performed even less well than the Soviet Union, though so also did Greece, while yields in Denmark, the Netherlands, Norway and Sweden were more than twice as great as those in the USSR. Output should also be considered in relation to population. Thus, while the Soviet Union and the rest of eastern Europe produced more cereals and fresh milk in the late 1980s than the Community, but less butter, cheese and meat (Table III.1), per capita output was very different, with the highest levels in the EFTA countries, followed by the Community, and much lower ones in eastern Europe.

The potential for competition between the various types of farm, and between the countries and trading blocs which have been referred to above, was great. Wheat, barley, potatoes, sugar beet, vegetables, dairy products and meat can be produced in many of the lowland areas of Europe, and most of the farms described above produced several of these in the 1980s. Other crops, especially those from the Mediterranean region, are somewhat more restricted in their distribution; but they, too, were often grown in several countries. Some upland areas and those with adverse physical environments, in contrast, were limited to pastoral activities. This meant that, in theory, farmers had great flexibility to respond to changing market conditions, though those with heavy capital investment in particular types of equipment, such as that for milking, often needed to keep it fully used in order to recoup their expenditure.

Table III.1 Average annual agricultural output in the late 1980s

	Cereals (1,000 tons)	Meat (1,000 tons)	Fresh milk (1,000 tons)	Butter, cheese and dried milk (tons)	Population (millions)
EC	176,000	40,200	114,000	8,600	323
EFTA	16,000	2,300	15,000	900	32
USSR	192,000	18,400	106,000	4,700	289
East Europe*	93,000	10,400	41,000	3,000	140

Source: FAO (1989)
* Eastern Europe other than the USSR

However, that competition has been severely restricted. Since the 1960s, the Community has maintained prices for the most important farm products at well above world market levels; and, up to the late 1980s, this encouraged farmers to increase their output by an average of two per cent per annum – increases which occurred in spite of the decline in land and labour in the industry noted above, and various attempts by the Community during the 1980s to restrict output (Commission 1987b). Thus it is that the controversial 'mountains' of surplus cereals and dairy products and wine 'lakes' have been created – surpluses which have had to be given away, dumped on world markets or destroyed. EFTA countries have adopted similar policies, with even higher levels of support for their farmers, with similar results. Meanwhile, eastern Europe moved from a position of broad self-sufficiency in temperate agricultural products in the 1960s to one of increasing deficit and dependence upon imports from North America, Western Europe and elsewhere. Table III.2 shows how the trade in cereals, in particular, had developed. Much more of the output of the Community and EFTA was traded with countries outside each group than in the cases of the USSR or the rest of eastern Europe; and the Community had a cumulative surplus of almost five billion dollars in its trade with the rest of the world between 1985 and 1988, two-thirds of which was accounted for by its exports to the communist countries. Two-thirds of the exports of the EFTA countries also went to those areas. It may also be noted that the USSR was the chief recipient of eastern European grain.

Table III.2 Trade in cereals, 1985–8 ($US billion)

To:	EC	EFTA	USSR	East Europe*	Others	Total
From:						
EC	21,776	465	2,840	800	5,012	30,893
EFTA	[illegible]	[illegible]	[illegible]	[illegible]	[illegible]	[illegible]

Source: UN (1990)
*Eastern Europe other than the USSR

The potential for further agricultural change

Thus, European agriculture ended the Fourth Wave as it had entered it, out of balance. Farmers in western Europe were overproducing many crops at a time when too little food of acceptable quality was reaching the people of much of eastern Europe. The structure of land-holding in much of southern Europe and Poland had not been adjusted to the technical advances in the industry, and there were too many people employed on the land in these countries and in Romania. Conversely, the huge collectivised and state farms were generally recognised to be too large, and there was still too much land in use in mountainous and other marginal environments. It was widely agreed that these problems were largely the fault of the price, trade and structural policies which governments had applied to farming; and that the collapse of Comecon, economic reform in eastern Europe and the newly-independent Soviet republics, the desire of those countries and of EFTA to improve their links with the European Community, and moves to reform the Community's Common Agricultural Policy, if carried through, would bring about major changes – changes which will be examined in Section V.

Energy

At the start of the fourth Long Wave, Europe consumed the coal equivalent of about 700,000,000 tonnes of fuel each year. Three-quarters of this was coal, mined from a large number of fields from the Asturias in Spain to the Kuzbas in western Siberia. Wood and peat were also burned in many places for domestic heating, while Romania and the Baku area of the Soviet Union produced petroleum. Oil was also imported from the Middle East. Industry, railways, the generation of electricity, and the production of gas depended almost entirely upon coal. But coal's position has been strongly challenged by oil and natural gas during the Fourth Wave, and the development of the energy industries during this period has been closely connected with the changing technologies of the production and use of both coal and its competitors.

Three aspects of those technologies have been of particular significance. Firstly, there have been marked improvements in labour productivity. The growth of the coal industry in Europe and elsewhere during the third Long Wave was achieved almost entirely through the construction of pits served by vertical shafts, worked by large numbers of miners. During the Fourth Wave, in contrast, an increasing quantity of coal has been extracted much more cheaply from huge open pits, some 300 metres deep, with the use of large-scale machinery, but relatively little labour. This coal has been able to compete in far-distant markets against shaft producers. Thus, coal from Australia and North

America has undercut that mined in western Europe, while producers in Colombia and South Africa have kept their costs low through the employment of cheap labour. Meanwhile, the cost of extracting oil and natural gas has proved to be less than that of the fuel equivalent of shaft-mined coal, even where those fuels have been exploited in the Arctic or offshore (International Energy Agency 1985).

Secondly, the transport of energy has been changed by the introduction of the pipeline and the electricity grid. The cost of moving petroleum and natural gas by pipe has been much lower than the hauling of coal by rail, and this has encouraged the use of these fuels, even where they have been located at great distances from the market. Several proposals have been considered for similar long-distance conveyor or slurry deliveries of coal, but little has been accomplished. Conversely, electricity grids have enabled fuels, including coal, to be consumed at source, transporting the energy from them very cheaply over many hundreds of kilometres.

Thirdly, not only have the demands for energy which can only be supplied by petroleum grown very greatly during the fourth Long Wave, but some of the markets which were previously supplied almost entirely by coal have been opened to other fuels, several of which are of higher calorific value in relation to weight, and more convenient for customers to handle. In particular, there has been a shift from the combustion of coal to provide steam power in factories, on the railways and for heating, to the use of electricity. One, completely new source of energy – nuclear fission – was invented during the Fourth Wave, and another – natural gas – which went unused, and often wasted, before the Second World War, has become one of Europe's most important sources of energy. Thus, by the early 1990s, most coal was being used directly for two purposes only – the generation of electricity and for coking.

The fuel industries have also been affected by concern for the natural environment. There has been a growing recognition that coal is one of the most

nuclear power stations after the fall of the communist governments in those countries.

The demand for energy rose sharply in all parts of Europe during the expansionary phase of the Fourth Wave, doubling or more between 1955 and 1973 in all except the United Kingdom, East Germany, Czechoslovakia,

Belgium and Hungary. Governments were concerned about shortages of coal and electricity; and in the 1960s, the Soviet Union and the countries around the North Sea took the opportunity to diversify their sources by exploiting their oil and gas deposits. Several countries began to build nuclear power stations, and the OPEC oil price rises in 1973 further encouraged producers of fuels in all parts of the world to increase output. However, they also depressed demand, and many of the new investments were coming on stream in the late 1970s and early 1980s at the time when the rate of growth in the world economy was declining. While the consumption of energy continued to rise sharply between 1973 and the mid-1980s throughout eastern Europe, the earlier growth came to an end amongst the larger consumers in the west, with the exception of Italy, the Netherlands and Spain, and this was followed by falls in eastern Europe in the late 1980s (United Nations 1991). The result has been a glut of fuels, steep falls in prices, and pressure on the more expensive producers, and especially on those in the coal industry, to abandon their activities.

Coal

At the bottom of the 1930s depression, more than half the world's coal, or just over 500,000,000 tonnes, was mined in Europe (Figure III.6). Forty per cent of this came from Great Britain; and Germany, the Soviet Union, France and Poland were also important producers. World output has risen fairly steadily since then, and was more than three times as great by the late 1980s. That in Europe rose to 945,000,000 tonnes in 1957, but growth since then has not kept pace with that in other parts of the world, and output had only reached 1,040,000,000 tonnes in 1988. However, there has been a marked contrast between the industries in eastern and western Europe. Communist Europe accounted for half of the continent's total in 1957; and Polish and Soviet output continued to increase thereafter, with the result that almost four-fifths came from those two countries by the late 1980s. Output by all the major western producers, in contrast, turned down after 1957, and more recently has fallen sharply as coal has been increasingly imported (United Nations 1991). Whereas communist Europe was a modest net exporter of coal in the late 1980s, net imports into the non-communist countries totalled about 105,000,000 tonnes in 1988, or half as much as they mined, much of which came from Poland and the Soviet Union, but more from outside Europe (International Energy Agency 1985). In short, both the demand for coal in western Europe and the ability to mine it at competitive prices have been declining since the 1950s, whereas the situation seems to have been quite different in the communist countries.

The development of the Soviet coal industry has been particularly impressive. Little coal was mined outwith the Donbas field of the eastern Ukraine before the 1930s, but the industry has spread out since then to the east and

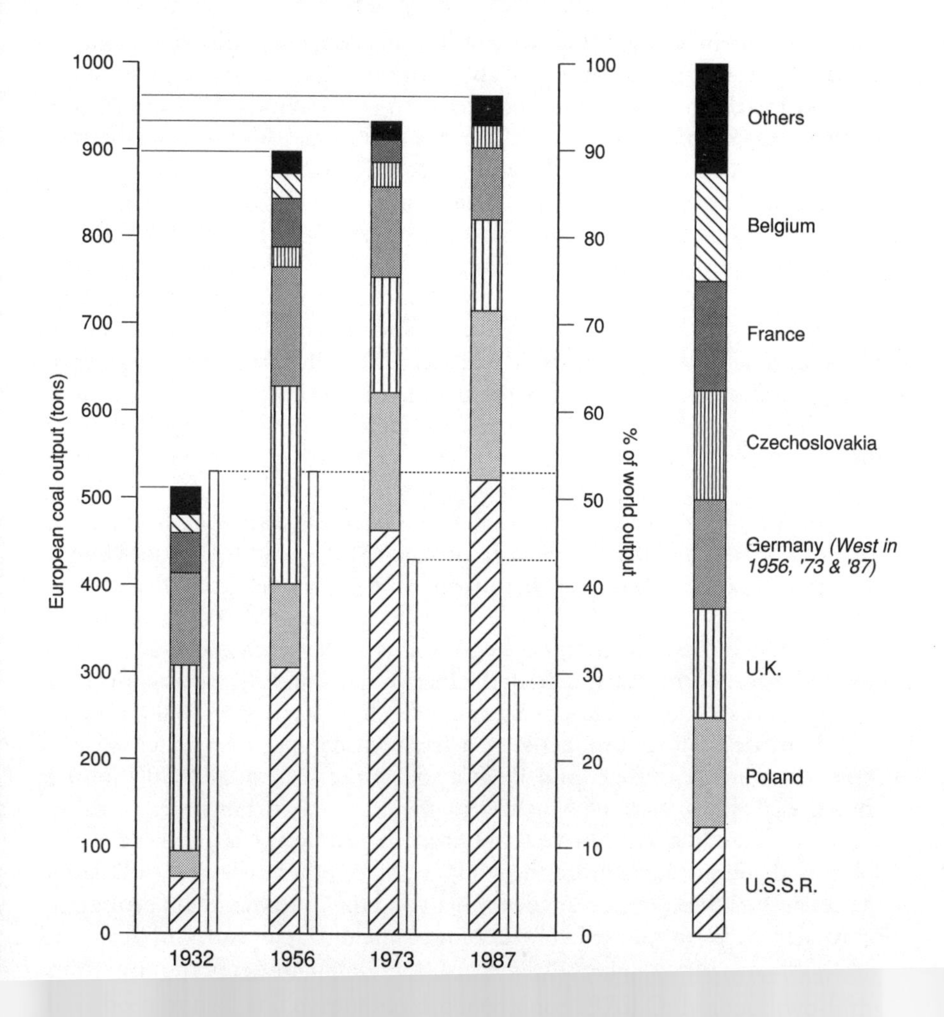

have been rising as deeper seams, many of which are also very narrow, have been mined, and output has declined since 1976. Only about two-fifths of Soviet coal was being raised there by the late 1980s, and many of the pits would probably be revealed to be sub-marginal if the Ukraine were to introduce a true market economy. Nevertheless, with an annual output of almost 200,000,000 tonnes, the Ukraine and Upper Silesia are the two most productive coalfields in Europe, followed by the Kuzbas and Ekibastuz. About a quarter of the Soviet coal output, or about 145,000,000 tonnes, came from the Kuzbas, a sixth from Ekibastuz, and a tenth from Karaganda. Vorkuta and the Urals produced most of the rest (Symons 1990, pp. 156-60). The Kuzbas contains thick seams, lying sufficiently close to the surface to permit opencast working, and its coal is generally at lesser depths than that of the Donbas. The field produces coking and steam coal which is used locally, but much is also sent to industries in the Urals. The Ekibastuz field, which, like that at Karaganda, lies in Kazakhstan, is mined exclusively by opencast methods, producing low-quality bituminous coal for local power stations and others in Siberia and the Urals. Several other huge fields lie even further to the east in Siberia and the Soviet Far East, but the cost of exploiting these on a large scale would seem to be prohibitive in the absence of substantial increases in the real price of other fuels.

Second among European producers of hard coal is Poland. The Upper Silesian field, including the Ostrava field in Czechoslovakia, was producing a total of about 210,000,000 tonnes in the late 1980s. As in the Soviet Union, output has been increased very sharply since the 1930s, and grew until the onset of the Polish crisis of 1980. This increase was achieved through the construction of new pits to mine deeper seams in the south and southwest of the field. Most of the coal is used in the metallurgical and electricity industries of Upper Silesia and Krakow, or is exported. Though raised from shaft mines of only modest labour productivity, it has been cheaper than much of that mined in western Europe; and Poland sold more than 30,000,000 tonnes abroad each year, some of which went to the Donbas, but more to other countries, including many in western Europe. The industry has, however, been subsidised and protected from the competition of other fuels; and, following the collapse of the communist government and the introduction of economic reforms in 1989, output fell. The Lublin coalfield, where work had begun in the 1970s with the aim of raising another 40,000,000 tonnes per annum from a depth of about 1,000 metres, was abandoned.

Only two fields in western Europe were major producers of coal by the early 1990s – the Ruhr and the Nottingham and Yorkshire field – both of which raised about 60,000,000 tonnes, largely for electricity generation or for coking. Unlike the Soviet and Upper Silesian fields, the output of both of these had declined during the Fourth Wave as the demand for coal fell in western Europe. Many small pits mining the shallower seams had been closed, and the industry had migrated to a small number of new and larger, but also deeper, pits to the north of the Ruhr and the east of the Nottingham–Yorkshire field. Even so, the adjustment does not appear to have been complete, for the German industry was still supported by a large government subsidy, and imports of cheap coal by the British electricity-generating industry were strictly controlled.

These fields, however, have fared better than many in western Europe, where the decline of the industry over the Fourth Wave has been very great. Hundreds of pits have been closed, and hundreds of thousands of jobs have disappeared. Many colliery settlements have lost their *raison d'être*, and huge efforts have been made by governments to reclaim land, create new jobs, and help miners to migrate to new pits. The number of pits in the United Kingdom fell from about a thousand in the 1930s to fifty in the early 1990s, and employment from about 800,000 to 50,000, with the possibility that there would be only a handful of pits and a few thousand jobs by the middle of the decade. Severe decline has also occurred in the French industry, especially in the Nord/Pas de Calais, and in the Belgian Sambre-Meuse field. The Dutch industry was completely closed.

Lignite

Lignite was used before the Second World War, but large-scale, open-pit mining enabled European output to be quadrupled between 1932 and 1960, when 612,000,000 tonnes were raised; by 1989 as much was being mined as hard coal. However, because of its much lower calorific content, its contribution to Europe's energy supply was less than half as great. A quarter of the total was raised in East Germany, from fields around Cottbus and Leipzig, and other major producers were the Soviet Union, West Germany (from the Rhenish field near Cologne), Czechoslovakia, Yugoslavia and Poland (United Nations 1991). Most of the Soviet output came from remote fields in central Siberia and the Asiatic republics, but some was raised from high-cost, shaft mines close to Moscow. Because of its low calorific content in relation to bulk, much has been burnt in electricity-generating stations located close to the pits; and in East Germany some has been made into briquettes or used in the chemical industry, all of which has led to appalling atmospheric pollution in Czechoslovakia, East Germany and elsewhere.

a sixth of the world's petroleum, or 30,000,000 tonnes, was produced in Europe in the early 1930s; but by 1960 output had increased six-fold, and by the 1980s it had more than quadrupled again, and represented a quarter of the world total. This came almost entirely from three countries – the Soviet Union, United Kingdom and Norway. The Soviet Union was by far the world's chief producer, with about 600,000,000 tonnes, or three-quarters, of the European output (United Nations 1991). Three-fifths came from Tyumen Oblast in western Siberia, and about a fifth from the Volga–Urals field. Oil from western Siberia has been sent by pipeline, largely to refineries west of the Urals, while that from the Volga–Urals field, which is located midway between the Moscow, Ukraine and Urals industrial regions, has been piped to all these areas and to eastern Europe.

The Volga–Urals field was first developed during the Second World War; and output increased rapidly in the 1940s and 1950s; but the western Siberian deposits have only been opened up since the 1960s. In all cases, output rose swiftly, but had reached some sort of plateau by the 1980s, with evidence that the most accessible deposits had been exploited, and that output could only be maintained if new wells were sunk or efforts made to increase the proportion of the oil extracted. Output from the Volga–Urals field fell by about a quarter during the 1980s. Production in western Siberia was also being threatened by the failure to maintain the pumping and pipeline equipment in an area of harsh climate and difficult terrain; and matters have been made worse by the failure of the Soviet industry to adopt the drilling and extraction methods which have been commonly used in market economies since the 1950s, with the result that the rate of drilling and the proportion and quality of the oil extracted are much lower than they need be.

The second major source of oil in Europe is the North Sea basin. Exploration began there in the 1960s, and output had reached 180,000,000 tonnes by the late 1980s, almost entirely from the British and Norwegian sectors. Many individual deposits exist within the basin, and further exploration in deeper waters north of Scotland may reveal yet more. However, the costs of extraction are very high; and many of the smaller fields or those in the deeper waters would not have been opened up if the price of oil had not risen four-fold in 1973, and doubled again in 1979. Much of the oil from the British sector is refined and consumed in the domestic market, but Norway exports a very large proportion of its output, chiefly to the rest of western Europe.

Natural gas

Natural gas was only of very minor importance in the 1930s in Europe. However, by the late 1980s it had grown to such an extent that it was contributing as much as coal or oil to the continent's energy requirements. Almost two-fifths of the world output came from the Soviet Union, and the other significant producers in Europe were Britain, France, Italy, the Netherlands and West Germany (United Nations 1991). Large-scale exploitation in the Soviet Union began in the 1950s, in the northern Caucasus, and later in the eastern Ukraine, at Orenburg in the Volga–Urals oil and gas field, in Turkmenistan and Uzbekistan. The most recently-opened fields have been in the Tyumen area of northwestern Siberia. In those fields which were exploited first, output rose rapidly, only to reach a plateau, and then begin to decline; but the central Asian, and especially the western Siberian, reserves appear to be very great: by the late 1980s, over half the Soviet output was being produced in western Siberia. The gas has been moved by pipeline to industrial regions in what was the Soviet Union, the rest of eastern Europe, and, more recently, to western Europe. Output in the rest of Europe has been small in comparison with the Soviet Union, and has come very largely from the Groningen field in the Netherlands and the North Sea basin, both of which contain extensive reserves. Dutch and Norwegian gas is sold to several western European countries.

The European energy market in the late 1980s

Taken together, Europe's production of energy had become dominated by the late 1980s by the Soviet Union (Figure III.7). Three-fifths of the total was produced there, and the next largest producers were the United Kingdom, with about a tenth, and Poland and West Germany, with about five per cent each. About two-fifths of the Soviet output came from oil, and a little less from natural gas. Hard coal supplied about a fifth. The contributions of lignite and hydro and nuclear power, though large in absolute terms, only amounted in total to about five per cent. Oil was also the leading component of British energy production, contributing about half the total, but was followed by coal, with about a third, and gas. Almost ninety per cent of Polish energy production and over half of West German, in contrast, was of hard coal.

The consumption of energy in Europe rose six-fold between the Great Slump and the late 1980s. At the start of the period, the demand for all except oil was met by production within the continent

III.8). The Soviet Union produced about thirty per cent more energy than it consumed, and Norway almost four times its needs, while the United Kingdom had a small surplus. Production and consumption in the Netherlands and Poland were in overall balance, but all the other countries were in deficit. Those with the largest shortfalls were West Germany, France, Italy and Spain; and western Europe as a whole produced only about three-fifths of its energy

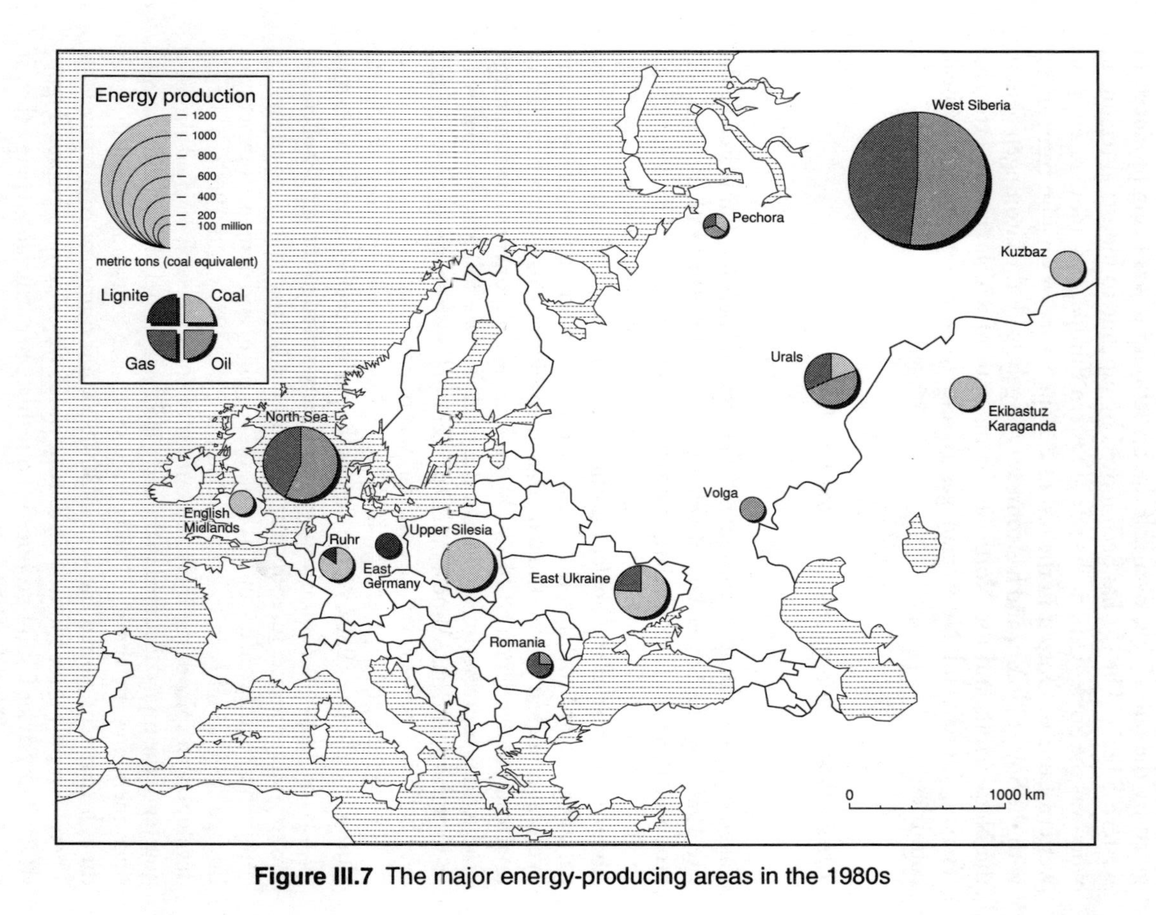

Figure III.7 The major energy-producing areas in the 1980s

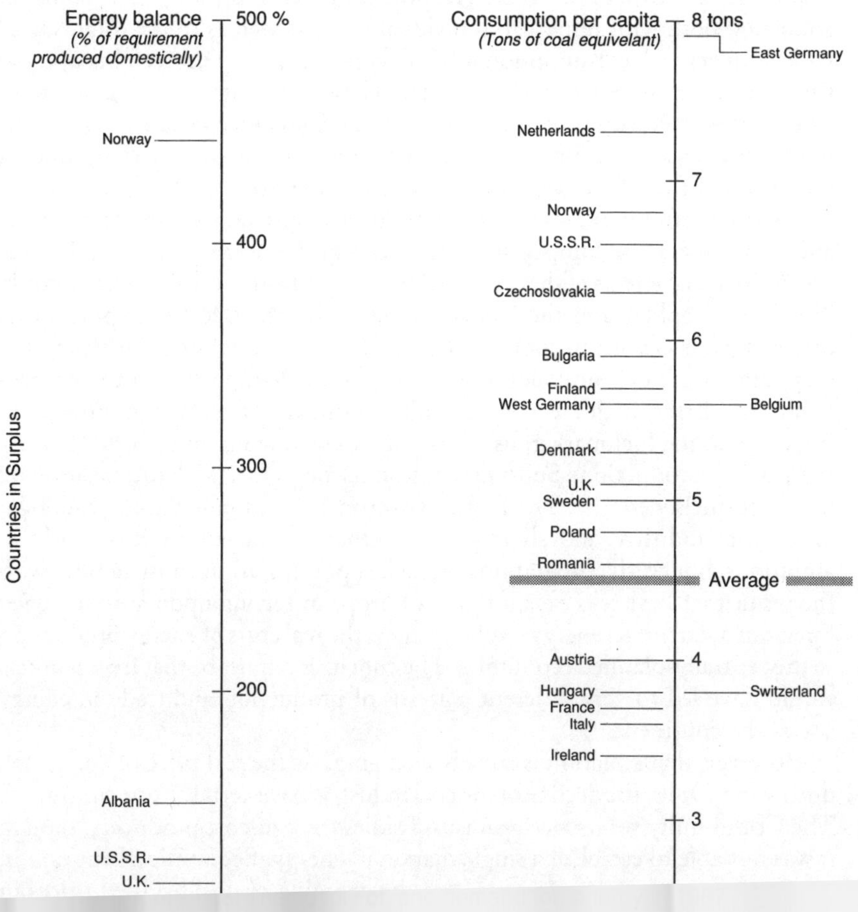

Figure III.8 The supply of, and demand for, energy in 1987
Source: United Nations (1991)

requirements. Eastern Europe, other than the Soviet Union, was obliged to import about a fifth of its needs. The production and consumption profiles of countries, both with respect to individual fuels, as well as to the total, varied widely. In general, consumption was higher per capita in northern Europe and the centrally-planned economies, than elsewhere (Figure III.8). Western Europe imported large quantities of oil, natural gas and coal, chiefly from the Arab countries and the Soviet Union. Eastern Europe also imported significant quantities of these fuels, almost all of which came from the USSR.

But this trade was a very imperfect reflection of the relative costs of producing and transporting the competing forms of energy. Concerns in western Europe about the social effects of the decline of the coal industry and about the security of energy supplies, and the Soviet Union's wish to seize the opportunities offered by fuel exports to control the economies of its satellite countries and to earn hard currency from sales to western Europe, had prompted the governments of all the major producers and consumers of energy in Europe to intervene in the fuel market, usually with a view to maintaining or increasing indigenous production. Subsidies, restraints on trade, and the taxation of imported fuels were rife. The French government responded to the rundown of its coal industry and shortage of alternative indigenous fuels with an ambitious, but costly, programme of nuclear power station construction, with the result that France is exceptional in Europe in relying upon atomic power for about a sixth of its energy. Nobody knew the real costs of energy production in the centrally-planned economies. The conclusion must be that freer markets would have led to very different patterns of production and trade in energy across the continent.

However, that situation is already changing. As the real price of energy fell during the 1980s, the decline of the coal industry in western Europe continued. The Community set its face against subsidies to high-cost producers, though it was not able to establish a single market in energy. Economic disruption in the former communist countries, and the charging of unsubsidised prices in hard currency for Soviet energy exports to them, had already begun to depress demand by the end of the 1980s. Poland's Lublin coalfield was abandoned; Soviet oil production was in decline; several nuclear power stations in eastern Europe were closed in the early 1990s; and plans for others were scrapped. In short, the capacity of the energy industries was being cut back. But the European energy market as a whole is not in surplus, and any long-term, world-wide economic growth associated with the expansionary phase of a new Long Wave is likely to lead to an increase in demand. Irrespective of the impact of any technical innovations which may alter the relative prices of fuels in a Fifth Wave, just as they have done during the Fourth, or open up new sources of energy, there is already much potential for change in the energy industries of Europe – potential which we shall return to in Section V.

Further reading

An introduction to the development of west European agriculture is provided by Tracy (1982), while its state in the 1980s is reviewed by Alexandratos (1990) in *European agriculture: Policy issues and options to 2000.* A more detailed assessment of the situation in Poland, following the collapse of communism, has been provided by the World Bank (1990) in *An agricultural strategy for Poland.*

The geography of energy supply in the 1980s is covered in some detail in the appropriate sections of Symons' *The Soviet Union* (1990), Turnock's *Eastern Europe: An economic and political geography* (1989), and Williams' *The Western European Economy* (1987).

CHAPTER 5

MANUFACTURING

Europe was one of the world's major centres of manufacturing industry in the 1930s, comparable with North America, and France, Germany, the Soviet Union and the United Kingdom were the leading European producers of manufactured goods. Belgium, Italy, the Netherlands and Sweden were also important. The Balkan countries, in contrast, were hardly industrialised. In other words, the role of manufacturing in the various economies was roughly the reverse of that of farming (Figure III.2). More than a third of the British worked in manufacturing, and more than a quarter in Germany, France, the Low Countries and Sweden. The figure in Italy was about a fifth, but elsewhere it was much lower, and less than a tenth in the Soviet Union.

After the Second World War, however, the picture changed rapidly, especially during the expansionary phase of the Fourth Kondratiev. Manufacturing grew rapidly throughout eastern and southern Europe; and, by the early 1970s, it provided more than a quarter of all employment in the Soviet Union and much of eastern Europe, and a somewhat smaller proportion in Greece and Yugoslavia. But growth in the industrialised countries of northwest Europe was slower. Thereafter, three groups of countries can be recognised. Those which were least industrialised continued to expand the role of manufacturing in total employment, and the most spectacular growth in the 1970s and 1980s was in Romania and Bulgaria. Those in which manufacturing had grown in the post-war years, such as the Soviet Union, Czechoslovakia, and Finland, showed little change; and those which had been most industrialised – Britain, Germany, France, the Low and alpine countries, and Sweden – all registered marked falls in the proportion of the labour force in manufacturing. This 'deindustrialisation' also affected Hungary, Italy and Spain. But, it was not accompanied by an equivalent fall in the contribution of manufacturing to GNP. Rather, it seems to have reflected sharp rises in labour productivity relative to other sectors of the economy.

Nevertheless, European manufacturing was facing problems almost everywhere by the 1980s. According to Williams (1991, p. 86), the competitive position of industry in the Community was being undermined by

> its less effective application and commercialization of R&D [than in America and Japan]. European R&D was fragmented along national lines and most EC companies were too small to compete in the global marketplace ... and were weakened by their dependency on small national markets and by wasteful duplication of research.

More particularly, they were slipping behind in technological innovation, and losing their share of world trade, in consumer electronics, computers and telecommunications. Britain, in particular, had fallen back, both in relation to the United States and the rest of Europe. Thus, by the 1980s, only West German firms were rivalling those in America and Japan in expenditure upon research and development, and in the number of patents applied for in more than one country – that is, for major innovations which require protection worldwide. Many branches of manufacturing were hiding behind import restrictions of one sort or another or being sustained by subsidies. But the situation was far worse in eastern Europe. Long before the late 1980s, the Soviet Union had come to rival the United States as the leading world producer of some, but by no means all, goods; and some of its aerospace and armament industries were particularly advanced. For the rest, however, the region had become isolated from the mainstream of technical innovation, was a byword for backwardness in both products and processes, and was riddled with overmanning and inefficiency.

It is not possible to describe here the contribution of all of the many branches of manufacturing to these generalised patterns of change in the industrial geography of the continent during the Fourth Wave, but four examples will be examined. Two may be categorised broadly as producer–good, and two consumer–good, industries. Two may also be classified as mature industries, that is, industries which were already well developed by the 1930s, while the other two are industries which have come into existence since then (Table III.3).

Steel

Steel-making was largely established during the Third Wave, when its fortunes were closely connected with those of the mining and shipbuilding industries, and with railways and construction. Demand from some of these has not been buoyant during the latter part of the Fourth Wave; but new uses have appeared for steel, in pipes for the oil and natural-gas industries, and sheet steel for the production of cars and domestic appliances. World output, which grew strongly during the Long Boom, peaked in 1974, and has shown no long-term tendency to rise since then. Meanwhile, some of the sources of raw material which influenced the location of the industry in the past have become exhausted, and others have been opened up. Moreover, costs of overseas coal and ore have been reduced relative to some of those in Europe by large-scale, open-pit production, and the introduction of bulk carriers. New producers, outwith Europe, with low labour costs, have entered the world market. The scale of production of bulk steel has been rising, and the basic oxygen method of manufacture and continuous casting have been replacing the open hearth in recent decades. More recently, 'mini-mills' – electric-arc furnaces which can respond more easily than the bulk, integrated steel mills to the requirements of customers for small quantities of a variety of high-quality, alloy steels, but which rely on close links with customers and access to supplies of their principal raw material, scrap – have been taking an increasing share of the market.

Europe made over half of the world's steel in the 1930s (Figure III.9). Germany, the Soviet Union, Britain and France were the chief producers, followed by Belgium, Luxembourg and Italy. By the late 1980s, however, the picture had altered markedly. World output was many times larger than at the bottom of the Great Slump; and European output of crude steel ingots had risen sharply to about 350,000,000 tonnes. Almost half of that was made in the Soviet Union, which had become the dominant producer in Europe, and a tenth in West Germany. Italy, France, Britain, Poland, Czechoslovakia and Romania each contributed about five per cent. In other words, production had spread widely amongst the countries of Europe during the Fourth Wave, and there were few which did not have a steel industry by the 1980s. Several of these, however, were very small. On the other hand, production had also begun, or been increased, in many countries outwith Europe, and Europe's contribution to world steel output had declined to about half the total.

By the late 1980s, the industry in Europe was located very largely in five types of site. Coalfields offering local supplies of coking coal, but which had also often possessed iron ore as well, were the most important in terms of output. The Donbas, Ruhr and Upper Silesia were the chief of these, all of which had a history going back to the nineteenth century, when the production of steel was closely bound up with the demands of local mining, railway and heavy-engineering industries. If the mills at the orefield at Krivoy Rog are added to

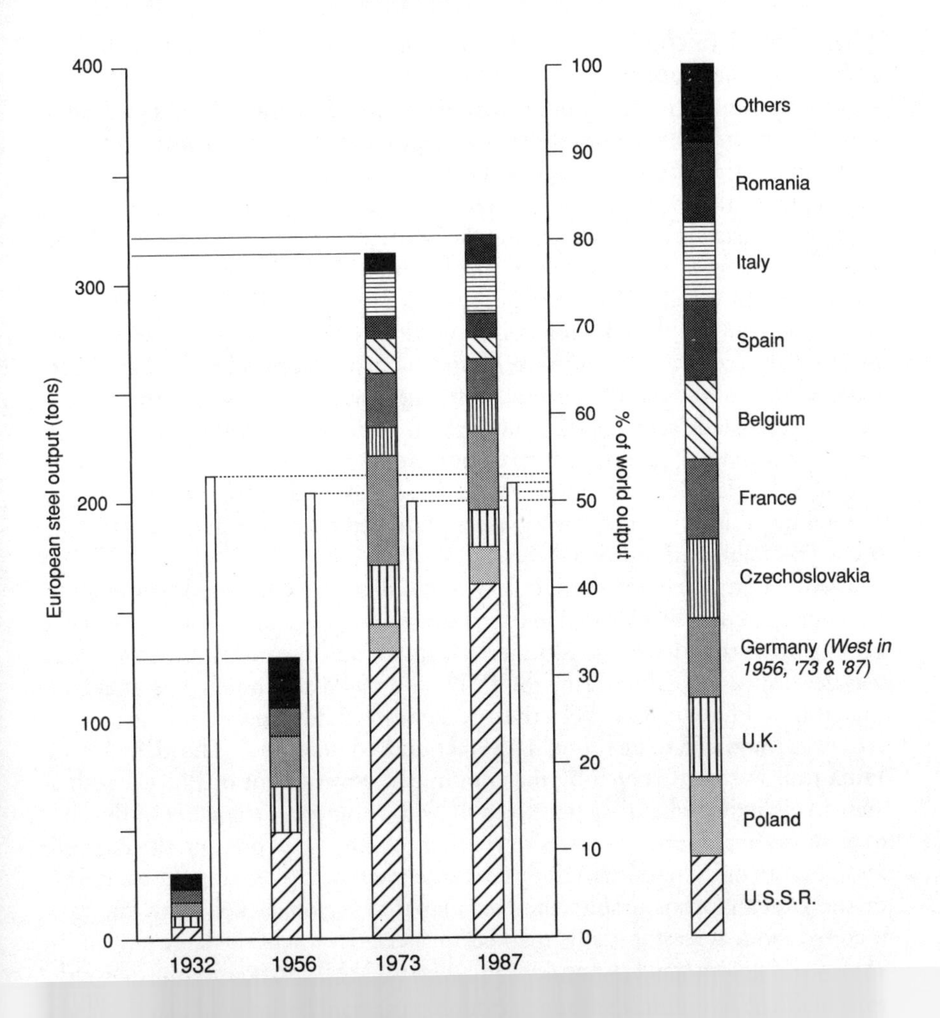

which steel has been traditionally associated, and the availability of imports of cheaper coal, have raised increasing doubts about the viability of coalfield sites in western Europe during the Fourth Wave, though not in eastern Europe.

Orefield sites, though in many cases having a longer history of production than the coalfields, were generally less important centres of the industry by the late 1980s. Chief amongst them were the central and southern Ural mountains, where more than 40,000,000 tonnes were produced annually, and the Krivoy Rog area of the Donbas.

Thirdly, and increasingly important, have been the break-of-bulk locations, usually at ports, which became very competitive as the cost of ocean transport of ore fell during the 1950s and 1960s. Many such sites have been developed, especially in Italy, where three-quarters of the output in the 1980s came from four major coastal complexes, and on the North Sea coasts; however, not all the available opportunities were taken. The British industry built new mills on the coast of South Wales and at Teesside, but failed to transfer the Scottish industry to the Clyde; while the growing Polish industry took advantage neither of sites on the Baltic coast, where imports of ore and exports of coal could have been handled, nor of those on the frontier with the Soviet Union, where the change of rail gauge made such handling of the large quantities of coking coal and ore which were traded between the two countries inevitable.

Fourthly, electric-arc producers, and those making specialist steels, have in general been closely tied to the high-precision engineering industries, often in the long-established industrial areas.

Lastly, a large part of the industry, including many of the developments mentioned above, was located in places chosen by governments with a view to serving other than narrowly commercial aims. Thus, the industry in the Urals was developed by Stalin during the 1930s and 1940s to a much greater extent than might otherwise have been the case, as a safeguard against German attack; coal has always had to be brought several hundred miles to it. The giant Nowa Huta mill was constructed by the communist government of Poland with a view to changing what they perceived to be the bourgeois character of the city of Krakow, but at some distance from either coking coal or ore; and the Bagnoli and Taranto mills in southern Italy were intended to help develop the economy of the Mezzogiorno, despite the fact that that region lacked both the raw materials and, at least initially, markets for steel. Several of the large new mills of the 1950s in eastern Europe – at Dunaujváros in Hungary, Eisenhüttenstadt in East Germany and Kosice in Slovakia – were also built in places which possess few advantages for the industry, and the development of steel-making in Albania and Yugoslavia owed more to the idea that it was essential to the Stalinist model of development that a state should possess its own capacity than to the technical requirements of the industry. Each of the constituent republics of Yugoslavia acquired its own steel mill, many of which were small and in high-cost locations.

Looking at the map of Europe, as a whole, it would appear that these five types of site can be grouped into a small number of rather large steel-making regions. Such regions are not cheek-by-jowl concentrations of mines, coke ovens, sinter plants, blast furnaces, rolling mills and fabricating yards, in which such plants enjoy short and dedicated transport links with each other, but large areas, each containing several groupings of industry, with which steel-making is closely connected. Viewed at this scale, the European steel industry in the early 1990s was located in five major regions, in each of which it had a complex history of development, range of production and set of links. Several of the regions crossed national frontiers. These regions, in order of output, were the Ruhr–Lorraine–Pas de Calais triangle, the Donbas–Krivoy Rog, the Urals, the Upper Silesia–Krakow–Ostrava complex, and the Moscow region, which together produced three-fifths of Europe's steel.

It is of interest to note that the steel industry has played a substantial role in some of the recent attempts at economic integration in Europe. Before the war, Stalin sought to establish an interconnected complex of coal, ore and steel production, linking the Kuzbas with the Urals. This was not, of course, an integration of the economies of different countries, and the presentation of the programme for the linked development of these widely separated areas did no more than make virtue out of the necessity of creating a major source of strategic materials beyond the range of German attack. It was considered, however, to be an important example of what might be possible. Thus, it was followed in the 1950s and after by the linking of the steel industry in the Soviet Union with those of eastern Europe, with large exchanges of coal and ore between Upper Silesia and Krivoy Rog, and dedicated, wide-gauge rail links between the Soviet Union and Upper Silesia and Kosice. There was also an attempt, through Comecon, to achieve a degree of specialisation in the production of steel among the eastern European countries; but Romania refused to cooperate. Meanwhile France, Germany, Italy and the Low Countries established the European Coal and Steel Community in 1951, in the anticipation of a growing demand for these products, and with a view to allowing that growth to be located in the most appropriate sites. In the event, the Community's High Authority proved to be incapable of doing so, or of managing the decline of the industry after 1974 in a rational manner. Instead of allowing competition within the Community, and with producers elsewhere, to determine which steel mills deserved to survive after the mid-1970s, it imposed quotas upon individual countries, and imports of steel into the Community were strictly controlled. Meanwhile, the

Steel has been a politically sensitive industry throughout the Fourth Wave, and the present scale, as well as the location, of production owes much to the involvement of governments. Not only eastern European governments, but also the Italian and Spanish, have been keen to build up their industries since the 1950s; and the French authorities have shown some reluctance to close mills in Lorraine and Nord when they became uncompetitive. The industry in Italy is in state ownership, and that in France was nationalised in 1981. British mills have been in and out of the public sector since the Second World War; but even when they were in private hands, decisions about the scale and location of investments have been strongly influenced by government. All have received state subsidies at one time or another, and subsidies to the Italian industry remain high.

Nevertheless, the industry has been facing a difficult situation since 1974, and this has applied in particular to the large-scale integrated mills in which so much of Europe's steel has been produced during the last Long Wave. Producers in western Europe have been subject to fierce competition from extra-European industries in export markets, and indirect competition from the import of goods containing steel, especially cars. There has also been some substitution of other materials, especially plastics, for steel. Third World imports have been strongly resisted, but subsidies to the industry have been reduced, and several of the older and less happily-located mills have closed. Production has fallen by between a third and a half since its peak in Belgium, Britain, France, Germany and Luxembourg, and by even more in Austria, the Netherlands and Switzerland. Employment has been halved. Output in eastern Europe, in contrast, continued to rise, with only one interruption in the late 1970s and early 1980s; but it has been much slower to introduce such improvements as the use of basic oxygen, continuous casting and electric furnaces than that in western Europe, and much of it is technically backward. The collapse of communist governments is expected to be followed by a severe pruning of all the heavy industries, including metallurgy, in the region. Some mills might be able to compete effectively with those in western Europe, if closer integration of the European space economy is allowed; but the production of bulk steel in Europe as a whole remains vulnerable to competition from elsewhere.

Jet aircraft

Nowhere have the technical and political influences which have been at work upon the geography of the manufacture of producer goods in Europe during the Fourth Kondratiev, and which have obliged producers in western Europe to undertake a substantial degree of integration, been so clearly demonstrated as in the case of jet aircraft.

The construction of piston-engined aircraft was well established in Britain, France and Germany by the 1930s, with smaller industries in several other European countries; but the invention of the jet engine gave rise to a new range of vehicles in the 1950s. These were capable of travelling much faster and further, at lower fuel costs per unit distance, and with less maintenance and fewer crew. Moreover, during the 1960s, their range and capacity increased substantially, not least as a result of the arms race of the Cold War. Thus, by the early 1970s, jet aircraft had come to occupy a critical role in military conflict; killed off all except short-distance passenger transport by sea; made inroads into long-distance passenger transport by rail and the movement of freight; and come to account for almost all of the value of the output of the aircraft industry.

However, the industry has been less dynamic since then. The last major breakthrough which proved to be commercially viable, the wide-bodied jet, of which the Boeing 747 range is the chief example, entered service in 1970. The supersonic Anglo-French Concorde, which appeared at about the same time, never covered its production costs, while its Soviet rival, Concordski, was cancelled. Improved versions have been produced of many of the planes in service, but no technical advance comparable with the jet has appeared. Innovation has also been undermined recently in the military sphere by the end of the Cold War, which has been accompanied by far-reaching proposals for disarmament, threatening not only the production of military aircraft both east and west of the former Iron Curtain, but perhaps removing an important spur to the development of new types of aeroplane.

Only a few countries possess the resources, or have the military pretensions, to support the manufacture of jet aircraft, for unlike the steel industry it has been at the forefront of technological advance during the Fourth Wave, and is complex. Planes are the product of lengthy and painstaking research and design; they contain many different components, and are very expensive. The design of a successful aircraft usually requires a large team of highly-skilled workers, while its production relies upon the manufacture and assembly of the frame, communications and control systems, and the engines. Only very large companies or governments can afford the huge start-up costs, and only the largest and wealthiest countries can provide the markets to justify the long production runs which are necessary to recoup them. Many are never recovered through the market, but are met by government subsidy. However, even

[illegible]

been limited only by the willingness of taxpayers to meet the bill. Government has also been the chief provider of research and development funds. In the 1980s, the French authorities were devoting more than half of their research and development funding to the industry, the British more than two-fifths, and the West Germans more than a quarter; only in the case of West Germany did any other industry receive a larger share (Klepper 1991b). The British and

French governments have also given support to the production of civilian planes by subsidising sales of aircraft or obliging national, flag-carrying airlines to buy domestically-manufactured planes, compensating them when their running costs have proved to be greater than those of rival aircraft. They have also intervened to restructure their industries in order to ensure their continuation, and taken a stake in their ownership since the early 1970s, though the British government subsequently sold its share again. The major West German producers were also brought together in the early 1990s. In short, the market for jet aircraft in western Europe has been firmly managed by governments: it is doubtful if much of the industry would have survived in the absence of government support, though it has to be acknowledged that the rival American aircraft companies have also been in receipt of massive subsidies.

The high cost of developing new planes has obliged the industry in western Europe to mount an increasing number of joint projects. Thus, Concorde was built by the British and French; and the Airbus is a French and German project, to which Britain contributes twenty per cent and Spain four per cent of the components. West German production has been almost entirely in the context of joint projects, while that in Italy has been largely concerned with the construction of American planes under licence. There have also been a number of joint ventures in conjunction with NATO in the production of military aircraft in western Europe. The Tornado fighter was built by the PANAVIA consortium of Britain, West Germany and Italy; and other consortia have been established to build the European Fighter Aircraft and a military transport plane. Thus, the industry is spread widely across western Europe, with branches or suppliers of components in most of its industrial regions, and a complex set of links between the various countries.

Only a few thousand jet aircraft are built in the world each year, and the United States and Soviet Union have been the leading producers, followed by Britain and France. The Soviet Union has insisted on building almost all of the planes which have been used by itself and the countries of eastern Europe since the Second World War, but several countries in western Europe have attempted to compete with the three major American suppliers. Thus, by the late 1980s, the countries of Europe fell into four groups. The Soviet Union built several hundred jet aircraft annually, and the industry there had a workforce of more than a million. Britain, France and Sweden designed and built much smaller numbers; and several other countries – Czechoslovakia, Italy, Spain, the Netherlands, Romania and West Germany – either built jets on licence, or were partners in consortia with the British, French, Soviet or other industries, or were major suppliers of components. British Aerospace employed about 130,000 people in 1990, and Aerospatiale and Dassault in France about half of that. One hundred thousand were employed across western Europe by the consortium companies and component supplier in connection with the European Fighter Aircraft. Several of the smaller countries in both eastern and western Europe, in contrast, did not play any significant part in the industry.

Aircraft design and production in the Soviet Union was undertaken by a small number of separate teams, each of which was responsible for several types of vehicle, some civilian, but mostly military. Indeed, the production of all aircraft was undertaken in association with defence requirements. Jet aeroplanes were assembled at a small number of large factories from Kiev and Tbilisi to Kazan and Tashkent; but components were drawn from a large number of factories, spread widely over the country, some of which made other goods as well. Most aircraft production in the 1930s had been in Moscow and the west, though new centres were established further east during and after the war. Thus, by the 1980s, jet aircraft were being manufactured in at least four different republics – Georgia, the Russian Federation, Tadzikhistan and the Ukraine – and the production of components was even more widespread, though the design teams were chiefly in Moscow (Symons 1990, p. 193).

The British and French industries, though much smaller than that of the Soviet Union, were also distributed among a number of sites. In each country there was a cluster of factories around the capital; the concentration in the Ile-de-France was particularly marked, with almost half of the French industry's employment, and sixty per cent of its research staff (Beckouche 1991). Other factories, such as those in northwest England and Toulouse, owed their location to the wish of pre-war governments to move their aircraft industries beyond the range of German bombers. The West German industry was centred on Bavaria and Hamburg, and all of these sites were supplied by several hundred manufacturers of components spread across most of the industrial regions in those countries, and in others.

Textiles

Like steel, the textile industry in Europe is rather old, and its history provides

for the import of raw materials and export of products, and in the associated urban settlements. By the end of the nineteenth century, hundreds of thousands of people were employed in the industry in Britain, France and Germany; and textiles were one of the largest, if not the largest, form of manufacturing in Europe. Cloth was sold on domestic markets but was increasingly exported from northwest Europe to other countries on the continent, and to colonies in the rest of the world, either directly or through the clothing industry. But, by the start of the Fourth Wave, the industry in northwest Europe had become vulnerable; since that time, the replacement of steam with electric power has freed producers from the coalfields, and countries with lower labour costs have been able to undercut it. Firms in Britain, Germany and elsewhere have retaliated by replacing labour with faster machines, introducing synthetic fibres, concentrating upon specialist, high-quality and fashion-related products, and looking to governments for subsidies and protection; but northwest Europe's dominance of the world's mass markets for textiles has gone.

Britain was the largest producer in Europe in the 1930s, followed by Germany, France, the Soviet Union, Italy, Belgium, Poland and Czechoslovakia, in approximately that order; however, this changed very greatly during the Fourth Wave. Governments in eastern Europe expanded their industries. Many mills were built, often in rural areas; and the established textile centres, such as the Moscow region, Lodz and Saxony, also operated at high levels of activity. Thus, by the 1980s, the Soviet Union, and especially the Russian Federation, was producing far more cloth than in the 1930s, and more than any other country in Europe (Figure III.10), while Poland and East Germany were also major producers, all working chiefly to supply their domestic markets. The industry also expanded in southern Europe, where it enjoyed low labour costs, but also government support. Thus, by the 1980s, Greek, Portuguese and Spanish producers were exporting to the rest of the European Community, and the industry was a major source of employment in all these countries.

However, the most spectacular development was in Italy, which had become the second largest producer of yarn and cloth on the continent, with mills not only in the traditional location of Lombardy, but also in many parts of the peninsula, in which labour was cheap relative to the rest of the Community. But labour was not the only reason for the relative success of the Italian industry. The substitution of fashionable for standard fabrics, and the replacement of large, integrated mills by small, specialist, design and production workshops, equipped with computer-based machinery, enabled the woollen industry of the Prato area, which had traditionally produced low-value cloth from the recycling of rags, to increase its output and maintain its employment (Piore and Sabel 1984, pp. 213–16). The contrast with the West Yorkshire shoddy industry, which persisted in its production of low-quality cloth woven from recycled fabrics, much of which had been exported to southern Europe and beyond, could not have been greater. Notwithstanding the recruitment of cheap labour from the Indian subcontinent during the 1950s and 1960s, and the introduction of three-shift working, Yorkshire shoddy-making collapsed.

The débâcle in Yorkshire was only part, however, of the sharp decline of the modern factory industry in many of those areas in which it had developed first in Europe, but which experienced falls in output and much steeper ones in employment. Indeed, so weak was it in several of the countries of northwest

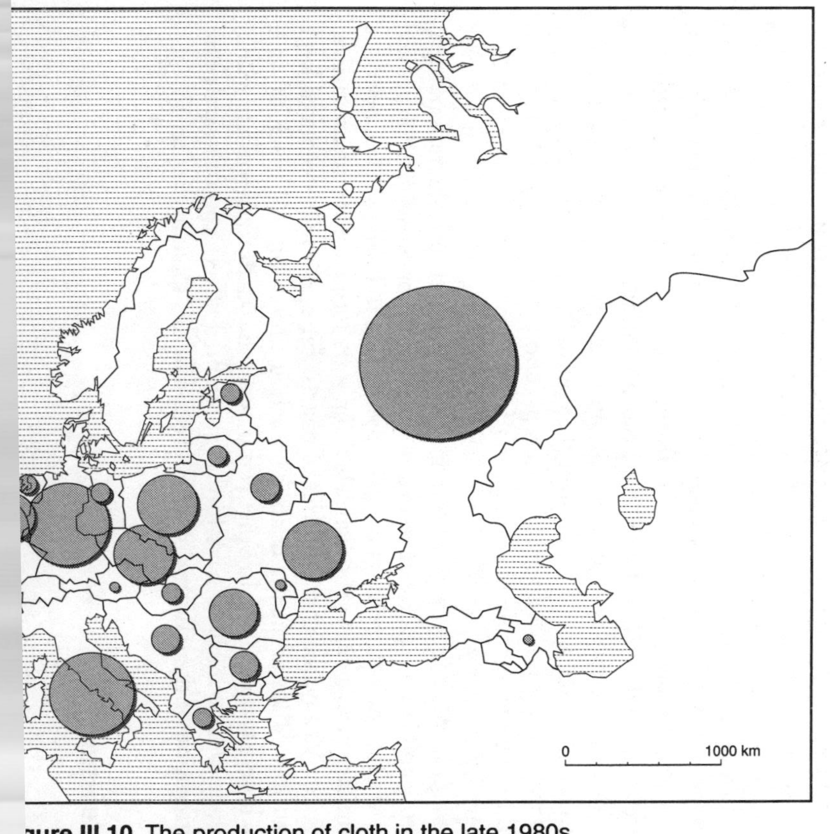

gure III.10 The production of cloth in the late 1980s
Source: United Nations (1991)

Europe, in the face of southern European and Third World competition, that it contracted not only in the declining phase of the wave, but also in the 1950s and 1960s. The British government financed extensive rationalisation and re-equipment programmes in both the cotton and woollen industries, and other governments also helped their industries to acquire more productive machinery. However, the concentration of the industry in the hands of a small number of multinational companies in Britain was followed by the transfer of much production to lower-cost, overseas sites, some of which were in southern Europe; and, by the 1980s, the great nineteenth-century swarms of textile mills in Britain, France and Belgium, with their associated coal mines, railways, warehouses and ancillary trades, were much reduced.

Thus, the countries of Europe fell into three groups with respect to the fortunes of the textile industry during the Fourth Kondratiev – the communist countries, those of Mediterranean Europe, and the northwest. All, however, had become vulnerable to competition from eastern Asia, Turkey and elsewhere by the early 1990s. That in northwest Europe, which had survived through its close links with the clothing industry and specialisation in high-quality and fashion fabrics, and that in southern Europe, have both depended in part for their survival since 1973 upon the Multi-Fibre Agreement – a voluntary arrangement through which imports into western Europe are restricted. Meanwhile the industries of eastern Europe, which produced large quantities of lower-quality cloth, were labour intensive, and much of their machinery was obsolete. In other words, any removal of trade barriers within Europe will be likely to have further substantial effects upon the scale and distribution of the industry. We shall return to this topic in Section V.

Television sets

Television sets, in contrast to textiles, are a consumer product of the Fourth Wave; and the development of their manufacture has been similar, in many respects, to that of other durable-use goods, such as refrigerators, washing machines and a wide variety of devices for home entertainment. However, by the late 1980s, television had proved itself to be more than just another household gadget. Watching it had become the third most time-consuming activity of the population, exceeded only by sleep and work; it had reoriented the film industry, which now concentrates principally upon the production of material for video cassettes, and advertising; and it had slashed cinema attendances (Dunnett 1990). Even in such countries as France and Spain, in which governments have maintained close controls over broadcasting until very recently, and in eastern Europe, where many programmes were dull and filled with rather obvious propaganda, almost all households possessed a television set. In other words, just as the introduction of jet aircraft has boosted the oil industry, and led to the development of airports, so television has not only encouraged a range of other new manufactures, but also stimulated the growth of associated service industries to the point where economic activity in the television industry, *sensu lato,* is far more important than the manufacture of the sets themselves.

The transmission of programmes in black and white began in Britain and Germany in the 1930s, and in most other European countries in the 1950s. The first pictures were of poor quality, and sets cost as much as a small car; but demand rose rapidly as improvements were made, and as the manufacture of components, and process of assembly, became large-scale, routine and cheap activities. Demand was further stimulated by the introduction of colour in the 1960s, which required the replacement of sets, and in western Europe by a wide range of other services which developed around the use of televisions in the home in the 1970s and 1980s. Cable and satellites, in particular, greatly increased the number of programmes which were available to viewers; and the video cassette, which allowed viewers to watch items at times other than those at which they were broadcast, and also material which was not broadcast at all, proved to be very popular. VCRs were also manufactured in the Soviet Union, but quality was low, output small, prices were high and they were not designed to play western tapes (Dunnett 1990, p. 189). Interactive television – videotext – became widespread in France in the 1980s.

However, the manufacture of televisions has not been brought together with that of the associated durable-use goods which have come to form the basis of much home entertainment, namely, video recorders, stereo systems and home computers, nor even with the aerials and satellite dishes which receive the signals, all of which tend to be manufactured and sold separately. As Piore and Sabel (1984, pp. 204–5) point out, there is no all-embracing pleasure machine, linking television with the other elements in the home-entertainment 'bundle', which is the equivalent of Ford's Model T car or IBM's 360 computer. Nor has the industry been able to supply an integrated market. Largely because

in the 1950s almost all countries in Europe joined in. However, by the end of the 1960s, Japan had already become the largest single manufacturer in the world; and by the 1980s it had been joined by South Korea. In the 1960s, the distribution of the industry in Europe roughly reflected that of population. Thus, the Soviet Union, West Germany, Britain, Italy and France were the chief producers, in that order, with the output of the Soviet Union more than twice that of West Germany. Much of the Soviet industry was in Russia, followed by the Ukraine, which manufactured about a third of Soviet sets. It is probable that, if it had not been protected, the western European industry would have been decimated in the 1970s by Asian competition; but imports were limited to small and medium-sized sets, that is, of 52 centimetres or less, and subjected to voluntary import restrictions. Thus, the industry continued to grow in most of these countries during the 1970s and 1980s, though in Britain and Germany this was increasingly a matter of Japanese firms opening branch plants as the indigenous ones either left the industry or were taken over by other European producers. However, by the early 1980s, the minimum efficient scale of production for cathode tubes was considered to be about one million units per annum, and that for the assembly of sets 400,000 (Dicken 1986, p. 331), both of which were larger than the markets in several of the smaller European countries. Thus, although the chief producers in western Europe – Philips in the Netherlands, Thomson in France and Nokia in Finland – all owned plants in other western European countries (and also, in the case of Philips and Thomson, in eastern Asia, from where they exported small-screen sets to Europe), several of the smaller countries in western Europe had ceased to make sets. All of the eastern European countries, in contrast, manufactured sets, even though their output was typically rather small (Figure III.11).

Although the industry grew throughout the Fourth Wave, and employed almost 100,000 in western Europe in the 1980s, its future looks uncertain. Most households in Europe have at least one set; and the development of television-based services has increasingly become concerned with novel uses for sets, sometimes in conjunction with new peripheral equipment, rather than with further improvements in the sets themselves. New and improved forms of receivers are, however, in existence, and the introduction of high-definition television will probably require the replacement of most existing equipment. There may, moreover, be a large market in eastern Europe, where sets are generally of poor quality, but the success of the European industry will depend crucially upon future trading arrangements with eastern Asia.

Summary

During the Fourth Wave, the production of, and trade in, manufactured goods in Europe changed very greatly. Some of these changes reflected the development of new products, such as jets and television; some, the declining competitive position of one part of the continent in long-established types of production, such as textiles, in relation to others and to the rest of the world; and some, government policies of industrial development, rationalisation and protection, such as those in the steel industry.

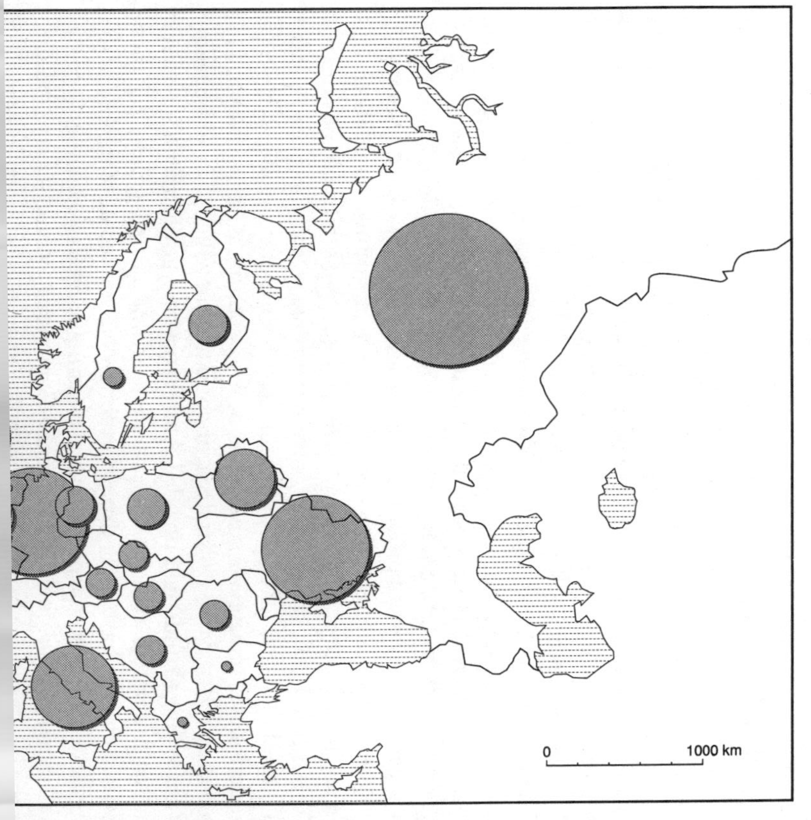

III.11 The production of television sets in the late 1980s
Source: United Nations (1991)

By the end of the period, manufacturing was contributing more than a quarter to the gross domestic product of almost all the countries of Europe, with very much higher nominal values in the centrally-planned economies (Figure III.2). However, the composition of the sector varied. Thus, engineering contributed rather more in West Germany and Sweden, while the food-processing, textile and clothing industries were important in Italy. Comparisons with eastern Europe are difficult, and employment may be a better guide than GDP. According to this measure, engineering was more important in East Germany and Czechoslovakia than elsewhere, while food processing was relatively large in Poland, Hungary and Bulgaria, and textiles and clothing in Romania. Not surprisingly, in view of its size and variety of local economic circumstances, the structure of employment in Soviet industry tended towards the average for the centrally-planned economies.

These patterns owed much to the intervention of governments. The authorities in eastern Europe gave very high priority to the expansion of manufacturing, and especially to the production of armaments and capital goods, but much less attention to items for private consumption. Nor did they manage to match western producers in innovation or resolve the question as to how to develop manufacturing once the supply of surplus, rural labour had been exhausted – once, that is, extensive economic growth had to be replaced by intensive. Meanwhile, many governments in western Europe 'picked winners', that is, they invested public funds in the manufacture of goods which were considered to have a bright future, or whose continued domestic production was considered to be of strategic importance, but which the private sector was not willing to undertake unaided. And everywhere, governments interfered with, or prevented, trade in at least some manufactured goods. All these policies, however, have come to be increasingly questioned since the end of the Long Boom; and the collapse of central planning in the east, together with the establishment of the Single Market in the Community, would seem to indicate that the involvement of the state in manufacturing will be much less direct in future. But, if that is the case, its scale and distribution across the continent may be subject to yet more change, and we shall return to this matter in Section V.

Further reading

The geography of European manufacturing is covered in some detail in the appropriate sections of Symons' *The Soviet Union* (1990), Turnock's *Eastern Europe: An economic and political geography* (1989), and Williams' *The Western European Economy* (1987). Aydalot and Keeble (1988) have edited a series of studies of *High Technology Industry and Innovative Environments: The European Experience*, which deals very largely with western Europe. Houseman (1991) provides an analysis of *Industrial Restructuring with Job Security: The Case of*

European Steel for the European Steel and Coal Community since 1974. Shepherd (1981) provides a brief comment on *Textile-industry Adjustment in Developed Countries* during the 1970s; Keesing and Wolf (1980) describe western Europe's *Textile Quotas against Developing Countries* at that time; and Hardill (1987) examines *The Regional Implications of Restructuring in the Wool Textile Industry*, with particular reference to Britain. *The World Aircraft Industry* (1986) is discussed by Todd and Simpson.

CHAPTER 6

THE SERVICE INDUSTRIES

Unlike the primary and secondary sectors, the role of the tertiary sector has increased everywhere in Europe since the 1930s, and become the largest source of employment and contributor to the gross domestic product in many of them (Figure III.2). Services accounted for about forty per cent of employment in Britain in the 1930s, about thirty per cent in France and Germany, twenty per cent in Italy, and a smaller proportion in eastern Europe and the Soviet Union. By the 1980s, in contrast, they accounted for more than half in almost all of western Europe, exceeding sixty per cent in Britain and France, and more than forty per cent in the Soviet Union. In Poland, Romania, Yugoslavia, and some of the other countries of eastern Europe, the proportion was between thirty and forty per cent.

These increases reflected the growth of a very wide range of activities, from education, health, and communications, to professional advice of many types, financial services, entertainment and tourism. They also reflect the labour-intensive nature of most services, and the limited opportunities which have existed within them in the past for the substitution of machinery for labour, and for economies of scale, in contrast to those in farming, the extractive industries and manufacturing. However, they are also an expression of the increasing differentiation and specialisation in the types of service which have become available. Long Wave theorists have given little attention to the service sector, and its recent growth calls this omission into question. Howells (1988, p. 89) reports the view of Barras that innovation in service industries, unlike that in those producing goods, tends to proceed from improvements in delivery to the development of new products – a 'reverse product cycle' – but it is clear that there has been much innovation in the sector since the 1930s, and that, therefore, the link between such developments and Long Waves may be just as strong or weak, depending upon one's view of Long Waves, as those in the rest of the economy.

One of the most significant innovations in the service sector during the Fourth Wave has been the growth and improvement in transport and communications, and this has affected the production of many other services by weakening the link between propinquity and supply. Unlike the production of goods, that of many services must be located at the market; and, in those cases in which services can only be supplied at particular places, those who wish to consume them must travel. Much effort has been made, however, during the Fourth Wave to obviate this constraint. Even before the Fourth Kondratiev it was not necessary for the producer and consumer of some services to meet, or for all the office-type operations of firms to be carried out in a single building, or for the administrative activity of manufacturing companies to be undertaken at the factory; and it has become even less so in recent years. It follows that there is, now, no intrinsic obstacle to trade in many services between countries, and that the integration of the economies of different countries may have a substantial effect upon the spatial arrangement of their production. In particular, those services which can be supplied at a distance – through postal, radio, telephone, but now also through computer networks, satellite and videotext connections – may be sold by producers in one country to those in others, while those which still require direct contact between supplier and customer may be traded through the movement of customers across borders or by the establishment of networks of foreign branches. It should also be noted that some of the most specialised services may only be supplied where there is a large market, or where there are particular conditions which allow them to be provided, and that this may mean that they may only be available in some countries, but not in others.

In the event, trade in services between the countries of Europe has been much less than that in goods. Government-run, administrative and public-order services, which are a major source of employment, have not been traded internationally, though there has been a degree of specialisation and integration in a number of activities, some of which are closely related to Europe, such as NATO, with its headquarters in Belgium, the Warsaw Pact, Comecon and the Community. Similarly, there has been very little international trade in educa-

countries. Much of this may now change, however, as a result of the institution of the Single Market in western Europe and the opening up of eastern Europe.

We shall now examine the changing geography of two major services which illustrate the changes which have been occurring as a result of innovation and integration during the Fourth Kondratiev – banking and tourism.

Banking

It is not easy to define the banking industry accurately. European banks have always provided a variety of services in connection with the handling and use of money. Some institutions specialise in the provision of 'wholesale' services, that is, those to governments and other banks and financial businesses; others rely heavily upon 'retail' services to the general public; and some supply both markets. But many other firms have begun to offer similar services during the last sixty years, especially in the retail sector, and now overlap and compete with those which call themselves banks in many western European countries. Some banks have responded to this challenge by expanding their own range of activities. However, developments have varied very widely across the continent, not least because of the plethora of national regulations which have grown up, as governments have sought to control the money supply and protect customers from bank failure – regulations which have fragmented the European banking market. Nevertheless, the financial industry, like many other services, has grown very greatly in western Europe during the Fourth Wave in customers, transactions and employment, and about two-and-a-half per cent of the labour force in the Community was employed in banking and finance by the 1980s. We shall examine the changing spatial pattern of the industry by considering the development of international financial centres and local banking services.

International financial centres

Reference was made in Section II to the relatively free market for capital in the nineteenth century in Europe, and the emergence of London and Paris as financial centres of world and European significance respectively provides an early example of the effects of economic integration. Notwithstanding the disappearance of Britain and France's role as perennial exporters of capital, and their replacement by New York and Tokyo, during the twentieth century, the continuing economies of agglomeration which London, in particular, has offered – with its wide range of specialist commodity and financial markets and associated professional services – have helped to maintain its status throughout the Fourth Kondratiev as the world's most important centre of international banking. 'The city' has become one of the three foci of the Eurocurrency market, which developed in the 1960s and 1970s along with New York and Tokyo; deregulation in the late 1980s attracted many foreign banks and securities houses to it, and it conducts three times as much business as Paris or Frankfurt. Meanwhile, Paris has become one of the most important futures markets in Europe; and the strength of the Deutschmark, coupled with the gradual deregulation of German financial markets and the importance of exports in the German economy, has made Frankfurt the second most important financial centre in Europe. Other major centres in Europe include Amsterdam, Brussels, Luxembourg – which has developed since the 1960s almost solely in connection with the Euromarkets – and Switzerland (Gardener and Molyneux, 1990, pp. 143–66).

Local banking services

In the 1930s, banks were confined almost entirely to one country or region, which they served through a network of branches, and governments exercised tight controls in order to protect customers from bank failure. However, this stability was the enemy of efficiency, and many banks in western Europe enjoyed a comfortable, oligopolistic relationship with their competitors. Moreover, the regulations, like the patterns of ownership and range of services, varied widely between countries; and thus the European banking market was fragmented along national lines. Some banks specialised in medium- and long-term loans to industry and commerce. Others acted as savings banks or sources of mortgages for the general public, and some offered a wide range of services. Some were owned by the state – a situation which became the norm in eastern Europe after the establishment of communist governments – some were joint-stock companies, some cooperatives, and some were privately-owned institutions. Some, such as those in Germany, were closely connected with major commercial and industrial concerns, whereas in other countries such links were banned. Few individuals held accounts in the major banks in the 1930s, and most wages and purchases were paid in cash. Many people in the more developed countries of northwest Europe, however, made use of mutual and postal institutions, offering savings facilities; but elsewhere, retail banking was only weakly developed. Bank transactions were very largely dependent upon

The deregulation of financial markets in the 1980s helped these institutions to extend their activities into the traditional stock-in-trade of banks, namely, deposits, payments and foreign exchange. However, some banks have retaliated by broadening their own activities, and have become less easily distinguishable from the many other firms which offer mortgages, pensions, life and other insurance, portfolio and securities management, and financial advice. The development of new financial services had progressed furthest in France, Germany, the Netherlands and Sweden; banks and kindred institutions have appeared in large numbers in all except the smallest settlements in western Europe; and employment has grown. That in British banks trebled during the Fourth Wave.

The provision of banking services was also much altered in the 1980s by the introduction of new technology. Transactions were increasingly handled through automatic cash dispensers, electronic point-of-sale instantaneous-debiting machines, and other credit card facilities, without reference to bank staff, as private networks connected branches, cash dispensers and tills to each bank's central computer. These innovations allowed branches to deal with a greatly increased volume of business, without commensurate increases in staff; but they also encouraged the merger of banks in order to spread the costs of the new equipment. Many small and regional banks were taken over, with subsequent rationalisations of head-office facilities and branch networks. By the early 1990s, there was no technical obstacle to any bank providing European-wide automatic credit and debit facilities. No bank, however, did so, not least because of the continuing existence of separate national bank-clearing systems in western Europe; and only a few offered limited services of this sort in other countries, usually in conjunction with local banks (O'Brien 1992, p. 55). No such connections existed, however, with banks in eastern Europe.

Nevertheless, there has been considerable integration of the banking industry in western Europe. The Swiss banks have long been repositories for foreign accounts; and the development of the Eurocurrency markets, which operate almost entirely through computer networks, and are world-wide, have allowed banks and enterprises to avoid many national restrictions on the large-scale movement of capital. West European countries have gradually opened their domestic markets to foreign banks, and a large number have found it advantageous to establish branches in Brussels (Wilson 1986). Several Community banks have offered reciprocal services to each others' customers, and mergers have occurred between some banks in member countries (Gardener and Molyneux 1990, pp. 208–13). Meanwhile, American Express has been processing all its European business through its Brighton office for several years, while the other card companies, and the much-longer-established traveller's cheque, have facilitated the integration of retail financial business, not only in Europe, but throughout the world.

The situation in eastern Europe was very different. All the countries of the area, except the Soviet Union, had been served in the 1930s by a variety of privately-owned banks, catering to commerce and industry, and a network of cooperative and post office savings banks, which were used by individuals. After the Second World War, however, the banks were taken into public ownership, and ceased to be independent commercial operations. Rather than making profits by borrowing short while lending long, their purpose became one of facilitating the circulation of money in the context of the central plan for investment, trade and consumption drawn up by the government. The range of services which they offered was very narrow; and branch networks were weakly developed, except in the case of the savings banks, which were represented in almost all towns and also many villages (Gowland 1992). In Poland, for instance, where there had been a strong tradition of cooperative societies in rural areas before the war, there were no less than 1,660 cooperative banks, with 2,700 cash counters, catering largely to the needs of people in small towns and villages, including many private farmers (World Bank 1990, pp. 231–2). Employment in banking increased, as did the number of transactions, though not to anywhere near the level in western Europe; but almost none of the new technology had been adopted by the early 1990s.

Tourism

Tourism has also grown strongly in Europe during the Fourth Wave. Few people took holidays away from home in the 1930s, and only a very small number ventured abroad. The number of places attracting foreign visitors in Europe was small. However, rising incomes, a decline in the real cost of foreign travel – in part the result of the introduction of jet aircraft – and the introduction of regular, paid holidays have turned international tourism into a major employer and source of income in several regions. Mass tourism has also been assisted by the introduction of computer-aided airline and accommodation booking and the construction of motorways, all of which have meant that the integration of the continent has probably proceeded further in this industry than in most other economic activities. The growth of tourism during the Fourth Wave seems to have occurred in three stages. At the start of the period, the industry was largely concentrated in northwest Europe, the French Riviera and the Alps, and was local, with resorts catering chiefly to regional or national

of the population of northwest Europe than of the Mediterranean countries was travelling abroad, while people in eastern Europe were subject to much restriction.

Almost all parts of the continent have attempted to promote their local tourist industry, and a very wide range of amenities has been offered to holidaymakers. But only in a few places has tourism become a significant part of the economy, and in even fewer has it been established as a year-round, as distinct from a seasonal, activity. Three broad types of region may be identified. The Mediterranean coasts, from Portugal to Greece, have been the principal centres of the industry, supplying cheap summer holidays to northern Europeans in search of hot, dry weather, but also being used by the French, Italians and Spanish themselves. There has been a rapid and large-scale development of coastal resorts in these countries since the 1950s, both of hotels for package holidays, and of villas and apartments. Employment, which is often of a casual nature, has been substantial. Some Spanish resorts have also been able to attract winter holidaymakers and the retired from northern Europe, though the numbers were only about a quarter of those at the peak of the summer season in the 1980s (OECD 1985). The Black Sea coasts of Bulgaria and the Crimea have offered similar climatic conditions for summer holidays to eastern Europeans and Soviet citizens respectively. Those of the Crimea, where successive Soviet leaders had their summer villas, acquired a somewhat similar status to that which has long been enjoyed by the Côte d'Azur, in western Europe, as a resort at which to be seen. Meanwhile, resorts on the coasts of northwest Europe, to which the general public went in very large numbers in the early days of mass tourism, have lost some of that trade.

Historic sites have provided a second focus for the industry, often catering for those touring by coach or car, but also many from outwith Europe. Almost all countries in Europe can offer attractions of this type, but the United Kingdom and the Italian cities of Florence, Rome and Venice are amongst the busiest. Indeed, such has been the growth of tourism that access to the most famous sites was increasingly being rationed during the 1970s and 1980s through restrictions on vehicular entry to some of the most historic cities, charging for entry to cathedrals, and the limitation of attendance at art galleries. Many attractions were, in effect, full at the peak of the season. It is sometimes difficult to separate the heritage element of tourism in cities from a more general interest in visiting foreign countries and their capital cities; and it is also the case that many 'tourists' in such places are those travelling on business. Thus, the level of activity in the hotel, restaurant and entertainment industries in London or Paris, Geneva or Vienna, depends as much on the importance of those cities to business and government as to their historic monuments. It may also reflect the growth in the conference business, which is often classified as another form of tourism, but which, like other business visits, tends to be less seasonal than holidaymaking. If the southern coastal resorts offered holidays for the general public, often at the lower end of the price range, those visiting capital cities and historic sites, though usually on shorter breaks or on tour, often spent more per capita per diem.

Mountainous areas, especially the Alps, provide a third focus for the industry, and one which enjoys a year-round season. Most visits to them are made in the summer, when many people travel by coach and car to admire the scenery; but they also enjoy a long winter season, based upon skiing and other sports. Skiing, in particular, has attracted very large numbers of tourists to Austria, France and Switzerland, leading to much expansion of existing settlements and the development of new resorts. However, the industry suffered from a shortage of snow at the start of several seasons in the 1980s, and there was increasing concern about the damage caused to mountain sides by the construction and use of pistes. Heli-skiing – using helicopters to gain access to the highest glaciers – has been banned in Austria and France. Problems have also occurred in the summer, when, such has been the intensity of use of some Austrian valleys, that they have been closed to mountain bikes and private cars.

The international trade in tourist services does not, of course, account for all the activity of the industry in any of these three types of location; in some, domestic tourism is of far more importance than that from abroad. For instance, almost all of those who have taken holidays in the Crimea in the past have come from the Soviet Union; there is much movement from the French cities to the Mediterranean coast and the Alps each year; and many people in western Europe take short breaks close to home, in addition to longer summer holidays. However, because no part of western Europe is far from another, and because, in spite of this, there are great contrasts in climate, heritage and scenery within it, the opportunities for international tourism have been very great. Furthermore, although most governments have promoted the industry in their countries (and in some cases have subsidised the construction of accommodation, transport facilities and other infrastructure), there have been few effective restrictions on such movements since the 1950s in western Europe, or on the ability of tour companies to provide facilities in countries other than their own. In other words, there has been something close to free trade in tourism. Several large companies have grown up offering complete holidays, including travel, accommodation and entertainment, in a variety of countries; and they have not hesitated to provide holidays in new places, in order to retain the interest of their customers. The hotel trade, especially in the larger cities, has also been taken over to a significant extent by international hotel chains [illegible]

[illegible]

France was highly favourable. Germany and the Netherlands, in contrast, had large negative balances (OECD 1985).

Elsewhere, and especially in eastern Europe and the Soviet Union, tourism contributed little to the economy. Many eastern European factories and other state-owned enterprises arranged summer holidays for their employees in their own guest-houses in the mountains or on the coast, and many individuals took accommodation in private houses in the same areas. Communist governments did not, however, give foreign tourism by their citizens a high priority, and guided such movement as did occur to preferred countries within the communist bloc. Most visits were by officially-organised groups on a reciprocal basis with others in the host country. Thus, a few Soviet citizens travelled abroad, chiefly to Bulgaria and East Germany, while some Poles were allowed to go to Hungary, but few to Romania or Yugoslavia. Independent foreign travel was strictly controlled. East Europeans were not generally allowed to hold passports, but had to apply for them before every foreign journey; and the authorities severely restricted the amount of foreign currency which was allowed for such visits. Very few Romanians were allowed out of their country. Increasing efforts were made to attract western visitors, and several western hotel chains built and ran hotels in some of the major cities in the 1970s and 1980s, but the number of western tourists remained small, not least because many of the other tourist facilities were in public ownership, and of low quality in comparison with those in western Europe. Standards of service were abysmal (Hall 1991, Poland 1987, pp. 509, 620).

Thus, there has been a spectacular growth of mass international tourism in Europe during the Fourth Wave. But tourism is volatile, for the public often seeks novelty, and reacts quickly in the face of economic difficulty by reducing expenditure. Adverse publicity about particular countries, strikes by air-traffic controllers or ferry crews, and especially disturbances involving threats to the safety of travellers, have all led the public to reduce their expenditure on holidays or to take their custom elsewhere. Thus, there was a decline in international tourism in the early and mid-1980s in general, and the spectacular growth of the summer package industry in Spain and of winter sports holidays in the Alps seems to have stopped. Martial law in Poland in the early 1980s halved the number of foreign visitors; the upheavals elsewhere in eastern Europe and the Soviet Union in the late 1980s have further damaged the small industry there; and the fighting in Yugoslavia in 1991 put an end, at least temporarily, to the largest of the international tourist industries in eastern Europe. It would appear that there is considerable potential for foreign tourism between the two halves of the continent, but its realisation will depend upon the improvement of facilities in the east, and a considerable increase in the wealth of those living there before they can afford foreign holidays of the sort which have become typical of western Europe. However, tourism may not only benefit from any new Long Boom in a Fifth Kondratiev, but also assist it to occur, for expenditure on travel tends to rise more rapidly than income in developed economies. We shall return to this topic in Section V.

Further reading

Readers wishing to consider the development of the banking industry in more detail are recommended to read Gardener and Molyneux's *Changes in Western European Banking* (1990) and *Finance in Eastern Europe* (1992), edited by Gowland.

Further information about tourism may be found in *Tourism and Economic Development in Eastern Europe and the Soviet Union* (1991), edited by Hall, and *Tourism and Economic Development: Western European Experiences* (1991), edited by Williams and Shaw.

More general accounts of the changing geography of the service sector in western Europe are given by Howells (1988), *Economic, Technological and Locational Trends in European Services*, and Illeris (1989), *Services and Regions in Europe.*

CHAPTER 7

THE DEVELOPING SPACE ECONOMY

Previous chapters in this section have set out some of the changes which have occurred recently in the three major sectors of the European economy – changes in the size and distribution of activities which have been related to their developing technology and to such integration as has already occurred within the continent – and attempted to provide a temporal framework for the discussion of them. But the choice of activities was necessarily selective; and the accounts of them, by themselves, do not provide an adequate description of the changing space economy as a whole. It is, therefore, to this that we must now turn. It will not be possible to give a comprehensive account of the regional economic geography of the whole continent, but several types of place within the space economy will be examined by way of illustrating the variety of experience which there has been in Europe during the Fourth Kondratiev. In particular, we shall consider:

— centres of decision making;
— the geography of research and development;
— industrial regions;
— rural areas; and
— the question of divergence, both within some of the larger countries and across the continent as a whole.

Centres of decision making

The development of the European space economy during the last Long Wave can be presented as a struggle between the various centres of decision making within the continent. Each of the three economic groupings of countries – the Community, Comecon and EFTA – has established headquarters from which it has operated; and decisions about the organisation and development of the European space economy have also been made in other places, some of which have been of equal or greater significance not only as centres for groups of

BOX 3

Long Waves in the space economy

The Long Wave theories outlined in Box 2 all imply that, just as there may be a variety of experience between different industries during any wave, different regions within the space economy may also experience a range of economic fortunes, that these fortunes will be related to the phases within each wave, and that some places will experience an increase in the competition for space within them, while others face stagnant or declining demands.

Innovations which lead to the development of new industries, with products which replace those of older industries, offer the most straightforward case of change in the space economy. During the expansion phase of a Long Wave, those areas which have been selected by new industries will be likely to enjoy the highest levels of investment and employment increase; and the price of land there and land-use intensity will probably be increasing. Areas whose economies are based upon old industries, in contrast, may be undergoing decline. The labour thus released may be able to migrate to the areas of growth, from which some wages may be remitted, and governments may also provide assistance for the declining areas; but the price of land and intensity of land use within them will probably be falling.

In the declining phase of a wave, in contrast, all areas may find themselves stagnating. The new industries, whose markets are now saturated, will have been obliged to turn from product to process innovation, or even to product differentiation, as a way of maintaining their level of output and of increasing productivity. Moreover, they are likely to be shedding labour, thus depriving the declining regions of outlets for their surplus labour; and such peripheral regions may suffer further if governments, faced with declining tax revenue and increasing payments to the unemployed, are obliged to cut the levels of regional

countries within the continent, but also as 'gateways' between Europe and the outside world. Thus, the most important decision-making centres in Europe by the 1980s were probably Brussels, Frankfurt, London, Moscow and Paris

(Figure III.12). The significance of each of these cities is attributable to different causes: that of Brussels to the development of the Community, that of London and Paris to their inherited roles as two of the world's financial and trading capitals; that of Moscow to its status as the capital of the Soviet Union and centre of the communist bloc; and that of Frankfurt to the redevelopment of West German economic strength after the Second World War.

The primary struggle within Europe has been between the Soviet model of development, run from Moscow, and that of the western European economies. If Greece, Italy or any of the other countries of western Europe had opted for central planning and the public ownership of the means of production, or been forced into the Soviet sphere of influence, as seemed possible after the Second World War, the role of Moscow would have been enhanced, while that of the western European centres would have been diminished. Conversely, the collapse of Comecon and the Soviet Union has greatly increased the opportunities for western banks and companies to extend their operations into eastern Europe, and for those countries to forge links with the Community, thus enlarging the decision-making activities of such places as Brussels, Frankfurt and London. Furthermore, those collapses have spawned a large number of new states, each with its own capital city, and so reduced the influence of Moscow still further.

There has also been competition between the western European centres, and the gradual widening and deepening of the Community has increased the role of Brussels, and also of those other cities in which its institutions are located, such as Luxembourg and Strasbourg. It is of interest to speculate on where the central institutions of any enlarged Community, incorporating some of the countries of eastern Europe, might be located; but it may be noted that the headquarters of the European Bank for Reconstruction and Development, which was set up in 1991 with the responsibility for channelling Community money to eastern Europe, were placed in London. However, the significance of the Community, and of those cities in which its institutions are located, is necessarily related to its powers. Attention has already been drawn to the fact that the Community's budget is very small in relation to the GDP of its members, and it should also be noted that its parliament has no significant legislative role; that the Community is not responsible for the defence of its members; and that it employs only about 23,000. In other words, the Community's limited degree of integration has restricted the development of its own centres of decision making; and the continuing influence of its members has enabled their principal centres to maintain their international attraction as financial markets, transport foci and places of influence. Thus, by the early 1990s, the monetary policy not only of Germany, but also of the Low Countries, was being run, in effect, by the Bundesbank; and Austria, Sweden and Switzerland, which were not members of the Community, had also linked their currencies to the Deutschmark. The central institutions of EFTA, which

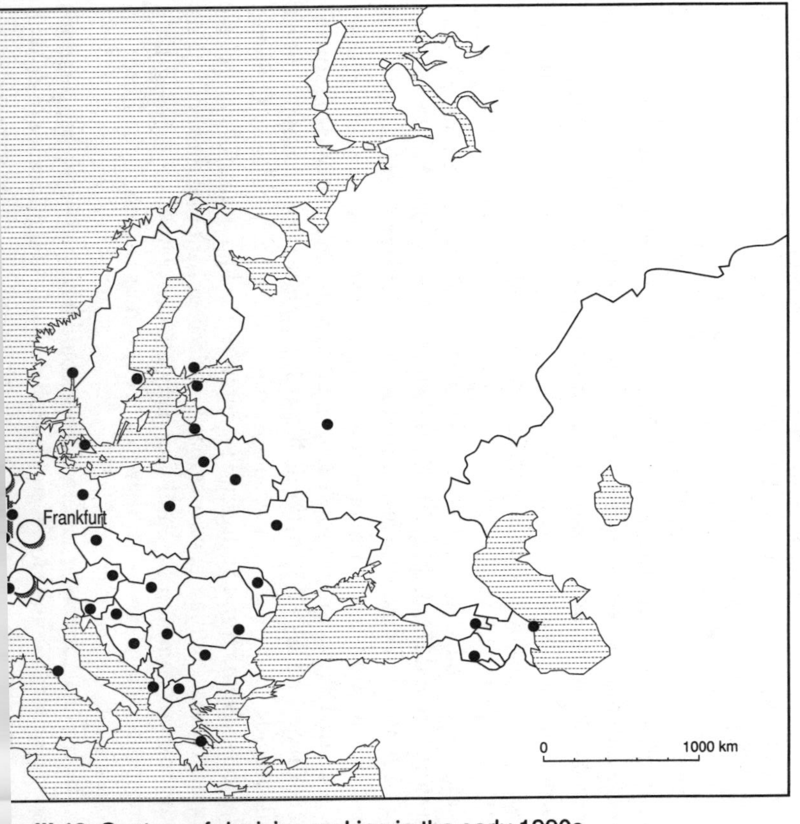

re III.12 Centres of decision making in the early 1990s

lost several of its members to the Community during the 1970s and 1980s, enjoyed even less power than those of the Community, and were tiny.

Competition between decision-making centres in eastern Europe, in contrast, appears to have been muted. Although several of the commissions of Comecon were distributed among the capital cities of the region – East Berlin, Budapest, Bucharest, Prague, Sofia and Warsaw – the headquarters and almost half of them were located in Moscow.

There is also a third tier of responsibility in Europe, below those of the economic groupings and capital cities, namely, that of the provincial cities. It has frequently been argued that the growing role of central government, and the increase in the scale of enterprise, in western Europe have both acted to move decision making away from such places during the Fourth Kondratiev, and to transfer it to the metropolis. But assertions of this sort generalise a variety of experience. Thus, it is, indeed, arguable that in those countries in which the settlement hierarchy was dominated by a primate city in the 1930s – Britain and France – capital cities are now more influential in matters to do with government and the management of enterprise than used to be the case, but that is not true of others. In Spain, for instance, Barcelona continues to compete with Madrid as a centre of economic influence, as do some of the other large coastal cities; while in the exceptional circumstances in West Germany since the Second World War, the deliberately insignificant nature of the capital has provided added scope for competition among such cities as Cologne, Hamburg, Munich and Stuttgart. Furthermore, the importance of some of the regional centres in these countries may be further enhanced if those of Spain's 'autonomous communities' and Germany's *länder* which are arguing for a 'Europe of regions', in which they would enjoy direct access to the European Commission, should succeed.

The regional capitals of eastern Europe could have had no such aspirations under central planning. However, while all decisions of significance to do with investment and employment were taken in the capitals, those responsible for planning under communism had a well-developed understanding of the concept of the regional hierarchy of service centres; and those cities which were designated as centres of regional government were generally provided with a wide range of cultural, educational and sporting facilities.

The geography of research and development

The models of the integrated space economy which were outlined in Section II hypothesised powerful links between research and development, innovation and the largest agglomerations, and especially those agglomerations with a manufacturing base. They suggested that, after integration, those agglomerations would become the centres of the most advanced forms of production for the whole of the space economy, at the expense of smaller centres in other countries.

Institutionalised research and development, like jet aircraft and televisions, is very much a creation of the last Long Wave. Of course, invention and innovation have always occurred; and before the 1930s, some of the largest firms had their own design teams, and research was sponsored by others. However, the scale of these activities was small, and their organisation weak, in comparison with what has developed since. The growth of these activities has been related in large part to the military needs of the major European powers, the emergence of large companies, and the general increase in educational facilities in Europe. Cities and regions which have been chosen for such activity in western Europe have experienced an influx of highly-paid labour, and investment in research laboratories; and they have attracted many other firms which hope to profit by their proximity to such activity. Meanwhile, centres of research and development in eastern Europe have also been the target of large government expenditures, and have acquired a degree of prestige.

As in so many other aspects of the development of Europe's space economy over the last Long Wave, however, three regions can be recognised with respect to research and development – the Soviet Union, the advanced industrial nations of northwest Europe, and the rest of eastern and southern Europe. The Soviet Union has promoted research and development on a scale which is probably larger than that of any of the other countries of Europe, and in many areas of the economy, but chiefly for military purposes. The Academy of Sciences was responsible for many large research institutes, whose programmes of work were related to the medium-term economic plans of the country; and design teams were established in the aerospace and other strategic industries. Much of this work occurred in Moscow, but many other major cities were also the seats of such organisations. The town of Akademgodorok, in western Siberia, was developed specifically as a centre for science and technology, close to the large, manufacturing city of Novosibirsk; there were also many 'closed

[illegible]

Eastern European products were generally inferior to those made in western Europe, and some have proved to be very dangerous. Several of the closed cities, in which nuclear research had been undertaken, have now been revealed to be highly polluted.

Some of the most important sources of innovation for western Europe, in contrast, lay not within the continent at all, but in the United States and, more recently, Japan. However, much research and development has also occurred within western Europe, chiefly in the advanced industrial nations. Thus, Britain, France, the Netherlands, Sweden and West Germany were spending about two per cent of their GDP on research and development in the early 1980s (Williams 1991, p. 153), much of which was financed by governments; and the Community also initiated research programmes in biotechnology, information technology and telecommunications, largely in conjunction with major companies. Many of the large firms also undertook their own research; the biggest spenders in western Europe in the early 1990s were Daimler-Benz, Siemens, Hoeschst, Bayer, VW and BASF, all of which were based in West Germany, Philips in the Netherlands, Fiat in Italy, and ABB and Roche in Switzerland, in that order. Much of this work was undertaken at or close to the headquarters and main manufacturing sites of these companies; and there were other clusters of research activity and associated manufacturing in such places as Cambridge, Grenoble, London, Paris, Toulouse and southern Sweden. The contrasts in performance between the countries of western Europe were, however, rather clear. By the 1980s, more than forty per cent of the foreign patent applications by western European companies came from West Germany, and the proportion was even higher in the industrial engine, motor vehicle, scientific instrument and chemical industries. Britain and France each filed about fifteen per cent of the total, chiefly in the chemical and defence-related industries, respectively; and Swiss companies about eight per cent (Cantwell 1992, Patel and Pavitt 1991, Welfens 1992).

The research and development centres in southern Germany are particularly noteworthy. The most important industries in Baden-Württemburg have been those which have been closely associated with the major innovations of the Fourth Kondratiev – engineering, cars and electronics – and the major companies of the area – Daimler-Benz, Bosch and AEG – have been amongst those which have devoted most resources to research and development. Furthermore, in addition to the research already being undertaken in Stuttgart and elsewhere, the *land* government has encouraged the further growth of these activities in three of its other cities – Heidelberg, Karlsruhe and Ulm (Bade and Kunzmann 1991). It should not be surprising, therefore, that Baden-Württemburg has became the most industrialised state within West Germany during the Fourth Kondratiev.

Many of the smaller countries, in contrast, were more the recipients of technical advances fashioned elsewhere, than their originators. Greece, Ireland and Spain each spent less than one per cent of their GDP on research and development in the early 1980s, and attracted little of the investment in high-technology industry. There were also marked contrasts within countries. More than two-thirds of the patent applications in Italy in the 1970s were from only three of the country's twenty regions – Lombardy, Piedmont and Emilia Romagna – all in the north, while the number from the Mezzogiorno was tiny (Thwaites and Alderman 1990). Something similar also occurred in eastern

Europe, where, although the organisation of research after the Second World War was everywhere similar to that of the Soviet Union, the most important development work, and the associated manufacturing industries, were located chiefly in that country.

Industrial regions

Reference has been made above to the growth of advanced forms of industry in those regions in Europe in which research and development have been concentrated over the Fourth Kondratiev, but they have not been the only areas in which manufacturing has grown.

Some of the most spectacular increases in manufacturing and mining, whether assessed in terms of output or of employment, have been in the long-established industrial regions of eastern Europe, most of which are based upon coalfields. Both the Stalinist emphasis upon heavy industry, and the recognition that increases in output could be met more cheaply in many cases by expanding existing mines and factories than by building anew, have favoured the further development of areas such as the Donbas, Urals and Upper Silesia since the Second World War, and especially in the 1950s and 1960s. Nor have other long-established industrial regions, such as those associated with textiles around Lodz and engineering in Upper Saxony, failed to increase their levels of activity. However, that expansion has not been without its problems. Even if output and employment have both been raised, productivity has been low in comparison with comparable industries in western Europe; these regions have been suffering from increasing shortages of housing and water, and many of them are dangerously polluted.

This has been in marked contrast to similar areas in northwest Europe, almost all of which have been in decline since the 1950s, as their coal, steel and

the small and medium-sized towns in such areas, whose economies were narrowly based upon these industries.

There is, of course, much industry outwith both the old industrial heartlands and the new concentrations of high-technology production, of which that established by multinational companies in the cheap-labour Mediterranean countries and Ireland or by the governments of eastern Europe in small and medium-sized towns in rural areas are important examples. Nor should it be forgotten that almost all the major commercial centres, including cities such as Berlin, Birmingham, Budapest, Kiev, Milan, St. Petersburg, and Warsaw, though lacking a significant raw-material base, have continued to be important and broadly-based centres of manufacturing throughout the Fourth Wave.

Rural areas

It might be thought that as the service sector, and especially that part of it concerned with personal services, has grown during the Fourth Kondratiev in all parts of Europe, and as the population has become increasingly urbanised, most areas within the space economy would have ceased to be dominated by marked concentrations of one type of economic activity, be it government and producer services, research and development, or manufacturing and mining, and become characterised by a broad range of them. This has not, however, been so, especially in rural areas, many of which have been obliged to adjust to the pressures created by substantial increases in farm productivity – which have taken place in the face of only a slow growth in the demand for farm products – and by the consequent shedding of labour, without the benefit of economic diversification.

The burden of adjustment in western Europe has fallen most clearly upon the most marginal areas, including many of those with the smallest farms. Investment in many of these has been inadequate to maintain the former level of activity, people have moved away, and some land has fallen out of use. The economies of their villages and small towns have been undermined. For example, the Massif Central of France now has less improved farmland, fewer houses, schools and shops, and less public transport than it did in the 1930s; and much concern was also expressed in West Germany in the 1950s and 1960s about the abandonment of land in many parts of the country – the so-called 'social fallow'. The decline of many of these areas would almost certainly have been greater but for the agricultural and regional subsidies which have been available for much of the period.

Much of rural Europe, however, falls into a second group of regions. These include a large part of the lowlands, from the Black Earth zone of the Russian Federation and Ukraine in the east to East Anglia and northern France, in the west, in which the natural conditions for farming have generally been more favourable than in those mentioned above. These are the areas in which farming has undergone major structural change as a result of government intervention of one sort or another since the 1930s, from collectivisation in eastern Europe to the Common Agricultural Policy in the Community. Though the details of change have varied considerably from place to place, scales of enterprise have been increased, methods of production have become mechanised, and yields have been rising in all of them; there has also been much labour shedding, and the rural populations have fallen. There has, however, been some variation in the timing of rural depopulation. Whereas people have been leaving such areas in western Europe since the 1950s, the decline has occurred more recently in much of eastern Europe. Nevertheless, rural populations have begun to fall sharply in the agricultural heartland of the Russian Federation, in Poland and in the Ukraine. Pallot (1991) draws attention to falls of between fourteen and twenty-three per cent in much of the Black Earth zone during the 1980s, and to smaller ones in many other farming regions in what was the Soviet Union.

But there is a third set of rural regions, in which the changes consequent upon increasing productivity in farming have been overwhelmed by those of counter-urbanisation. In western Europe, but also in parts of southern Poland and around Budapest, people have moved out of the larger settlements to the countryside or to those smaller towns and villages which have offered them visual, historic or other amenities – in other words, a superior 'quality of life'. Many of these people have commuted to work; some, however, have taken advantage of modern systems of communication to conduct their businesses from home, often at very great distances from their city offices; and a large number of retired incomers have spread themselves even more widely across the most pleasant rural areas. Counter-urbanisation has affected many areas, and not all of those in western Europe have been adjacent to the large cities, but, wherever it has occurred, it has led to the 'gentrification' of the countryside, and often to conflicts with agriculture and a shortage of housing for local people.

Divergence

Several different types of place have been mentioned in this chapter; places

shown little change since then. That in agriculture has declined throughout the post-war period; that in manufacturing and mining was marked by substantial increases during the Long Boom, but has shown losses in most of the subsequent years, and especially in the periods of recession; and that in services has grown in almost every year, with peaks in 1971, 1979 and 1987. Even in the years of deepest recession, the level of employment in services has usually been maintained. However, the regional impact of these changes has been rather varied (Bade and Kunzmann 1991). Almost all of the major agglomerations participated in the growth of the Long Boom. Thereafter, however, there has been a rather clear contrast between the Ruhr and Wuppertal agglomerations, in which there have been large falls in manufacturing and mining, and only small increases in services; much of the rest of northern Germany and the Saar, in which the falls in manufacturing and mining have been offset to a greater extent by the growth in service industries; and the south, especially the Stuttgart, Karlsruhe and Munich agglomerations, in which the growth of services has been particularly strong, and the decline of manufacturing jobs rather small. Similar contrasts have appeared in the growth of the different types of service. Thus, although service employment increased in all agglomerations between 1976 and 1986, that growth was chiefly in personal services. The number of jobs in producer services, by comparison, only grew faster than that in personal services in the Munich, Stuttgart, Aachen, Karlsruhe and Frankfurt agglomerations; there was little growth in the Ruhr, Wuppertal or Berlin. Furthermore, there has been a marked difference between the centres of agglomerations, which have tended to perform much less well in all these respects, and the rest of the country, including the outer areas of the agglomerations, where counter-urbanisation has been strong. In other words, although the number of jobs in manufacturing has been falling, while that in services has been growing, the secondary sector seems to have done rather better in regions in which services grew most strongly since the mid-1970s, while the service sector has shown little growth in those regions in which manufacturing and mining have declined most.

A similar correlation seems to have occurred in France, where, in the south of the country, services have grown quite strongly, and losses of jobs in manufacturing have been among the smallest. The Nord-Pas de Calais and Lorraine regions, in contrast, have suffered considerable decline in the coal and iron mining, steel and textile industries since the mid-1970s, and have enjoyed little growth in the tertiary sector. Meanwhile, the Ile-de-France, despite losing many of the less-skilled jobs in manufacturing since the mid-1970s, has experienced marked growth in producer services, which has further strengthened its dominant position within the country in those activities (de Gaudemar and Prud'homme 1991).

In other words, there have been great changes in the economic geography of both countries during the Fourth Wave. The question is, however, whether those changes have led to a convergence of the standards of living among their different regions, or to the opposite. It is clear that there has been a marked and general increase in welfare since the 1930s, but governments in both countries have, nevertheless, been able to point to 'leading' and 'lagging' regions. In 1987, the European Commission expressed concern about no less than six groups of lagging regions within the Community, which it identified as follows:

— agricultural regions;
— less-developed regions;
— declining industrial regions;
— urban problem regions;
— peripheral regions; and
— frontier regions;

examples of which existed in both France and West Germany, as well as elsewhere.

There may also be good reason to believe that, notwithstanding strongly egalitarian policies, there were 'leading' and 'lagging' regions within the Soviet Union under central planning; and Bater (1989, pp. 244–63) and Liebowitz (1991) have both drawn attention to wide differences in the standards of living amongst its constituent republics in the 1980s, some of which are indicated in Table II.1. In general, standards seem to have been highest in the northwest, in a band of territory from the Baltic republics and St. Petersburg through the Moscow region, and upper Volga to the southern Urals, while Moldova and the Caucasian republics were much poorer. There also seems to have been a significant difference between urban areas, which tended to have higher standards, and the countryside. It is true that the Soviet Union inherited marked regional contrasts in welfare from the previous Tsarist system, and that standards in the Baltic republics were relatively high, prior to the Second World War, but it would appear that these differences were not eradicated, and that there was a tendency to concentrate investment and facilities in the larger towns and industrial regions.

However, the clearest case of divergence under communism was in Yugoslavia, where, in spite of the transfer of resources from the rich republics to the poor, the devolution of much of the planning of the economy to those republics led to a rapid widening of the gap in living standards between Slovenia and Croatia, on the one hand, and Bosnia and Kosovo, on the other, between

stagnate, and, at worst, lose some of their economic functions. It would appear that, notwithstanding the limited degree of integration in Europe during the last Long Wave, there has, indeed, been competition between centres of decision making and between agglomerations, and that some have been relatively successful while other have not. Furthermore, just as some regions within individual countries have prospered more than others, so there appear to have been changes amongst the countries of Europe during the Fourth Wave. Comparisons are difficult because of the lack of comparable data concerning GNP for the 1930s and 1980s, the changes in international boundaries during the period, and doubts about how to measure the value of output in eastern Europe under central planning; and so a series of measures of the standard of living in the 1930s have been used for that period, and these have been compared with the World Bank estimates of GNP per capita in the mid-1970s and late 1980s (Figure III.13). Countries for which data is available have been placed according to their relation to the median value.

It would appear that, in the 1930s, the highest standards of living were in northwest Europe; that France, Italy, Estonia, Finland and Latvia were somewhat less well off; and that the lowest standards were in southeastern Europe and the Soviet Union. Czechoslovakia was the most developed of the eastern European countries, followed by Hungary and Poland, with the others in the region rather far behind.

There appears to have been some convergence since that time, at least within each of the two major economic groupings. Progress had already been made in that direction in eastern Europe by the mid-1970s; and the USSR, in particular, had improved its position. It would also appear that convergence has continued since, for, by the late 1980s, all the countries of the area had rather similar GNPs per capita; but it is important to note that this was only because of large falls in the values for two of the leading countries of the mid-1970s – Czechoslovakia and Poland. There also appears to have been some convergence among the original members of the Community, both between the 1930s and the mid-1970s, and since, though the rank order has changed somewhat. The five countries which have been members of EFTA throughout its existence, in contrast, have shown no convergence.

The most noticeable changes over the period, however, are those between the three groups. Thus, the EFTA countries have maintained their status as the richest in Europe, and Finland, in particular, has progressed relative to the rest of the continent. The Community countries have, similarly, retained their position between the EFTA countries and those of eastern Europe, though Britain and the Netherlands have both fallen markedly in relation to other members of the group. But it is the poor performance of the eastern bloc, especially since the mid-1970s, which is most apparent. Figure III.1 suggested that that group enjoyed more rapid rates of growth during the 1950s and 1960s than western Europe, but fell behind thereafter, and this would seem to be borne out by Figure III.13. By the late 1980s, the countries of eastern Europe were firmly at the bottom of the European league. It is this divergence, especially in the declining phase of the Fourth Kondratiev, which lay behind the collapse of the communist governments of eastern Europe, the abandonment of central planning, and requests for closer economic integration with western Europe.

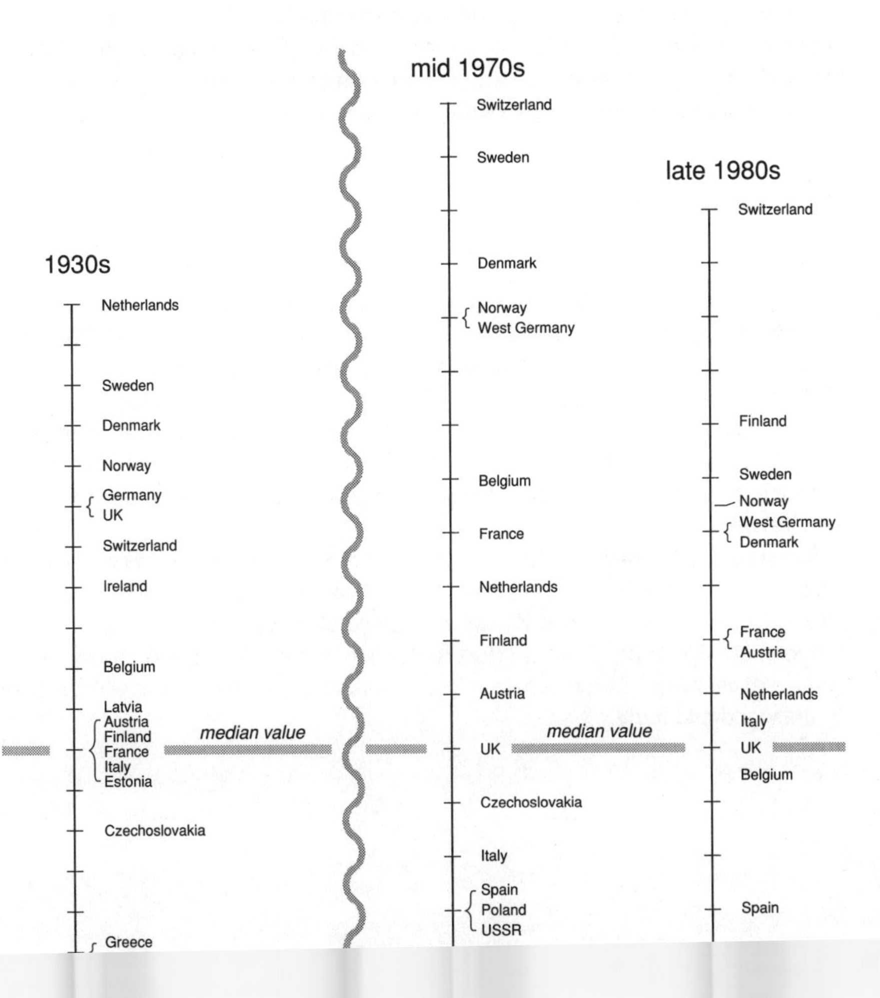
1930s
Netherlands
Sweden
Denmark
Norway
Germany
UK
Switzerland
Ireland
Belgium
Latvia
Austria
Finland
France
Italy
Estonia
median value
Czechoslovakia
Greece
USSR
mid 1970s
Switzerland
Sweden
Denmark
Norway
West Germany
Belgium
France
Netherlands
Finland
Austria
UK
median value
Czechoslovakia
Italy
Spain
Poland
USSR
late 1980s
Switzerland
Finland
Sweden
Norway
West Germany
Denmark
France
Austria
Netherlands
Italy
UK
Belgium
Spain
Poland
Romania

However, any future integration will inevitably expose the comparative advantages of some parts of the continent, and the disadvantages of others, even more clearly. It is, therefore, to the examination of this underlying geographical form, and of the economic rents which it represents, that we must now progress.

Further reading

Seers and Vaitsos (1980) have given an account of *Integration and Unequal Development: The Experience of the EEC* during the early years of the Common Market, while Molle and Cappellin have assessed the *Regional Impact of Community Policies in Europe* more recently (1988). Rodwin and Sazanami's *Industrial Change and Regional Economic Transformation* (1991) compares aggregate change in manufacturing and mining, on the one hand, with that in services, and especially producer services, on the other, in the leading countries of western Europe since the mid-1970s.

Marshall (1987) has provided a commentary on Long Wave theory, and an analysis of sectoral and regional change in Britain in each Kondratiev since the Industrial Revolution, in *Long Waves in Regional Development*.

Freeman, Sharp and Walker (1991) and Klein and Welfens (1992) have edited groups of essays on Europe's technological performance, competition with the rest of the world and trade.

Section IV
The map of economic rents

The future form of the European space economy will be determined by many factors. One will be the institutional framework, which was outlined in Section II. Another will be the processes of change which are already at work, especially those connected with the technology of production, some of which were discussed in Section III. And a third will be the map of economic rents.

Europe is not homogeneous. Some of it is richly endowed with natural resources. Other parts are poor. Some areas within it are easily reached; others are relatively inaccessible. The characteristics of site and situation vary widely between one place and another. Of course, these characteristics only become apparent when revealed, and in some cases enhanced, by technology and investment. Minerals are only of value if a use has been found for them. Accessibility is only created if routes are constructed. But wherever such developments have occurred, they show that some areas are more profitable for

[illegible]

very great importance in determining the use to which the various parts of Europe have been put in the recent past, and the intensity of that use, and which will continue to do so. This section will describe some of these – agricultural potential, sources of energy, tourist amenity, pollution and other environmental degradation, the availability of labour and accessibility to markets. It will also outline the link between the changing security situation in Europe and the opportunities and risks for economic development.

Agricultural potential

More land is used for agriculture in Europe than for any other economic activity, with the possible exception of forestry; and in most countries the industry continues to make a significant, if declining, contribution to employment and the gross domestic product.

Two broad groups of field crops – those of the cool temperate latitudes and of the Mediterranean – may be cultivated in Europe. The main cereals – barley and wheat – and sugar beet, roots, potatoes and oil crops can be grown in many places south of the sixtieth parallel, while maize, citrus fruits, vines and olives are confined to its most southerly areas (Figure IV.1). Pasture grasses and clover are more successful in northern Europe, and it follows that that area has something of an advantage in dairy products. Rice, sugar cane and tea can only be grown in a very few, restricted locations. However, agricultural potential varies widely within these broad regions; and areas of high potential, and also marginal regions, may both be identified.

Three sets of conditions determine that potential – climatic hazards, topography and soils. No part of the continent is free from climatic hazards; but, in general, conditions deteriorate away from the lowlands of eastern England, northern France, the Low Countries and central Germany. Precipitation increases towards the west, restricting the chances of harvests ripening. Conversely, it declines towards the east, with an increasing possibility of drought, until desert conditions are reached around the lower Volga in Russia. Precipitation also becomes increasingly seasonal towards the Mediterranean. As a result, much of lowland Europe suffers from a water deficit; and one which increases towards both the east and south of the continent, especially during the growing season. These conditions pose problems of aeolian soil erosion and associated dust-storms in the Black Earth region of Russia, in southwest Siberia and in the eastern Ukraine (Symons 1990, pp. 71–4). Temperatures fall towards the north in Europe; and the incidence of late-spring and early-autumn frosts increases, thus preventing the successful cultivation of Mediterranean crops in much of Europe north of the Massif Central, central uplands of Germany and the Carpathians, and of almost all crops in the open north of sixty degrees. They also display increasing seasonality towards the east, thus obliging farmers to sow lower-yielding spring crops. Farmers have sought to offset these limitations in the past by irrigating or covering crops, and, in so doing, have often more than recouped the capital outlay through increases in the yield and quality of their products, and by being able to harvest crops out of season, when

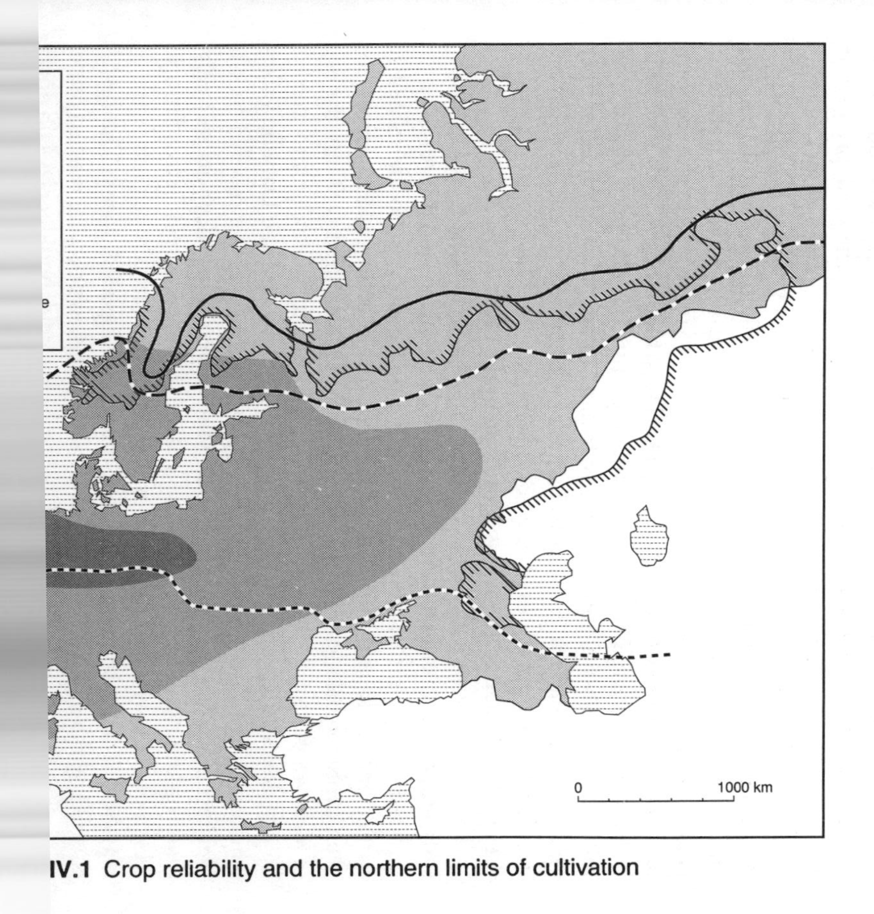

IV.1 Crop reliability and the northern limits of cultivation

prices are high; but much scope remains for both these types of intensification, especially in southern and eastern Europe.

Farming has become increasingly constrained by topography in recent times. Whereas small-scale, semi-subsistence and unmechanised farms could make use of steeply-sloping and small parcels of land, mechanised production requires large, gently-sloping sites, uninterrupted by outcrops of rock or other hazards. Not surprisingly, large areas of the uplands of southern Europe, which have been cultivated in the past with the aid of terracing, have been abandoned; and many of those which remain in use are in areas in which the transfer of labour from the primary to the secondary and tertiary sectors in the economy has yet to be completed, and the structure of farms modernised. Such areas must be regarded as marginal. Much mountain pasture has also been abandoned, following the substitution of intensive feeding of animals and birds for open grazing; and, where it remains in use, it also often reflects the fact that the industry has not yet adjusted fully, or is being supported for social reasons, or those of landscape aesthetics, as is the case in the Swiss Alps.

The pattern of agriculture has also been affected in the past by the quality of soils, and continues to be so, in spite of such methods of land improvement as under-draining, fertilisation and irrigation. Soil quality is closely related to parent material, and that, in turn, depends in many places upon the geomorphological history of the site during the Quaternary Era. Thus, the belt of loess which runs from northern France to the eastern Ukraine and western Siberia and also covers much of southern Germany and the Danube valley, which was laid down while much of northern Europe was covered by the Pleistocene ice sheets, is most favoured in this respect. These deposits are freely-draining and stone-free, and increase in depth from west to east across Europe. Much of the lowland to the north of that belt, however, is much less fertile. It may be divided into three broad, but often interdigitated, zones. The first is covered by the relatively infertile sands and gravels, which were washed out of the front of the glaciers; the second, by the heavy, cold, boulder clay laid down under their forward edges; and the third, which is the most northerly of all, is not covered at all, but is an area scraped bare by the ice, and characterised by exposed rock and confused drainage. This sequence of parent materials is broadly represented in Figure IV.2. After the decay of the glaciers, chernozem soils developed widely on the loess in eastern Europe, under steppe vegetation; and brown forest soils appeared not only on the loess, but many other parent materials, in the lowlands of western Europe. Both soils are capable of giving high yields of field crops. Further north, however, inferior materials and greater leaching have produced podsols of increasing acidity and decreasing depth and fertility. Areas to the south of the loess also pose problems. Soils in the eastern Ukraine and lower Volga, in which the climate is semi-arid and the summers are hot, are susceptible to both wind and water erosion, and to salination following irrigation. Much of southern Europe, and especially the mountains of the three Mediterranean peninsulas, is also prone to soil erosion.

The use of rural land in Europe broadly reflects these environmental constraints. Only the lower slopes of the mountains of southern Europe are farmed; and much of the central uplands, from the Massif Central to the Bohemian diamond, is forested. Large areas of sandy soils on the north European plain are also wooded, as is much of the area north of sixty degrees. However, the intensity with which farmland was used in the 1980s did not accurately reflect the detailed pattern of its fertility. Some areas of only moderate quality, in places as different as Denmark and Greece, were intensively cultivated, while the potential of others, especially in the Soviet Union, was far from fully exploited. Contrasts in yields across the continent were wide (Figure III.4); but the differences almost certainly reflected government policies with regard to farm ownership and incomes, as much as natural fertility.

Fuels

Europe has been a major consumer of fuels ever since the Industrial Revolution, and the most accessible of the continent's deposits have already been used. Imports have increased substantially during the last Long Wave; and, by the 1980s, the continent had a trade deficit with the rest of the world in both coal and oil. Great concern was expressed in western Europe at the peak of the Long Boom about the future availability of both domestic and imported supplies, and similar fears have been voiced more recently about the Soviet Union's stocks of oil and gas. These fears are groundless. The stock of fuels within Europe remains large; and the question is one of the relative price of extracting them, and of economising in their use or introducing alternatives to them, rather than of facing a sudden exhaustion of supplies. Nor do we know the full extent of the mineral resources of the continent, because the search for them

subsequently became the Scottish highlands to the north and the Variscan Front (roughly along the Ardennes, Bohemian massif and Carpathians) to the south. The second covered what are now the east European platform and west Siberian lowland. Some of these areas were swampy from time to time, and were covered with layers of vegetable matter, resulting eventually in many seams of coal; but these deposits were subject to several later periods of erosion, faulting

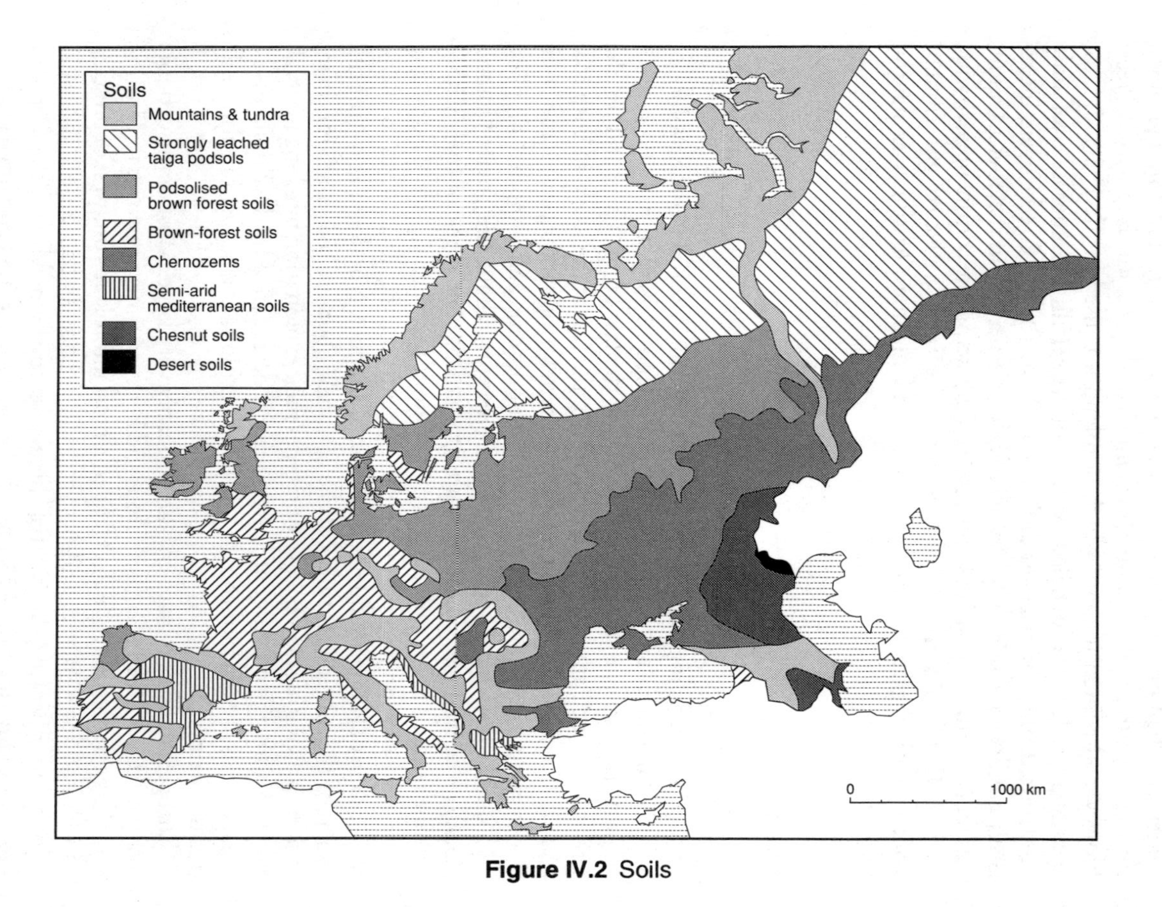

Figure IV.2 Soils

and gentle folding, with the consequence that they are now truncated in many places, covered unconformably with younger rocks, and divided into a number of basins (Mackowsky 1968, Nalivkin 1973). Mining has occurred where the coal seams are exposed on or near the edges of those basins, or where they are within a thousand metres of the surface. Upper Palaeozoic deposits were also widespread to the south of the Variscan Front; but many have been eroded subsequently, covered by deep deposits of more recent sediments, or highly folded; and the area only possesses small deposits of workable coal in such places as the margins of the Massif Central, the Asturias, and the Balkans. Many of the deposits in northern Europe were also too deep for profitable mining in the 1980s; but increases in the price of coal might encourage the resumption of mining in the Lublin field of eastern Poland, the deepening of operations at the Selby field with a view to exploiting other seams there, the opening of new mines in the Vale of Belvoir and elsewhere in the English Midlands, and the extension of mining down the dipslope north of the Ruhr into the Munster basin and towards the centre of the Upper Silesian basin. Moreover, there is some coal lying nearer to the surface which was not extracted by underground working in the past, but which is now potentially accessible by opencast methods. In other words, there are substantial deposits of coal still available within short distances of almost all the areas which were the chief centres of mining in Europe during the Fourth Kondratiev.

The situation with regard to sub-bituminous coals is somewhat similar. Marine transgressions across the North European Plain from Triassic to Miocene times led to the creation of extensive coastal marshes, and eventually to large deposits of brown coals in the west Siberian basin, on the Russian platform, in the Elbe Bay (underlying much of what was East Germany and west central Poland), and the Cologne Bay. Those deposits which lie closest to the surface have been extensively mined by opencast means during the twentieth century; but downfaulted blocks still contain substantial reserves, though at depths which make them more expensive to

fields; and a further thirty-six contain smaller fields. Some contain several fields. Almost all lie north and east of the Ardennes–Sudeten–Carpathian line of uplands, with the largest in western Siberia and the Volga–Urals basin. A few also exist in the Pannonian basin. Output from several of the oilfields which were exploited first, such as those in Azerbaijan and Romania, has been declining for many years; and even that from the Volga–Urals basin, which was

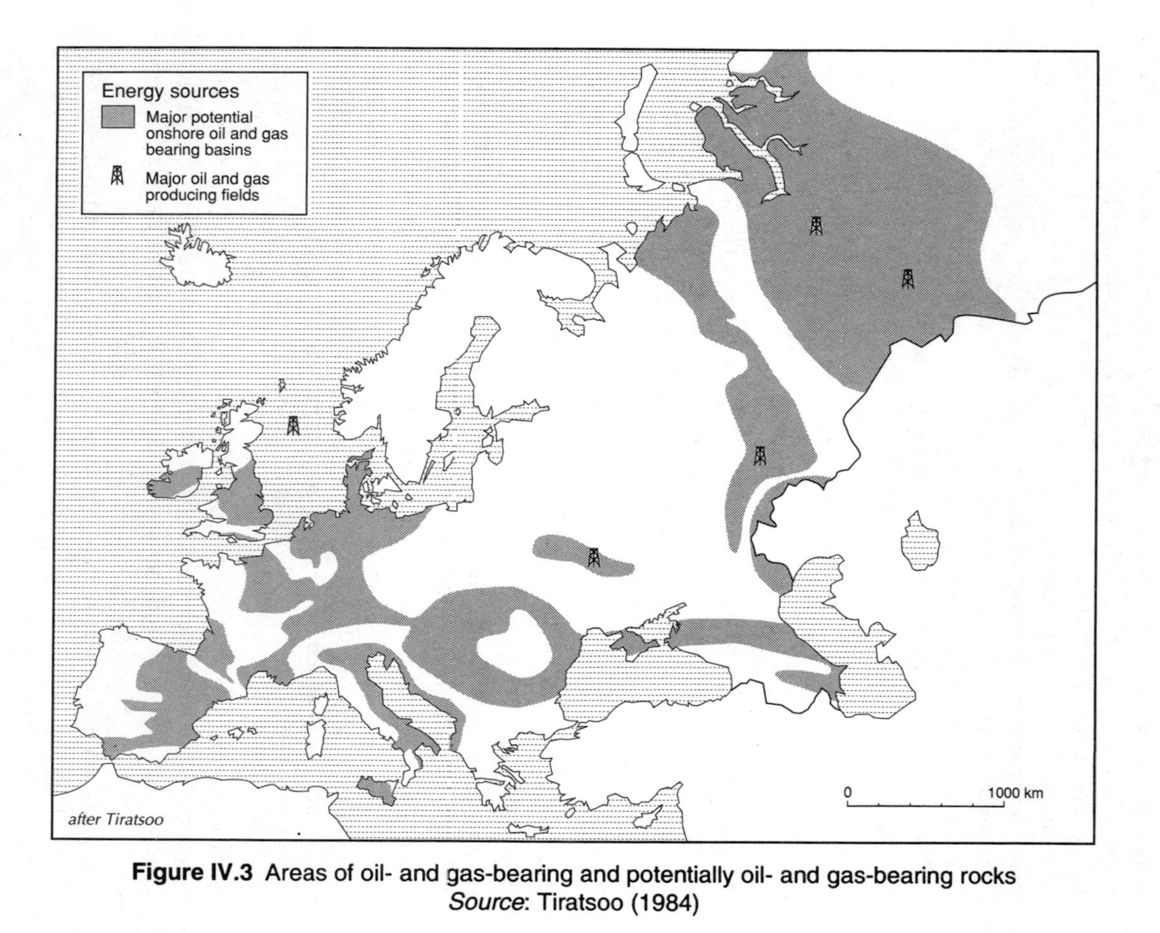

Figure IV.3 Areas of oil- and gas-bearing and potentially oil- and gas-bearing rocks
Source: Tiratsoo (1984)

developed between the late 1940s and the 1960s, has been falling more recently. Nevertheless, all major basins have proven reserves which are substantial in relation to recent output. This is particularly the case in western Siberia, which is second only to the Arabian Gulf in its potential (Tiratsoo, 1984, p. 124). Reserves of natural gas in the most important of the producing fields, and again especially in western Siberia, are also sufficient to last well into the twenty-first century, at present rates of output. The most promising prospects for the discovery of further oil and gasfields lie in eastern Siberia, in what were the Soviet, central-Asian republics, and offshore in the shallow waters of the Arctic Ocean, the Black and Caspian Seas and the Sea of Azov, on the southern Baltic shelf, and on the continental shelf north of the British Isles and west of Norway. It is also likely that, in keeping with the history of exploitation of most basins, a number of fields still await discovery in western Siberia, west of the Urals, and, perhaps, in other areas which have already been opened up, but that these will be small in comparison with those which are currently being exploited.

The growth of the European economy during the Fourth Wave was accompanied by a marked increase in the use of fuel, and especially fossil fuels. Future economic growth may be less energy intensive, not least because the price of fuels may have to increase somewhat to reflect the higher costs of extraction from less accessible sites; but there is no reason to believe that there will be an absolute shortage of such fuels in Europe during a Fifth Kondratiev. There may, however, be further changes in the balance of use between rival fuels, which will result in falls in output from some sites and the opening of sources of alternative fuels, all of which will be examined in more detail in Section V.

Tourist amenity

abandonment of officially-approved state tourism, with its visits to war cemeteries and 'monuments to socialist achievement'; and the establishment of a free market for western tourists and tour companies in the area, will almost certainly lead to a re-evaluation of its potential.

The opportunities for 'sun, sand and sea' holidays, which have done so much to develop the coastal areas of Mediterranean Europe since the 1960s, have also been exploited to some degree on the Black Sea coasts of Bulgaria, Romania and the Crimea, but to only a limited extent on other parts of that littoral. Yet the summer climate of the whole coast from the Bosphorus to Batumi, in its temperatures and sunshine, is the equal of that in Greece and Spain; and the Crimean and Georgian coasts, if somewhat wetter, are backed by spectacular mountain scenery. Similarly, in winter there are areas of eastern Europe which offer snow conditions which are as good for skiing, if not better, than those in the Alps, but have been much less developed, especially the Caucasus, the Rhodope Massif in Bulgaria, and the Carpathians. The scenery of the Caucasus and the Carpathians is also comparable with that of many of the resorts in the Alps which are visited by tourists in summer; and there are a number of spas which, though somewhat neglected under the communist governments, could be restored as luxury holiday centres, providing conference and sporting, in addition to medical, facilities. Nor has the potential of eastern Europe's history been fully exploited. Many towns and villages in the area are still largely composed of buildings in traditional styles; a remarkable collection of medieval and Renaissance monasteries exists in Bulgaria, Moldova and Romania; and cities which have retained their historic centres, such as Krakow, Prague and St. Petersburg, have the potential to attract the sort of attention which has been lavished upon such places as Avignon, Edinburgh and Siena. Much scope exists for the packaging of visits, either for the holiday or conference trade, in which tourists make use of a variety of amenities within an area. Southern Poland has a particularly rich and varied potential, including the city of Krakow, the salt-mine museum at Wieliczka, the journey by raft through the Dunajec gorge, and the Tatry Mountains, much of which can be enjoyed at most times of year.

However, the successful exploitation of all these amenities depends upon the provision of accommodation, catering, transport and entertainment on a much larger scale, and to the standard expected in western Europe. This may be achieved most rapidly through the widespread establishment of western tour companies and hotel groups, with their computer-booking systems, in eastern Europe; and we shall return to this matter in Section V.

Environmental degradation

Not all sites, however, possess the potential they once had, whether it be for farming, mineral extraction, tourism or other activities. The rent which they might once have yielded has been reduced and some areas have become worthless. Degradation has many causes, and occurs on many scales, within the space economy; but the result is always the same, namely, a reduction in the demand for such sites, and a fall in the intensity with which they are used. Reversal of the process often requires action by governments, either to restrain the way in which businesses use land, thus reducing their profitability, or to clear up the mess that has been left. Some damage seems to be beyond repair.

The most seriously damaged areas of Europe would appear to be those in which resources which could have been preserved have been destroyed. Chief amongst these are the areas which have suffered soil erosion, but there are others which have been damaged by subsidence or poisoning of the soil. Soil erosion has been widespread in southern Europe for many centuries, and was counteracted early by the terracing of slopes. Nevertheless, large parts of the steeply-sloping lands in the Balkans and in southern Italy and Iberia have lost their soil, and are now of little use for either agriculture or forestry. It is, of course, the case that such terrain is not suited to the large-scale, mechanised methods preferred by either industry today; but the removal of their tree cover has also led to the deterioration of climates in neighbouring areas, especially to a reduction in precipitation, and to the sedimentation of their rivers, to more erratic river regimes, and to flooding. What is more, a quarter of the land in Mediterranean Europe was continuing to lose soil at a rate of ten tonnes per hectare per annum or more in the 1980s (Grenon and Batisse 1989, pp. 217–19). There is also little soil left in many of the upland areas of northwest Europe, especially the British Isles, as a result of forest clearance in the distant past. Furthermore, the cultivation of more gently-sloping land in semi-arid areas, especially in the Ukraine, the Volga lands and the Virgin Lands of southwestern Siberia and northern Kazakhstan, has led to both wind and water erosion, and to a reduction of agricultural potential. Breburda (1990) reports that irrigation has leached humus from the upper horizons of the loess soils, while the use of heavy machinery has compacted them, increased run-off, and encouraged gully erosion. The planting of shelter belts, contour ploughing and other techniques have halted these losses in some places; but, in others, land has been put back to grass, and extensive grazing has replaced more intensive cultivation. In some parts of the Virgin Lands, erosion began as soon as the soil was cultivated, and much land was damaged (Stebelsky 1987).

Soil damage, as distinct from soil loss, has been on a somewhat smaller scale

Thirdly, soil has been poisoned by radioactive materials following the Chelyabinsk explosion of 1958, that at Chernobyl in 1986, and other accidents. Some areas have received such heavy deposits of particles that they will not be usable again for many years. Twenty-eight thousand square kilometres of Belarus, Russia and the Ukraine received five Curies or more of radiation per square kilometre from Chernobyl, and a further 48,000 square kilometres received between one and five Curies. An area of approximately thirty kilometres around the power station has been closed to most economic activities, and to farming, forestry and water supply in particular. About a quarter of this area was farmland and the rest forest. Some 116,000 people have had to be resettled, and it is estimated that a further 700,000 may also have to move eventually (Savchenko 1991). In other words, about a quarter of Belarus and large areas of northwest Ukraine were seriously poisoned. Not surprisingly, many of the other nuclear power stations of Russian design in eastern Europe have been closed, and there are grave doubts about the safety of the areas surrounding the remainder. Much less information is available about radioactive pollution in the central Urals, and in connection with some of the USSR's 'closed' cities in which nuclear experiments and the manufacture of weapons were conducted; but all such areas will probably be unattractive to new investment, especially that from the west. There are also large areas outwith the European space economy, as it has been delimited for the purposes of this study, in the deserts of Kazakhstan, on Novaya Zemlya and in the Kara Sea, which have been used to test nuclear weapons or dump nuclear waste, whose potential usefulness has also been much reduced thereby.

Atmospheric pollution also poses other threats for particular activities and regions of Europe. The continent's forests have been adversely affected, especially during the last Long Wave, by acid rain, dust and other pollutants. Large numbers of trees in almost all those countries of central and eastern Europe which lie in the path of the prevailing winds have been poisoned by the effluents of the major centres of industry and population further west, with consequent losses in the potential yield of timber and in the scenic attraction of some mountain areas, especially the Alps and Carpathians. Pollution of the atmosphere has also been very great in many of the major industrial regions; and, while short-range pollution has been much reduced in western Europe, the problem in the east remains severe. In particular, the areas in which substantial quantities of coal, either brown or black, are burnt, or in which there are large cement, chemical or metallurgical factories, and in which rates of illness and death are increasing, are likely to be unattractive to western investors. The Donbas, Urals, Upper Silesia, Upper Saxony, and industrial regions of Czechoslovakia, Romania, and elsewhere, have been rendered filthy and dangerous by such pollution in the recent past. Moreover, Europe may also be about to suffer from a decrease in the ozone layer, again the result of atmospheric pollution. The threat is restricted initially to northern Europe, and to spring and early summer; but, if the depletion continues, the dangers of sunbathing will increase; and regions whose economies are heavily dependent upon coastal tourism or outdoor sports may be faced with major changes in the type of holiday facilities which are required. Alternatively, tourists may go elsewhere.

The continent's water resources have also been degraded. Water has always been in short supply in some regions, restricting the development of agriculture, industry and settlement, and in many places agriculture has only survived because such supplies as have existed have been carefully husbanded. The edge of the œcumene in the Volga region and north Kazakhstan has been determined largely by that limitation. However, changes in the scale and methods of both agriculture and industry have posed a variety of threats to supplies in many areas. The cultivation of the Soviet steppes has been but the largest case of increasing demands in almost all those parts of the continent in which there is a summer deficit: demands which have led not only to reductions in the availability of water for other purposes, but also to falling water tables and the poisoning of groundwater by fertilisers, herbicides and pesticides. Water supplies have also suffered greatly from pollution by manufacturing and mining, and from the dumping of raw sewage. In general, these problems have been worst in eastern Europe. The shortage of water has meant that industries which require large quantities, such as electricity generation, have increasingly been obliged to create their own supplies by the construction of barrages and reservoirs, or to seek coastal sites or areas of high precipitation, many of which are remote from the major centres of population; and it was announced in the last days of the Soviet Union that water shortages would lead to falls of about a third in the production of coking coal, iron and steel in the Ukraine by the year 2005 (Marples 1991, p. 112). Many tourist areas in southern Europe also face acute shortages of water in the summer, which can only be alleviated by bringing it from long distances or making other expensive provision, such as the use of desalination. Those on the Adriatic and Black Seas were also experiencing high levels of marine pollution (Komarov 1980, pp. 37–8).

Reference has already been made to the continent's forests, both in connection with their early and unfortunate clearance in some mountain areas of southern Europe, and also with the damage which has been inflicted on them more recently in central, eastern and northern Europe by atmospheric pollution. It should be noted, however, that the quality of many of the forests in Russia, both west of the Urals and in western Siberia, has also been reduced by

[illegible]

In view of these and other problems, it should not be surprising that increasing concern was expressed in Europe about environmental degradation during the last Long Wave. The powers of environmental protection agencies were strengthened almost everywhere during the 1970s; and debate about these matters increased in eastern Europe after the introduction of *glasnost* in 1985, and again after the fall of the communist governments. Some of the worst sources of industrial pollution, such as the aluminium refinery at Skawina, near Krakow, and the nuclear power stations in what was East Germany, have already been closed, and production in others, such as the Nowa Huta steel works, reduced. Many other primitive and polluting factories in eastern Europe are also likely to be shut in the near future, not least because the high costs of installing the necessary filters and other machinery will make them uneconomic; and programmes for the construction of coal-fired and nuclear power stations have been cut back in several countries. The introduction of market pricing there will do much to cut back on the waste of energy, timber and water. Meanwhile, it has become increasingly difficult in northwest Europe to obtain permission for any large industrial development on a site which has not hitherto been built over. The continent is not, however, uniformly rigorous in the matter of environmental protection; and, wherever there are high levels of unemployment, priority is likely to be given to new development. The countries of northwest Europe have adopted the most stringent land-use and environmental controls, but southern Europe is generally thought to be less demanding (Williams 1987, p. 168), and requests for stricter controls in eastern Europe may be muted until unemployment there begins to fall.

Population

The population of Europe represents both a source of labour and a set of markets. The number of people in each country was given in Table II.1, but the significance of this information may be more clearly conveyed by a map. Figure IV.4 shows how population is concentrated in a small number of conurbations and their environs, several of which coalesce to form two axes, along the Rhine and the belt from northern France to the Donbas, which intersect in the Low Countries and northwest Germany. It also indicates the other concentrations in England and northern Italy, and the way in which population density declines away from the axes, towards the edge of the European space economy. In other words, the point of greatest population potential probably lies in the middle Rhine valley, and the significance of this distribution is enhanced by the much higher levels of wealth in northwest Europe than in the rest of the continent (Figure II.4). A map of the costs of labour, in contrast, would be broadly the reverse of this picture, with the lowest real wages in eastern and southern Europe.

However, unlike the other matters which influence the map of economic rents, population is not fixed in its location. Considerable fears have been expressed about the possibility that, following the collapse of the communist governments in eastern Europe and the abandonment of their restrictive policies on emigration, there will be mass movements of people from eastern to western Europe – people who will be difficult and costly to house, and for

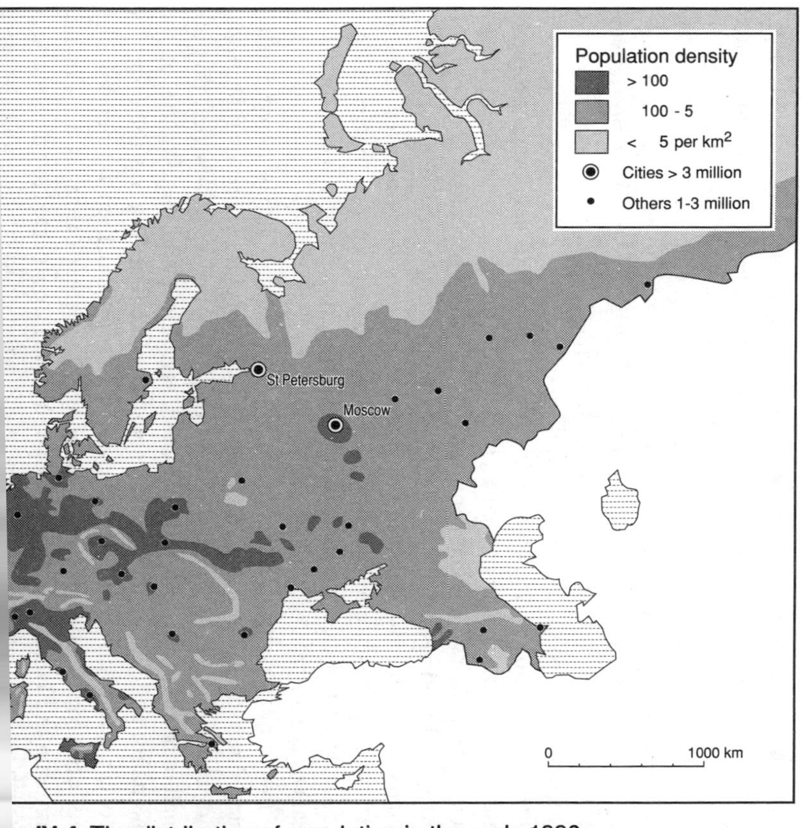

re IV.4 The distribution of population in the early 1990s

whom there will not be sufficient jobs. Many millions of Czechs, Germans, Poles and Russians either fled at the end of the Second World War, or were moved to lands which had been evacuated, and thousands of East Germans moved to the West each day during the summer of 1961 in the expectation that they would soon be prevented from doing so by the building of a wall across Berlin. Movements of this type were happening again in the early 1990s, as the Soviet Union and Yugoslavia unravelled. There was, however, considerable reluctance in western Europe to allow political, let alone economic, refugees to move other than to areas in which the majority of their compatriots lived; and it is likely that, where such people have a national state to which they could go, they will not be welcome in third countries. Croatian refugees from Bosnia were being encouraged to move to Croatia, not Britain. Much of the economic aid which was sent to the Russian Federation in the early 1990s was designed to prevent economic breakdown on a scale which would encourage people to move westwards, and, in particular, to persuade the ethnic Germans to remain there. Nevertheless, marked contrasts in the levels of pay and of job opportunities persist between one part of the continent and another; there is considerable potential for the migration of ethnic minorities who find themselves in adverse conditions; and economic reform in eastern Europe may shake out labour on such a scale that there may be a surplus in much of that area for many years to come.

Two other aspects of the future supply of labour may also be noted. Firstly, the demographic transition is now complete almost everywhere within Europe; and, although rates of population growth do vary between countries, they are small in comparison with those between, say, Russia and the Ukraine, on the one hand, and the former Soviet republics of central Asia, on the other, or between the countries of Mediterranean Europe and their former colonies in North Africa. The exceptions amongst the larger countries are Poland, Romania and Yugoslavia, where the populations are expected to grow by about a tenth by 2020, and Germany, where it is expected to fall by about the same amount. The highest rates of natural increase are in Albania, Armenia and Azerbaijan. Similarly, annual increases in the number of those of working age during the 1990s will be very small in most countries, and declining. Only in Poland, where the number will rise by about one per cent per annum – more than in any of the other of the more populous countries of the continent – and in Britain and the Ukraine, with increases of about 0.3 per cent per annum, is there no evidence of such a decline. In Germany, in contrast, the labour force will fall throughout the period; and, before the end of the century, it will also be declining by about 0.4 per cent per annum in Italy, and somewhat more slowly in several smaller countries in western Europe (World Bank 1992). In other words, while population growth may be exerting much less pressure on people to migrate than in the past, labour shortages may begin to appear in some countries in western Europe in the near future.

Secondly, the supply of illiterate landless labourers, which provided so much of the labour for the growing mining and manufacturing industries in the past, beginning with the Irish in nineteenth-century Britain and ending with the Yugoslav *gastarbeiter* in West Germany in the 1970s, has almost entirely disappeared. This is not to say that standards of education and labour skill are everywhere the same in Europe, or that the unemployed of eastern Europe would not be willing to work for a pittance in northwest Europe, if they were allowed to do so. Jones (1990) has drawn attention to the fact that many of the ethnic Germans in eastern Europe are not as skilled as those in comparable occupations in West Germany, or fluent in German. But the establishment of compulsory education and the great movements of labour from countryside to town, and from farming to manufacturing and service employment, in Europe since the 1930s mean that the population is now better educated and more experienced than ever before. Moreover, many young people are fluent in one or more of the major western European languages, and may, thus, be more widely employable than in the past.

Transport and communications

An integrated space economy must, by definition, be one in which its regions are connected with each other, and in which goods, information and labour can move from places of supply to those of demand. No part of the European space economy is unconnected with the rest; but the frequency, speed and variety of links vary greatly as between one area and another; and some national boundaries are reinforced by the existence of different and incompatible transport and communication systems. Scandinavia, other than Denmark, and the islands around the edge of the continent are necessarily less well connected with the rest of Europe than many other parts of the continent.

the rise of road and air transport during the Fourth Kondratiev, and the introduction of digital telephones and fax, have greatly increased the flexibility of communication, these facilities are not uniformly available across Europe. We shall consider the movement of freight, passengers and messages in turn, and the facilities for each of them.

During the Fourth Wave, the methods used for the movement of freight changed dramatically. The role of railways declined relatively throughout the continent, and absolutely in much of western Europe. That of inland waterways, which had been minor, declined further, while those of pipelines and air increased. However, the most important growth was in road transport, which, by the 1980s, accounted for almost all short-distance movements, and also much of the long-distance traffic. The result has been that, while access to railways and ports continues to be important for the exploitation and supply of bulky raw materials, door-to-door transport of smaller and more valuable loads can now be supplied wherever places are linked by all-weather roads.

Nevertheless, as in so many other aspects of Europe's space economy, this general picture conceals wide variations. More than sixty per cent of the ton-kilometres of freight traffic in the Soviet Union in the 1980s was carried by rail, and another twenty – oil and gas – by pipeline. Less than a tenth went by road. Rail transport was also common in the other countries of eastern Europe (Poland 1987, p. 600). However, the network of railways in what was the Soviet Union is sparse; and the gauge change at the frontiers means that most, but not all, goods must be trans-shipped before they can pass into other parts of eastern Europe. Nor is the transport of goods, and especially those connected with agriculture, to railheads in the former Soviet Union easy, for many roads are unmetalled, and become waterlogged in autumn and spring.

In western Europe, in contrast, less than a third of freight was carried on the railways by the 1980s, and in Britain, Italy and Spain only about a tenth. There is no doubt that the post-war construction of a dense net of motorways in northwest Europe (Figure IV.5) has encouraged the transfer of freight to the roads, though it would appear that this was not a necessary condition everywhere. Spain, which was slower than most to construct motorways, but whose rail gauge is different from that of the rest of western Europe, depended upon the road transport to a greater extent than any other country. It is unlikely, in view of this dominance of road transport, that the rail link under the Channel will do much, if anything, to reduce the effective distance between Britain and the rest of Europe for the carriage of freight. On the other hand, the removal of internal borders within the Community in 1993 will speed freight traffic between its contiguous members.

The market for passenger transport, especially over long distances, is very varied. The longest journeys, whether for business or pleasure, have come increasingly to rely upon aircraft, while shorter ones have taken advantage of the growing network of motorways. Nevertheless, rail transport retains a significant role, and the continent is served by many long-distance trains, each of which links major cities in several countries. As with freight, more passenger traffic goes by air and road in western Europe than further east, where the railways retain a greater role.

The supply of air transport is clearly linked to market potential. Firstly, the size and number of airports varies with the density and wealth of the popula-

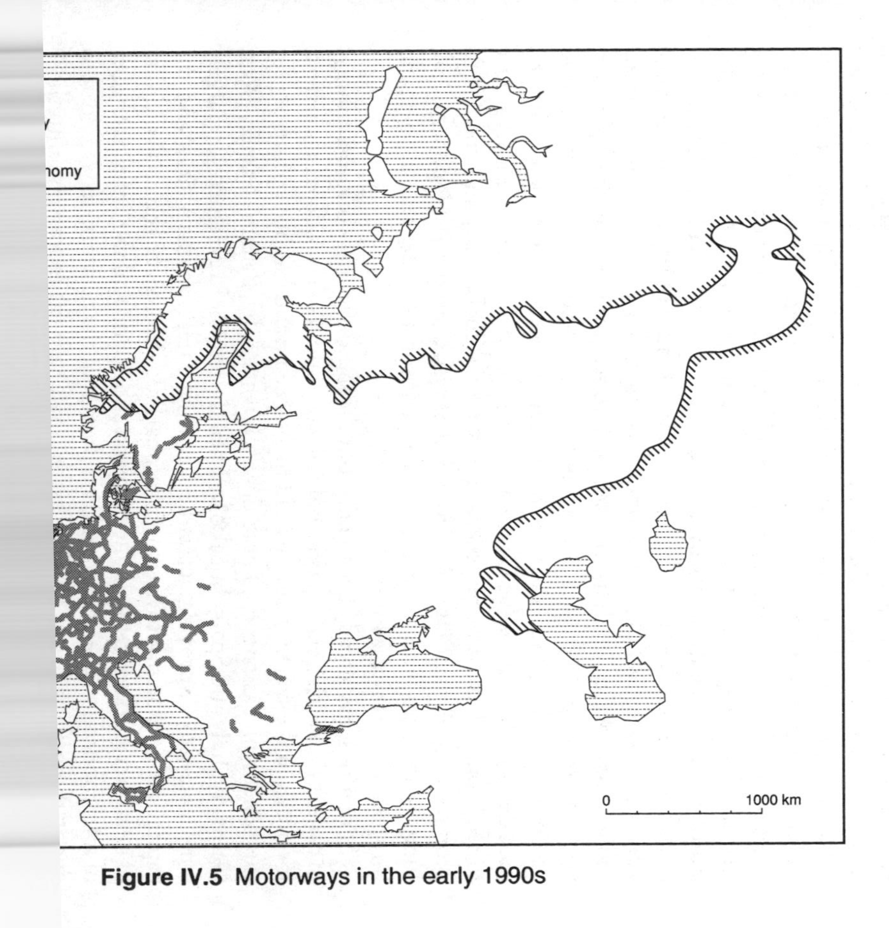

Figure IV.5 Motorways in the early 1990s

tion; and this is reinforced by the major airlines, most of which operate some form of 'hub and spoke' network, in which they provide feeder services from areas of lesser demand to the major airports, and long-haul services from them to other countries within Europe and beyond. The hub airport for national carriers is usually that at the capital city, though Frankfurt in Germany, Amsterdam in the Netherlands, and Zurich in Switzerland are exceptions. Proximity to hub airports is, therefore, to be preferred to locations elsewhere. Heathrow, which is the busiest airport in Europe, has also benefited from the demand for transport between London and those major cities of northwest Europe that are at distances over which road or rail would be just as fast elsewhere, but are longer and more irksome because of the need to cross the Channel. Heathrow has been expanded several times as it has approached the limits of its capacity, but it has not been able to accommodate all the flights that wish to use it; and Gatwick, Luton and Stansted have all been developed to accommodate both scheduled and charter services. Other major airports include Frankfurt, Paris De Gaulle and Orly, and Amsterdam – all lying close to the point of maximum population potential in Europe; and the 1980s promotion of Amsterdam as London's alternative airport – 'Hop, Schiphol, Jump' – sums up both the structure of air transport services and the demand for them in northwest Europe.

Something has already been said about the motorway network and railways in connection with freight traffic; but railways should be considered again here, for much of the recent investment in high-speed trains has been primarily for the benefit of passengers. These developments – by Britain, France, West Germany, Italy and Spain, but also by Poland – have been designed very largely with a view to improving access between the chief provincial cities and the capital, rather than improving international links. Moreover, the small number of new lines and services in France, Poland and Spain, and the limited number of interconnections between them and the rest of the network, have tended to divide those countries to a greater extent than have the motorways into those areas which enjoy easy access to improved means of passenger transport and those which are distant from them.

Telephone, fax, computer, mobile telephone and other networks also facilitate the integration of the space economy. Indeed, they do away with distance where they exist; but they do not do away with geography, because they also divide those areas which are served by them from those which are not. To be unconnected to subscriber trunk dialling, and other advanced communications systems, is to be far away from those places which are; and those areas which are not so connected are inferior sites for many forms of business. Even within western Europe, the density of connections of the most advanced forms of telecommunications varies, being highest in metropolitan regions, such as the Ile-de-France and southeast of England, and lower in Greece, Ireland, Iberia and the Mezzogiorno (Gillespie 1987, Howells 1990). The Community, acknowledging the significance of telecommunications for economic development, has been attempting to remedy the relative backwardness of these areas under its STAR (Special Telecommunications Action for Regional Development) programme.

Once equipment is installed, however, it is the price of sending messages which determines the map of economic rents; yet the prices of intra-Community telephone calls also exhibit a pattern of peripheral disadvantage, with much higher charges for calls to other member countries from Greece, Ireland, Portugal and Spain, and also from Italy, than from the rest of the Community (Mansell 1990). Nevertheless, it is even more expensive to contact non-Community Europe. For example, British Telecom charges twice as much at peak times to call the other countries within the Community and Switzerland as it does to make long-distance calls within Britain; almost three times as much to call the other EFTA countries and Czechoslovakia, Hungary and Poland; somewhat more again for calls to Albania, Bulgaria and Yugoslavia; and more than five times as much to ring Romania or the former Soviet republics. However, the picture is not as simple as these examples might suggest. Modern telecommunications offer a wide range of services, with a corresponding variety of tariffs, and in many countries there is much cross-subsidisation. Thus, prices for telecommunication services as a whole, as distinct from simple calls, are high in Germany, but cheap in Ireland and Portugal – a situation which Ireland has attempted to employ to attract foreign, computer-based, data-processing and financial services (Howells 1990).

But whatever the problems in western Europe, the situation in eastern Europe is much worse. As with the speed of trains and the quality of air services and roads, the further east and south one goes, the less frequent and the poorer do modern systems of communication become. Whereas there were more than five hundred telephones per thousand people in most of the countries of northwest Europe in the 1980s, the number in Czechoslovakia and East Germany was about two hundred, and in Poland and the Soviet Union one hundred (Figure IV.6). What is more, only limited subscriber trunk dialling

Security

The return to capital also depends upon social stability and external security; and areas in which one or both of these are threatened will be unattractive to most forms of business. Since the end of the Second World War, Europe,

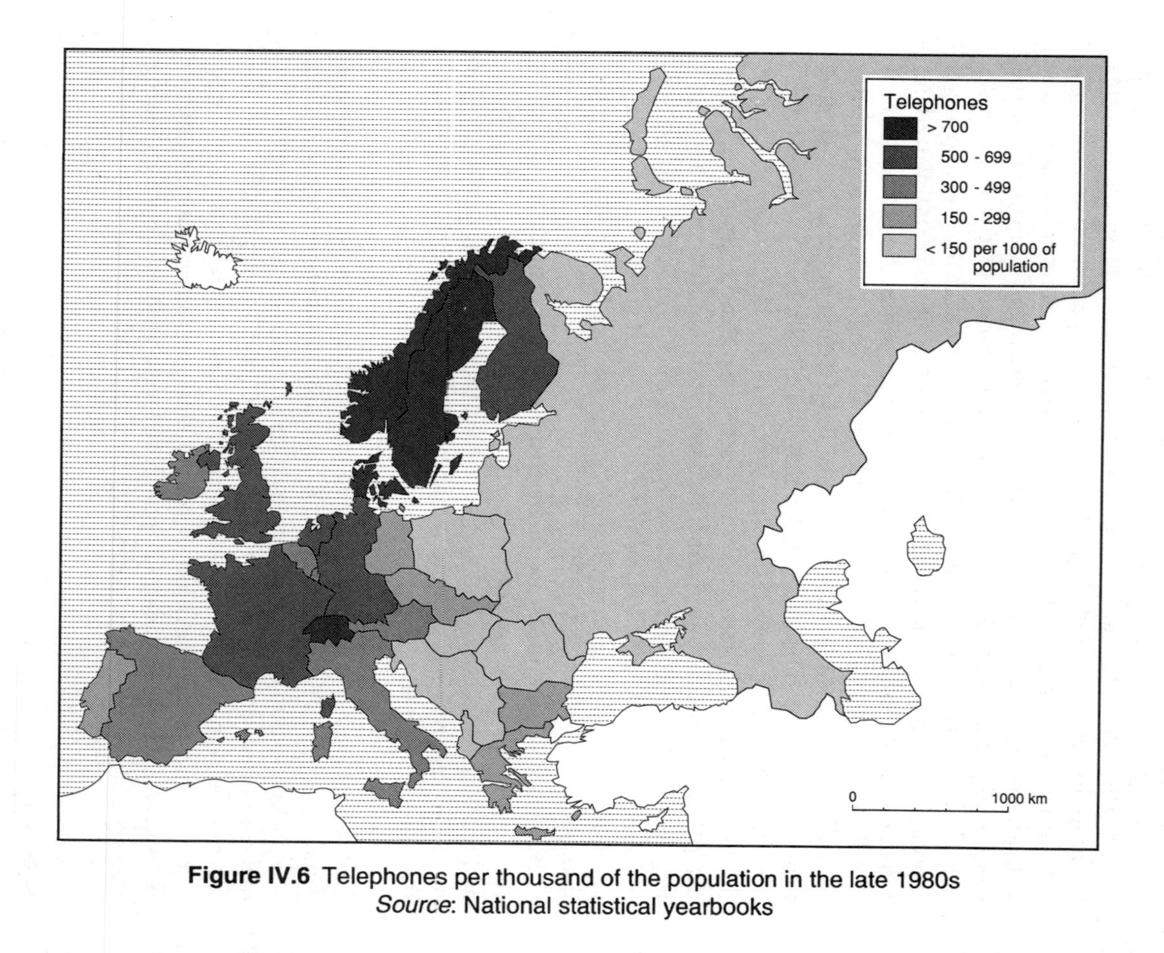

Figure IV.6 Telephones per thousand of the population in the late 1980s
Source: National statistical yearbooks

though divided into two camps, has offered a very stable environment, in which investors have been able to act with a considerable degree of confidence. However, the political changes of 1989–91 have not only removed the Iron Curtain, thus redefining the locations of all parts of the continent, but have also allowed many local conflicts to develop, and provided a context in which others may appear in the future.

The fall of the Berlin Wall and the Iron Curtain, the collapse of the Soviet Union, and the end of the Cold War, would appear to have altered the relative, as distinct from the absolute, location of several groups of places in Europe. Prior to these changes, the continent contained not one space economy, but two, each of which was focused upon its own heartland. Strategic industries, especially in eastern Europe, were located well away from the border between east and west; and transport links were designed in part to provide for access to, but not across, it. Much land at or near the border was taken over for military purposes, and large areas on either side of it were condemned to the status of the periphery. Others, however, benefited from their border status. In particular, ports with access to warm water, or which controlled the entrances to those water bodies which formed part of the Iron Curtain – the Baltic, Mediterranean and Black Seas – or from which the North Atlantic could be controlled, acquired great strategic importance, and were used as military bases. The White Sea and Kola peninsula, Kaliningrad, and the Crimean ports were all intensively developed for military purposes, just as the Clyde and Gibraltar were. But the European civil war is now over. Transport links across the former Iron Curtain in central Europe are being improved. Much military land is being released, and garrisons and naval bases, from Poland to the Atlantic, are being closed. More closures will follow as disarmament continues, and many future investment decisions will place a premium upon access to the other half of Europe, rather than on being at a safe distance from it. Interest in Arctic sea routes may wane (Samoteikin 1987). The defence ministries of Europe must now weigh the declining risks facing them within the

processes of economic interchange were being disrupted in some regions; and the affected areas had either ceased to be a part of the space economy or their importance within it was being sharply reduced as population fled and buildings and equipment were destroyed. Many of these disputes concern ethnic minorities, though that is not to say that the presence of such minorities in a country automatically leads to such problems, as Switzerland demonstrates.

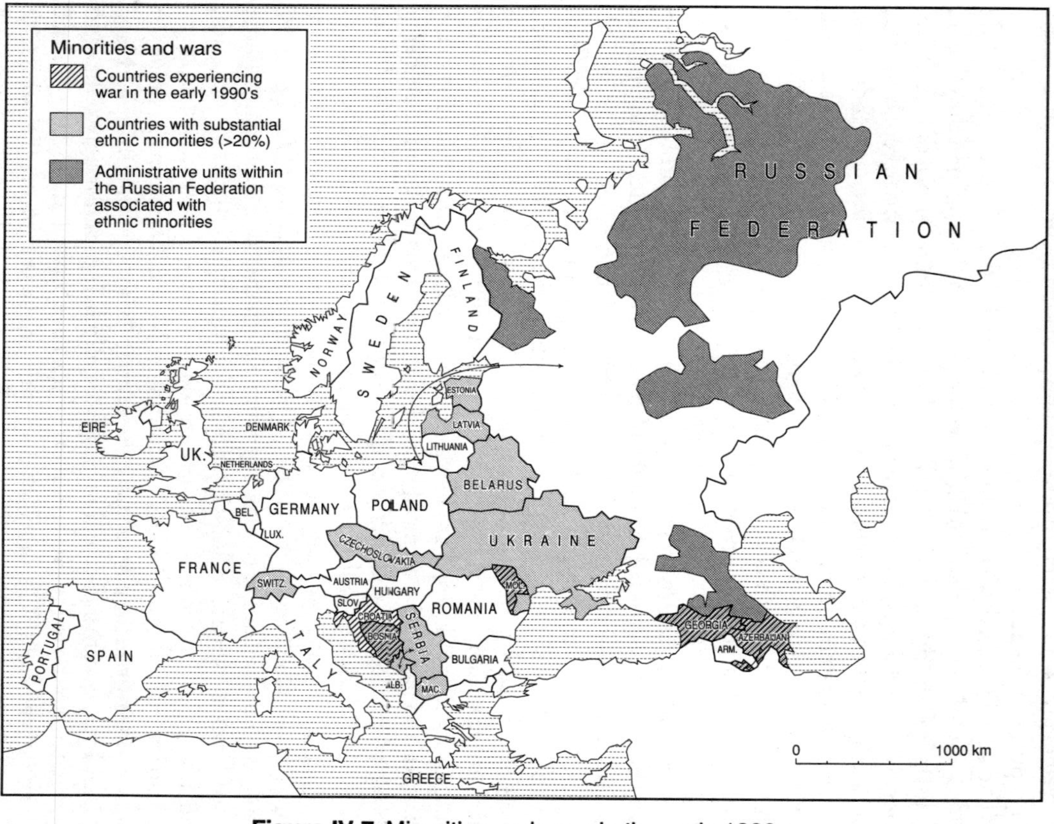

Figure IV.7 Minorities and wars in the early 1990s

The Balkans and Caucasus were the most seriously affected in the early 1990s, though some others, such as the Basque country of Spain and Northern Ireland, were suffering from occasional terrorism. Moreover, there is a threat of serious instability in the Russian Federation, where thirty-one ethnic minorities have long been accorded the form, if not the fact, of independent control of some of their activities through the Soviet administrative structure of Autonomous Republics, Oblasts or Okrugs. In so far as Russia has already agreed to grant its ethnic Germans the right to re-establish an autonomous region on the Volga, and withdrawn from what was the Chechen Autonomous Republic, following its declaration of independence, the principle of self-determination has been conceded; and the Ukraine has promised the Crimea substantial control over its own development. What is more, there are large Russian minorities in many of the former republics of the Soviet Union, and especially Estonia, Latvia and the Ukraine, which may give rise to political tensions there.

Nor should it be forgotten that there are also groups whose wish, though it be for political union such as that which occurred between East and West Germany in 1990, may also prove to be disruptive. Moldova may be reunited with Romania, and Kosovo may wish to join Albania, but such unions are likely to be disputed. Furthermore, if they should be achieved, they may set off requests for a variety of other boundary changes to bring, say, the Magyars in Slovakia, Transylvania and the Vojvodina within Hungary, provoking yet more conflicts which would inevitably militate against any form of cooperation between neighbouring states.

Conclusion

This section has given some details of a few of the resources, both natural and human, of the various parts of Europe: resources which will inevitably form the

technology of production – with its overtones of scales of enterprise, thresholds of demand, functional regions and periodicities of change – and the institutional arrangements which nations make to protect their economic interests. It is to that future geography that we must now progress.

Further reading

Some indication of the likely distribution of oil reserves in Europe is given in *Oilfields of the world* (1984) by Tiratsoo.

Considerable detail has been given about the problems of environmental degradation in Czechoslovakia by Carter (1985), in Poland by Kramer (1987), and in the Soviet Union by Komarov (1980) and Singleton (1987). Marples' (1991) *Ukraine under Perestroika: Ecology, economy and the worker's revolt* describes how some of the ecological problems facing that country, especially those associated with the Chernobyl accident and the supply of water for irrigation and industry, gradually became known under *perestroika*.

Ahnström (1990) gives an account of the evolution of the working population in western Europe since the 1950s.

Advances in telecommunications and their impact upon the economic geography of western Europe are considered by Hall and Preston (1988) in *The Carrier Wave: New information technology and the geography of innovation, 1846–2003.*

Section V
Common European home?

So, what will happen now? The Iron Curtain has fallen. The West has won the war of 'peaceful coexistence' which the Soviet leader of the 1950s and 1960s, Khrushchev, declared. East Germany has been swallowed by West Germany. Comecon has been wound up; and the eastern European countries, including the former Soviet republics, have declared themselves in favour of the market and closer links with the European Community. The immediate prospect facing them is of economic restructuring and unemployment. Their hope is for rapid growth thereafter. EFTA countries – inhibited in the past by the political overtones of the Common Market from applying for full membership of it – are now doing so; and the former president of the Soviet Union, Gorbachev, has spoken of the establishment of a 'common European home'. More specifically, the future economic geography of Europe may be affected by all of the following:

texts about the economic geography of the continent which were reviewed in Section I; and is one which requires an examination of the working of the space economy of Europe as a whole, rather than of the individual countries or blocs within it. Economic integration, if it should occur, may lead to the sort of changes which were set out in the models described in Section II. But the space economy of an integrated Europe will also inevitably be conditioned by trends in industries such as those which were outlined in Section III, by the latest innovations, and by the map of economic rents. So, what will happen now? This section will assess the likelihood that the countries of Europe will agree to establish free markets at home, and closer integration abroad; the effect of such changes upon the distribution of those industries which were discussed in Section III; and the broad form of the space economy at the end of the expansionary phase of a fifth Kondratiev, in, say, 2020.

Institutional change

In spite of the overwhelming desire among the states of western Europe after 1945 to put an end to wars between them, and the belief that this might best be achieved by binding their economies together, progress towards that target has been slow. Though European integration has been discussed for more than forty years, the Community has yet to take the critical step of instituting a single currency; and, even if some members do so by the end of the century, it is unlikely that all will be able, or willing, to bring their economies up to the standards of the strongest, and thus be able to participate. Nor may they be able to do so thereafter, unless strong economic growth leads to convergence similar to that which occurred in western Europe during the Long Boom. Meanwhile, although it may be relatively easy for the EFTA countries, which already have very close economic ties with the Community, to join it, probably in the late 1990s, the changes that the former command economies of eastern Europe will be obliged to make will be much greater.

Furthermore, although many governments in the east were talking about European integration in the early 1990s, several were practising the opposite. The former Soviet republics may eventually seek links with the Community; but the establishment of separate currencies, and the substitution of intra- for inter-republican trade, was fragmenting the space economy of eastern Europe, rather than binding it together. The strengthening of nationalist sentiment there is likely to inhibit the movement of labour; and territorial disputes, and especially violence, between some countries will deter investors. Nor has the full unravelling of the various ethnic groups within the former Soviet republics been completed; and in such an unravelling the autonomous administrative regions of various types may also try to assert control over their economic relations with the rest of the world, ignoring, where they wish, their traditional trading links with what was the Soviet Union. Meanwhile, Czechoslovakia has been divided into two independent, but loosely federated, states; and a settlement has yet to be reached in Yugoslavia. Members of the erstwhile trading group, Comecon, are less constrained to maintain their links with each other than hitherto. There will be much 'growing apart' in eastern Europe during the 1990s, though this does not mean that there can be no new, simultaneous 'coming together' between the states of the area and those of western Europe.

It is unlikely, however, that this will be achieved quickly. Siebert (1991, p. 67) suggests that three groups of reforms – creating a new institutional infrastructure, achieving monetary stability, and adjusting the economy thereafter – will be necessary before the countries of eastern Europe can enter the Community. More particularly, commodity and factor markets must be freed, state aids to industry abolished, currency convertibility and budgetary and fiscal stability achieved, the appropriate legal framework established, and the consequential adjustments to the structure and activities of enterprises carried out, including the privatisation of most of them. What is more, those who have run the centrally-planned economies, and who have little interest in the introduction of market disciplines or ability to exploit the opportunities which they offer, must be retrained or replaced. This will take many years, and the opening of the eastern economies to those of the west can only be achieved gradually, as they occur. Nevertheless, they may be a prerequisite of large-scale foreign direct investment (Inotai 1991).

Recent experience in East Germany indicates the scale of the task. The instantaneous achievement there in 1990 of the first two of Siebert's changes, albeit involving a highly damaging three- to four-fold revaluation of the East German Mark, drove unemployment up to levels not seen since the Great Depression. The Treuhand, the organisation charged with the privatisation of several thousand publicly-owned enterprises, has found it necessary to close many of them, and to reduce employment substantially in most of the others, in order to make them sufficiently productive to attract buyers; and the former Federal Republic has been obliged to make huge transfer payments to East Germans, not least to persuade them not to move to West Germany. Siebert (p. 68) claims that:

> In the medium term of four to five years and especially in the longer run German economic integration will be [illegible]

[illegible] received assistance on the same scale, or is likely to do so. Given that East Germany was considered to be the most efficient of the centrally-planned economies, it follows that the levels of investment in infrastructure and labour skills, and the rationalisation of enterprises, which will be required in the other countries of eastern Europe will probably be even greater. These tasks will take many years; and it is very unlikely that any other eastern European country will

BOX 4

Germany

Three of the most important countries of Europe have recently re-emerged after periods in which they have been either divided or submerged in larger states. Each is likely to play a major role in the development of the European space economy in future.

The union of the German Democratic and Federal republics in 1990 brought together the largest economy in western Europe, with a population of 61,000,000, and that of the most developed in the eastern part of the continent, with 16,000,000 people, to create the most populous country in Europe apart from the Russian Federation. The Germany which thus emerged was smaller than that which had entered the Second World War, having lost Silesia, eastern Pomerania and east Prussia to Poland and the Soviet Union in 1945, and was by no means one of the most extensive states in Europe. However, it has by far the largest GNP, and one of the highest GNPs per capita in Europe. It also lies at the intersection of two of the major routeways across the continent – those of the Rhine valley, which links northern Italy, the Rhone valley, the Alpine countries and the Danube basin with the Low Countries and North Atlantic, and of the Hellweg, which runs from northern France to Upper Saxony, Silesia and the Ukraine. If any country can be said to form the core of the European space economy, it is Germany.

The West German space economy is articulated around a series of large cities and agglomerations. The most populous of these is the Ruhr, which is the location of much of the German coal, steel, heavy engineering and chemical industries. Others include Berlin, Cologne, Frankfurt, Hamburg and Munich. While the old industrial agglomerations of the Ruhr, Saar and Wuppertal have struggled during the declining phase of the Fourth Kondratiev to maintain levels of employment and to attract service industries in sufficient numbers to offset the decline in mining and manufacturing, the southern cities have been particularly successful in building up research and development and advanced forms of manufacturing since 1945. Eastern areas of the former Federal Republic, in contrast, have suffered from their peripheral location during the period of communist government in Czechoslovakia and East Germany.

The immediate consequences of integration for East Germany were disastrous. West German products replaced many of those made locally; trade links with the former members of Comecon were disrupted; many factories were closed; large collective farms had difficulty in disposing of their goods; and unemployment rose sharply. The consequences for West Germany were more mixed. Producers in the west gained a new market, and investors were able to acquire assets cheaply through the privatisation process. However, the German government was obliged not only to assist the unemployed in the east on a massive scale, but also to divert much investment to the Russian Federation in order to ensure the removal of Russian troops from East Germany and persuade the ethnic Germans in Russia, most of whom do not speak German but have a right to settle in Germany, to remain there.

There will also be longer-term consequences. Erstwhile frontier zones within Germany, and between Germany, Czechoslovakia and Poland will cease to be as isolated as before. On the other hand, East Germany will continue to face problems of adjustment, not least in the polluted industrial areas of Upper Saxony. Dresden, which was once the equivalent of Frankfurt and Munich, but was largely destroyed during the Second World War, has still to be fully rebuilt. But it is the future of Berlin which will be of particular interest. During the nineteenth century, as the capital of one of Europe's strongest states, it developed as a centre of government, transport, financial and cultural services, and of manufacturing. Much of this has been undermined, however, by the post-war division of the city, the isolation of West Berlin behind the Wall – a city without a hinterland – and the neglect of East Berlin; and some of these functions have been taken over by other cities in West Germany. Once Berlin resumes its capital role, it may become the centre for these activities again, and may be seen as a suitable location for institutions having links with eastern Europe. Alternatively, it may not.

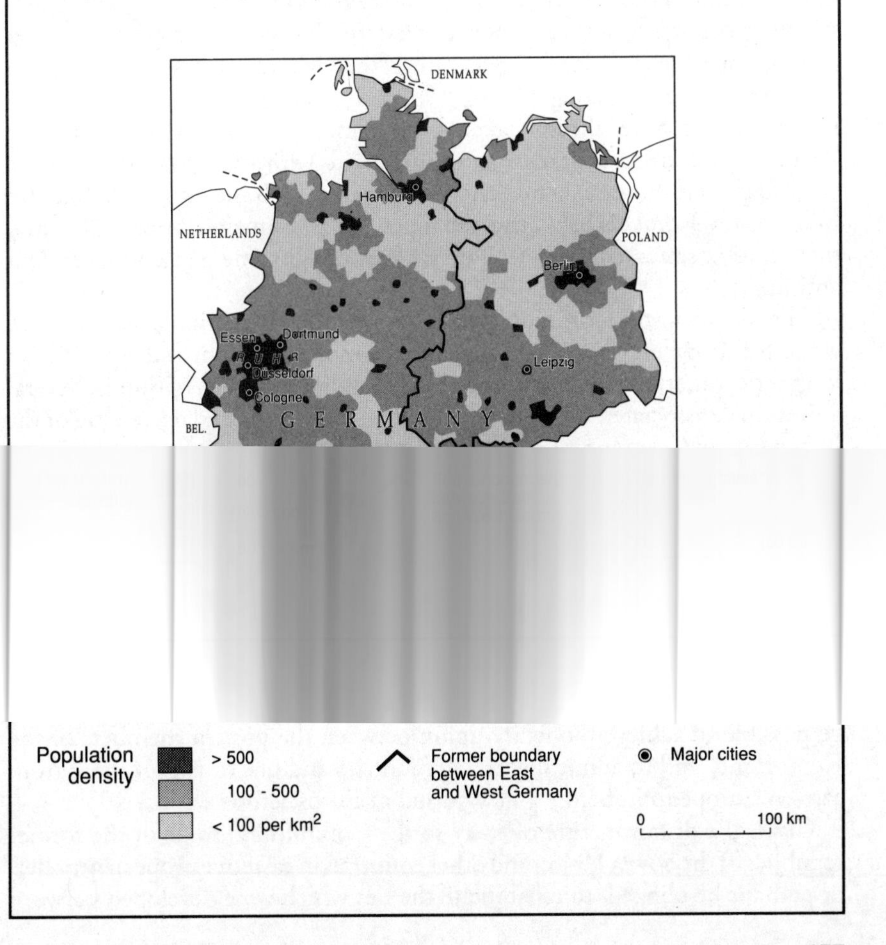

be able to participate in a truly common market, let alone a monetary union, with western Europe until well after the turn of the century. Meanwhile, if unemployment and other hardships arising out of restructuring should breed social unrest and political extremism – and the inter-war years show that this is very likely – progress towards both reform and integration may be delayed or reversed.

Early indications suggest that Hungary may be best placed to achieve the transition to the free market and integration with western Europe, followed by the Czech lands. The country has a longer history of experimenting with economic reform than any other in eastern Europe, stretching back to 1968; it was the target for no less than one-third of the western investment projects registered in eastern Europe in 1991; and by 1991 Germany had replaced the Soviet Union as its chief trading partner. Czechoslovakia has also benefited from a high level of western investment and increasing trade, especially with Germany, in the early 1990s. Both countries have technical norms which are rather similar to those of Germany, traditional economic links with German-speaking countries, and are closer to western Europe than any of the other eastern states except Poland. Furthermore, their labour is far cheaper than that in West Germany (Clough 1991, 1992). Several of the major western car manufacturers have already taken over plants in these countries, and in Poland, and set up factories to manufacture parts, with a view to supplying both local and west European markets from them (Dobosiewicz 1992, 72–6). Bulgaria and Romania have attracted much less investment (Inotai 1991); and the successor states to the Soviet Union have only just emerged as independent entities.

The history of the Community suggests that the integration of eastern with western Europe may be closely related to economic growth, and especially to long-term variations, such as those of the Kondratiev Cycle, within it. Several writers have associated the relatively rapid establishment and deepening of the links between Community members, culminating in the admission of Britain, Denmark and Ireland in 1973, with the growing prosperity in western Europe during the Long Boom. They have contrasted that with what has been called the Eurosclerosis of the period between then and the mid-1980s, and have suggested that there may be a connection between new moves towards both the deepening and widening of the Community and the renewal of economic growth of the late 1980s (Siebert 1991, Tsoukalis 1991). If such a pattern were to be repeated, with a twenty- to thirty-year period of faster growth, ending at some time around 2020, followed by one of economic difficulty, it might only be possible to achieve monetary union between the present members of the Community and to admit the EFTA countries and one or two of those from eastern Europe to it, before a new period of Eurosclerosis set in.

Given the distant nature of entry to the Community, some of the former republics of the Soviet Union and other countries in eastern Europe may prefer, or perhaps be obliged, to rehabilitate the ties which were developed between them under Russian hegemony. McAuley (1991) has provided a sobering analysis of the situation facing Lithuania, in which he concludes that the supply-side shock to that country's economy from its separation from the rest of what was the Soviet Union will probably cause a fall in the standard of living four times that experienced by Britain after the oil price rises of 1973 and 1979. Moreover, he points out that the prospects for the country from any closer integration with western Europe are bleak. There are few activities in which it enjoys a comparative advantage, and little local capital to finance the necessary economic restructuring and improvement in productivity. Nor is there any reason for believing that foreign capital will find Lithuania more attractive than other peripheral areas, such as Portugal or Third World countries, as a site for manufacturing unless it offers access to some larger market, such as a revived rouble zone which includes the Russian Federation. Even so, Lithuania must compete with Belarus, Estonia, Georgia, Latvia, and other newly-independent states which find themselves in similar circumstances. Governments in eastern Europe may, therefore, have little alternative but to encourage both newly-privatised enterprises and any which remain in state ownership to trade with those which are likely to have similar technical standards, working practices and levels of productivity; that is, with those elsewhere in the region, rather than opening their markets to western producers.

Any eventual economic revival of the Russian Federation may also encourage such states to rehabilitate their former links. Whatever further fragmentation occurs along ethnic lines in that country (see Box 5), it is likely that the Federation will remain the largest and most populous country on the continent, and the one with the most natural resources. As such, it will be attractive to western investors, including multinational companies, and may benefit from substantial inflows of both money and expertise, just as Tsarist Russia did in the late nineteenth century. Developments of this sort would enable the country to treat with western Europe from a position of strength, and also to influence [illegible]

groups of countries – the Commonwealth of Independent States, the Baltic republics, the post-communist governments of Czechoslovakia, Hungary and Poland, and the Black Sea countries, amongst others – had all indicated interest in new economic cooperation, at least with others in the same group, within a short time of the collapse of Comecon and the Soviet Union. Merritt (1991, pp. 93–113) has suggested that they should begin by establishing an eastern

European payments union, similar to that which provided the foundation for the regeneration of trade in western Europe in the 1950s.

But it is to be hoped that eastern Europe will not be forced back into the economic isolation of the communist period, for there seems to be little doubt that the integration of eastern with western Europe could prove to be a positive supply-side shock of very great proportions to the continent as a whole. If the economic growth associated with the establishment of the Single Market within the Community does indeed increase its GDP by between 4.25 and 6.5 per cent (Cecchini 1988), or by even more (Baldwin 1989), that associated with the linking of eastern and western Europe has the potential to be much larger. Initially, with productivity running much below that in western Europe and environmental damage much greater, many activities in the east will prove to be uncompetitive; and economic activity will fall as some are closed. There are reasons, however, for believing that growth thereafter could be rapid. Siebert (1991, pp. 68–80) suggests that the potential for increased specialisation and trade by them is great. He argues that, because much of the capital stock in eastern Europe is obsolete, or of poor quality, or in the wrong industries, investment will be required on a large scale; that the market will offer greatly enhanced incentives to entrepreneurs and labour to raise efficiency and productivity; and that, because the workforce is highly educated and skilled, it will be able to respond to these incentives. He foresees that capital will be attracted from the west, once problems to do with the ownership of property and the convertibility of the currencies have been solved, while cheap labour may migrate into western Europe and hold down wage rates there. In a word, Europe's inequalities could spark the upturn of the fifth Kondratiev.

The composition and arrangement of the European space economy will also depend upon the way in which the links between the continent and the rest of the world develop. Any closer integration within Europe will be likely to increase the movement of goods, services, capital and labour within the continent; and – to the extent that both eastern and western Europe find superior substitutes within the continent for non-European imports – that integration is likely to lead to the expansion of intra-European trade at the expense of that with other continents. That does not guarantee, however, that the barriers which Europe has placed in the way of imports from the rest of the world will be removed. Even if there are continuing attempts under GATT to relax the restraints on trade, it is likely that any dismantling of agricultural protection, or of non-tariff barriers on manufactured goods from the Third World, will be slow and much disputed within Europe. Nor is it likely that large-scale immigration will be permitted into western Europe, either from the east of the continent or further afield. Movements of capital, in contrast, are likely to become increasingly independent of European authorities as central planning in eastern Europe is replaced by the market, and as companies in western Europe and elsewhere seek to enlarge their market shares.

Perhaps the two most immediate tests of the willingness of the European countries to extend their economic integration more widely will be those of Turkey, which has long sought entry to the Community, and of the former Soviet republics of central Asia. Turkey, a large and populous country with a standard of living which was only half of that of the poorest member of the Community, and a poor record on human rights, has been an associate of the Community since 1963, but was refused entry in 1990. The central Asian republics, in contrast, have shown every intention of distancing themselves from Europe. Since the collapse of the Soviet Union, they have been seeking links with those neighbours with whom they have linguistic and religious connections, and especially Iran, Pakistan and Turkey. Nevertheless, they were major suppliers of fuels to the Soviet Union, and their development may depend in large part upon continued sales in European markets.

All this suggests that the space economy of Europe may be somewhat more closely integrated by 2020 than it was in the early 1990s. The EFTA countries, the Czech lands, Hungary and Poland, but not Slovakia, may have joined the Community; and most, but not all, members may be operating through a common currency. The economies of some members, such as Greece, Poland and Portugal, may not, however, have developed sufficiently to allow them to participate in these more advanced stages. Russia, the Ukraine and most of the other countries in eastern Europe will probably have entered into free-trade agreements with the Community and each other, covering both goods and services, though not, perhaps, agricultural products. Movements of labour between the Community and the other countries of Europe will probably also be somewhat easier than in the early 1990s, but are unlikely to be entirely unrestricted. Capital markets, in contrast, will be highly integrated. We may conclude that, notwithstanding the revolutions which have already occurred in eastern Europe, the economies of the continent will not be fully integrated by the year 2020. There will be no common European home.

Agriculture

By the late 1980s, agricultural output in Europe as a whole was almost in balance with demand, for, although there were large deficits in temperate crops, meat and dairy products in eastern Europe, there were surpluses of these products in the western countries. It is unlikely that the demand for farm goods will increase significantly up to the year 2020. Population, as a whole, will grow very slowly; current levels of nutrition are more than adequate; and the income elasticity of demand for food is low (Alexandratos 1990). Rising incomes in eastern Europe may lead to a demand for higher-quality and more processed food; but any dietary movement away from alcohol, fats and meat, of the sort which has already occurred in parts of northwest Europe, will reduce the demand for land in pastoral areas, and that given over to fodder crops and viticulture.

During the Fourth Wave, agriculture in much of Europe suffered from relatively low levels of return, substituted capital for labour, and was restructured into large-scale or intensive forms of production. Improvements in productivity followed, especially in western Europe, where the output of many crops and animal products rose much faster than demand. Many of these trends seem likely to continue. In particular, there are great opportunities for intensification, using present methods of production, in many parts of the continent; and biotechnology will probably permit further development through the introduction of drought-resistant and salt-tolerant strains, expansion of soil-less cultivation, and improvements in the quality, yield and variety of crops. But, if such changes occur, and if agricultural markets throughout the continent become more open, competitive pressures upon farmers will increase, less land will be required for farming, and the retreat from the hills and the cooler lands will continue.

However, the speed and extent to which these changes occur will be closely connected with those in the institutional framework of the industry, especially as they affect the prices of farm products. During the period of communist rule in eastern Europe, prices were held down; both the quantity and quality of the food supplied by the public sector were inadequate; imports, especially of fodder crops, rose; and sales from private plots thrived. But, in the absence of accurate price signals, investment in agriculture did not always go to the most appropriate areas. Free-market prices are likely to be higher than those which have been received by farmers in the recent past, and to encourage them to intensify those activities in which profits can be earned. But the full effect of such a change is unlikely to occur unless the collective and state farms are privatised, or transformed into genuine cooperatives in which members have a real incentive to respond to market signals. Many of the present farms may be too large to be worked efficiently and may need to be broken up, with many of their subsidiary activities, which are often not directly connected with agriculture, hived off. However, the equipment and infrastructure of agriculture has been constructed in line with the present, very large, scale of operations; senior personnel may have to be retrained or replaced; and the tradition of collective social organisation, which is particularly strong in many of the villages of the former Soviet Union, will need to be modified substantially if these changes are to be effective. Moreover, improvements are necessary in the transport and processing of farm products, if the large-scale waste which occurred under central planning is to be eliminated. It may be many years before the institutional structure of the industry, and those of its suppliers and markets, can be reformed to the point at which a free market can operate smoothly in much of eastern Europe.

Once such reforms are achieved, the potential for increases in output is great. Breburda (1990) reports that research farms have demonstrated that yields of grain, sugar beet and sunflowers from the loess soils of Moldova, Russia and the Ukraine could be raised by between one-and-a-half and three times, though he goes on to warn that methods of land improvement and cultivation, as well as the types of crop which are grown, need to be fitted much more closely than in the past to the characteristics of soils in each locality. Similarly, the World Bank (1990, p.21) has estimated that an increase of between fifteen and twenty per cent in the yields of the major cereals, a twenty per cent increase in potatoes, and a ten per cent increase in sugar beet should be possible within a few years in Poland. However, increases in output in these areas would probably reduce prices to farmers elsewhere in the same countries, thus leading to a decline in the intensity of land use in peripheral regions, and its abandonment in those which were thus rendered sub-marginal. Alternatively, export markets might be sought in western Europe, but it is doubtful whether any trade would be permitted which would reduce the prices, or undermine agriculture in peripheral areas there. The experience of East Germany is instructive in this regard. It was suggested in 1991 that output could increase by between twenty and thirty per cent if West German methods were employed, and that the country could be transformed from being a net grain importer to a major exporter within two or three years. However, the application of the Community's Agricultural Policy entailed an immediate fall of a fifth in milk production, a culling of a quarter of the dairy herd, and the set-aside of six per cent of the [illegible]

fodder crops will rise, thus encouraging domestic production; and, if Community barriers to Polish exports are removed, and the agricultural processing industry is modernised, Polish farmers should be able to compete with those in western Europe in the production of most temperate crops. It is a measure of the opportunities which are available to agriculture in Poland that the World Bank foresaw in 1990 that the country would be able to supply most domestic needs at prices well below those facing people within the Community, and also export speciality crops on a large scale without the need for subsidy. Such developments would encourage farm amalgamation, land consolidation, and investment. They will be impeded, however, unless many of the part-time and elderly farmers leave the industry, and the farm-supply and food-processing monopolies are broken up and privatised. The World Bank was of the view that substantial structural change would be unlikely before the later 1990s (World Bank 1990, pp. 6–27).

Conversely, in western Europe, the Community's Common Agricultural Policy, and similar forms of support in the EFTA countries, have raised farm incomes far above the levels which would have existed if the region had been integrated with world agricultural markets, and have encouraged the intensification of land use in many areas. Nevertheless, this support has not been sufficient to prevent the continued decline in employment, or the abandonment or transfer of some of the poorest farmland to other uses. There have been widespread calls for a reduction in the level of price support and the opening of western European markets to imports from elsewhere, both of which would have considerable effects upon the pattern of agriculture. The Swedish government began to reduce its support for agriculture in 1990; by 1995 it intends to abolish price supports, reduce subsidies, and target the remaining help to the north of the country, where, it is freely admitted, most farming would otherwise be abandoned. It is encouraging farmers to take up forestry or to devote land to nature conservation, and anticipates that five per cent of the country's farmland will be transferred to these activities (Sweden 1990). In Finland, the government fears that entry to the Community will lead to a fall of a third in farm output and a quarter in employment, once national levels of agricultural support and aid for sparsely populated areas are reduced to Community levels (Marshall 1992). However, it is unlikely that change in western Europe as a whole will be rapid. Concerns about the incomes of farmers, the effect of further agricultural decline on peripheral and relatively poor communities, and the long-term security of food supplies, are all likely to limit the pace of reform; and the pattern of farming in Europe is unlikely to come into line with that of fertility. Rather, proposals of the sort made by the Community in the early 1990s are likely to be preferred. Under these, farmers would be paid to set aside land, irrespective of its quality or the efficiency of the enterprises to which it belonged, while the Community will continue to protect its markets from the farm products of eastern Europe and elsewhere. Nor is it probable that, as the demand for farmland falls, the elaborate systems of planning, which have been adopted in many countries with a view to protecting it from development, and which have distorted the allocation of land among competing uses, will be relaxed.

Energy

European demands for energy grew very substantially during the Fourth Kondratiev, especially during the Long Boom; new fuels were brought into use; and new sources on the periphery of the European space economy were exploited. It is highly unlikely that there will be an equivalent increase in demand during the period up to 2020; but that is not to say that there will not be further shifts between fuels, and in the spatial arrangement of both the demand for and supply of energy.

The demand for energy in Europe as a whole may be no higher in 2020 than it was in the late 1980s. That in eastern Europe, which has fallen since the late 1980s, is likely to decline still further during the 1990s. The initial fall was caused by the disruption of trade, following the collapse of Comecon and the Soviet Union; and further falls are likely as the sharp adjustment of prices up to world levels discourages waste, and the economies of the region are restructured, with a shift away from heavy industry and into services. Furthermore, any worldwide economic growth in the expansionary phase of a fifth Kondratiev which leads to a general increase in the demand for fuels, and thus in energy prices, will encourage greater efficiency in their use throughout the continent.

The future for coal, in particular, seems to be problematic. The introduction of market prices in eastern Europe is likely to cut demand, the abolition of subsidies and other forms of protection in western Europe will force the closure of many pits, and pressures throughout the continent for reductions in the emission of pollutants from power stations will encourage generating companies to seek other fuels. Cecchini (1988, p. 20) has suggested that, once a truly Single Market is established in energy inside the Community, the price of coal in Germany could fall by fifty per cent, and that in Britain by twenty-five per

[illegible]

find markets; there may be no [illegible]
2020.

Some pits are also likely to be closed in eastern Europe, especially if there is little growth in the overall demand for energy there. Those in the Ukraine which have been mining thin seams at great depths may be particularly vulnerable. Opencast mining, in contrast, is likely to continue to be a major source of fuel, especially in southwest Siberia and north Kazakhstan. Marples

(1991, pp. 175–200) reports extensive discussions within the Soviet Union during the late 1980s about the declining production and high costs of coal from the Donbas in comparison with that from Karaganda and the Kuzbas, and proposals to double the output in the Kuzbas and send large quantities of coking coal to the Ukraine by rail. Whether, following economic reform, this will prove to be either necessary or profitable is doubtful; and, following the break-up of the Soviet Union, that from Karaganda will be an international movement – from Kazakhstan. However, it may be more feasible to use even larger quantities of coal from Ekibastuz, Karaganda and the Kuzbas than at present to generate electricity which can be sent to other parts of eastern Europe through the existing grid. It would also be possible to link the electricity grids of eastern and western Europe – which are already connected through what was East Germany and Finland – more closely, so that power could flow between the various time zones of the continent more freely than at present. Thus, Poland might be able to buy Russian electricity, while Polish coal-fired stations simultaneously provide some of the electricity which is presently generated by those in Germany and by nuclear stations in France, but only if governments feel able to allow the establishment of a truly free energy market.

The market for oil and gas in Europe is also likely to change markedly. Prices in western Europe will probably rise from the low levels of the late 1980s, not least because 'carbon taxes' may be imposed on all fossil fuels in an attempt to restrain their use, and because of the sharp fall which has occurred in the output of oil and gas in Russia since the late 1980s. Meanwhile, economic reform in eastern Europe has already led to sharp increases in the prices of oil and gas there, and more may follow. On the other hand, there will probably be considerable extra demands for oil for transport and gas for electricity generation. Altogether, the consumption of both oil and gas in Europe will probably continue to increase up to 2020, though that growth may well be much slower than in the 1950s and 1960s. Much of that increase may have to be met from Russia, and in particular from the Caspian Sea basin, the Volga and western Siberia, where there is a good chance that large deposits which can be easily exploited remain to be found; and western Europe may be increasingly supplied by pipeline from these areas by 2020. Concern has been expressed about the future of Russian supplies, not so much in terms of the exhaustion of reserves, but because the low quality of extraction technology is leaving substantial quantities below ground, and wasting much that is raised through leakage. However, it is likely that rising prices will encourage western companies to undertake joint operations with the Russians, using better technology, the exploitation of smaller deposits, and the search for new ones.

Other fuels are likely to be of much less significance. Several nuclear stations in eastern Europe have been closed since the Chernobyl accident; more closures are planned; and almost all of those in existence in the late 1980s in Europe will have reached the end of their lives by 2020. Very few new stations were being built in the early 1990s, and it is unlikely that this situation will change unless the safety of stations and the problems of nuclear-waste disposal can be solved. Some of the burning of lignite in East Germany, which provided most of its energy, but also caused much atmospheric pollution, is to be replaced by gas from West Germany (Nello 1991, p. 255). Ambitious schemes for diverting water from northerly-flowing rivers in Russia to the south of the country have been abandoned, and fears are being expressed about the effect of yet more hydro-electric projects upon the Alps. New sources of electricity, from solar, wind and wave power and nuclear fusion, all of which have been the subjects of much experimentation in the recent past, may be developed further. More use is likely to be made locally of all three of the sources of renewable energy; but none is likely to become capable of yielding large and controlled quantities of electricity at prices which are competitive with that generated from opencast coal or gas in the period up to 2020, while the technical problems associated with fusion are unlikely to be solved in time for it to be able to be brought into widespread use by that date.

Mellor and Smith, writing in 1979 (pp. 161–2), summarised the energy supply situation in Europe as follows:

> Siberia has no doubt a most significant role to play in Europe – both East and West – as a source of energy, whether for oil or gas, or also electricity from water, thermal or nuclear generators. Energy supplies will become increasingly critical in Europe around the end of the present century and local resources puny compared with the Siberian potential. The large diameter pipeline or the super-high tension transmission line could play as vital a role in European energy supply in the year 2000 and beyond as the mammoth tanker does in the 1970s. The development of these Eurasian energy and raw material supplies will depend upon financial and technical wealth ... it may rest upon aid from advanced Western economies with wealth and know-how.

Notwithstanding the political and economic changes since then, only the [illegible] seem to have been invalidated.

[illegible]

if output were to be increased. Meanwhile, [illegible] in western Siberia and northern Kazakhstan is unlikely to be accompanied by the creation of large settlements, for modern extraction tends to be a capital- rather than a labour-intensive activity; and, as the demand for energy is increasingly met by oil, gas and electricity, proximity to sources of fuel will become less important in industrial location decisions.

BOX 5

The Russian Federation

Three of the most important countries of Europe have recently re-emerged after periods in which they have been either divided or submerged in larger states. Each is likely to play a major role in the development of the European space economy in future.

The Russian Federation is the largest country in Europe. Much of it lies beyond the Ural mountains in Asia, but, as was argued in Section I, those parts of southwestern Siberia which are relatively densely populated are intimately connected with areas west of the Urals, and thus form part of the European space economy. That economy covers only about four million square kilometres, or less than a quarter of the country; but it is still half of the total for Europe. Russia is also the most populous country on the continent, with about 130,000,000 people living within the boundaries of the European space economy, though at one of the lowest average densities, of about thirty per square kilometre.

The Russian Federation became an independent country on the break-up of the Soviet Union in 1991; and its boundaries are not very different from those of Russia in about 1650, before its defeat of the Swedes, partition of Poland, and conquest of the Ukraine and central Asia. Nevertheless, it is neither ethnically homogeneous, nor everywhere stable. As its name indicates, it is made up of a number of administrative areas, some of which are associated with non-Russian peoples who have been granted limited powers over the management of their economies. The government of the Federation has agreed to revive a German autonomous region near Saratov on the Volga; and some of the Chechen, Ingush and Ossetian peoples of the northern Caucasus have been agitating for independence or closer links with the Caucasian republics.

In spite of its huge size, the Russian space economy was highly integrated under central planning, and was characterised by large-scale movements of freight over long distances. It was equally strongly connected with the other republics in what was the Soviet Union. Several commentators have argued that some, and perhaps much, of the transport of freight could have been avoided – that the space economy was over-integrated. However, it is clear that, even after economic reform, transport is likely to be crucial to such a large space economy, for that economy is articulated around a small number of regions: the Black Earth zone, the Urals industrial complex and the Kuzbas – each of which has a rather specific and complementary endowment of natural resources – and the Moscow metropolitan region, and St. Petersburg and its environs. There are also a host of other important regions, ranging from the eastern Donbas to the oil and gas fields of the Volga and western Siberia.

The future form of the Russian space economy will depend upon the degree to which the Stalinist model of development is replaced by the free market, the ways in which the Federation restructures its trade with the other successor states of the Soviet Union and countries of eastern Europe, and the links which it forges with the rest of the continent.

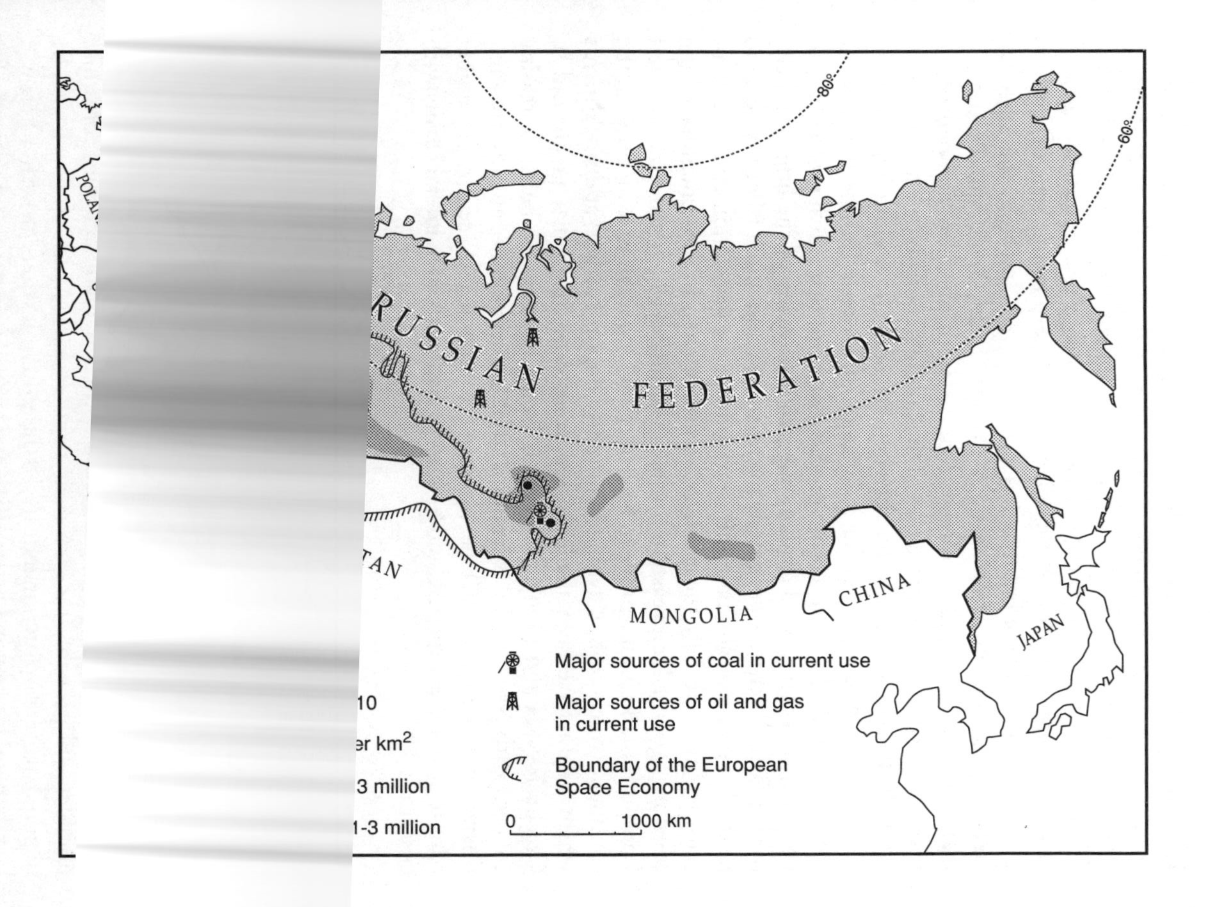
80°
60°
RUSSIAN FEDERATION
MONGOLIA
CHINA
JAPAN
TAN
10
er km²
3 million
1-3 million
Major sources of coal in current use
Major sources of oil and gas in current use
Boundary of the European Space Economy
0
1000 km

Manufacturing

It is probable that the influence of manufacturing on the form of the European space economy will also decline over the period to 2020. Those countries in western Europe which experienced a fall in employment during the 1970s and 1980s, suggesting that they might be about to enter a 'post-industrial' age, will face continuing competition not only from the cheap-labour areas of southern Europe to which some industry has already moved, and from the 'tigers' of eastern Asia, but also from eastern Europe. Even Greek and Portuguese manufacturers may find it difficult to beat eastern European competitors on cost. Meanwhile, any continuation of the failure in northwest Europe to keep up with the pace of innovation elsewhere in the world will undermine high-technology manufacturing there. Changes in eastern Europe will also be concerned with the need to raise productivity, but to a much greater extent. Early experience in East Germany suggests that many of the huge publicly-owned factories there were grossly overmanned, and much labour is likely to be shed. There may also be a shift from some of the heavy industries in eastern Europe, and especially those related to armaments, to those manufacturing consumer goods. Those eastern European countries which gain access to west European markets may prove to be attractive to companies from outwith the continent which wish to avoid Community import barriers; and investments which might have been made in, say, Ireland or Spain may go instead to Czechoslovakia and Hungary. There is likely, however, to be an increasing concern with product sophistication and differentiation throughout the continent; and industries will be increasingly attracted to centres of higher education or other expertise, and to those that allow them to interact easily with customers.

Steel

The scale and location of the steel industry in 2020 may be very different from that of the early 1990s.

The demand for steel in Europe as a whole is unlikely to grow as rapidly as it did during the Fourth Wave. That of the heavy industries in eastern Europe may fall, but the oil and gas industries and those manufacturing consumer durables will probably increase their requirements. Much steel will also be required in the construction industry, if the economies there grow, for there will be a demand for new and better office, factory and warehouse capacity, and for improvements in the rail and motorway networks.

The supply of steel may, however, be subject to radical change. Whether or not there is any reduction in demand, many of the mills which are currently in use are already old; others will become obsolete, and there will be much investment in the industry. That investment is unlikely, however, to replicate the existing spatial arrangement of production. Five types of location were mentioned in the discussion of the industry in Section III – coalfield, orefield, break-of-bulk, market, and 'political'. It is likely, as economic reform and privatisation in eastern Europe, and the Community's Competition Policy in the west, come to bear upon all manufacturers, that sites whose choice was 'political' will become increasingly vulnerable. Thus, the giant mills which were built in the 1950s at Dunauváros, Eisenhüttenstadt, Kosice and Nowa Huta, which lack adequate local supplies of raw materials or markets, are all likely to be closed, as are some of those in Italy. Nor may coalfield sites be as attractive as before if the traditional form of bulk production, using coke, is increasingly replaced early in the next century by the direct reduction of iron ore, using natural gas. While natural gas can be supplied in large quantities to almost any part of Europe, such a development will favour those areas to which gas and ore can be brought most readily, of which the Russian and Ukrainian orefields, and coastal sites around the North Sea, would appear to be the most significant. Moreover, left to make their own decisions, steelmakers are likely to prefer sites which give access to a range of raw materials and markets, while paying close attention to labour and other costs. Thus, they are likely to prefer break-of-bulk sites on the Baltic, Black and North Sea coasts, which can be supplied with domestically-produced raw materials by rail and foreign ores by bulk carrier, and from where steel can be distributed to both home and overseas markets. More steel may also be produced in mini-mills, in which small quantities of high-quality, specialist alloys are made from scrap in electric furnaces. Mini-mills are likely to be sited in many types of industrial region, and not only the traditional coalfield and orefield locations. They are not, however, likely to employ thousands of workers, after the manner of the steel industry throughout [illegible] before the early 1970s; but will be merely one element within most [illegible] In short,

[illegible]

will depend in part upon [illegible] in western Europe have done since the mid-1970s, and on their replacement of old-fashioned, open-hearth production with the use of basic oxygen and continuous casting. It will also be related to the costs which they may be obliged to incur in reducing the industry's high levels of atmospheric and other pollution. Nevertheless, they are thought to pose a threat; producers in the Community are to be protected until after the year 2000 from Czech,

Hungarian and Polish competition. However, if and when imports are allowed into western Europe, they may not only come from the rest of the continent, and countries such as Brazil and South Korea may be able to undercut eastern European products. Producers in those countries may also be able to penetrate eastern Europe's domestic markets, if they are allowed to do so; and a truly free market in steel throughout Europe and between Europe and the rest of the world would probably mean that most of the manufacture of bulk steel in Europe would disappear. It is unlikely that this will be allowed to happen in either eastern or western Europe before 2020.

Jet aircraft

The aerospace industry, in contrast, is likely to be rather stable up to 2020. The demand for military aircraft will probably decrease, following the end of the Cold War, and the development of new aeroplanes may be slowed. That part of the industry in both the former Soviet Union and western Europe may decline; but governments are unlikely to sanction massive reductions in its capacity while conflicts of interest continue between Europe and other parts of the world. Nor are they likely to agree to open tendering and procurement procedures, covering the whole continent, for the supply of such aircraft in the absence of much closer political links or some pan-European defence treaty. Rather, the western European consortia which were established in conjunction with NATO are likely to continue, while Russia will probably be the largest manufacturer of military planes in eastern Europe.

The demand for civil aircraft, in contrast, may increase. The carriage of both passengers and freight was growing rapidly during the declining phase of the fourth Long Wave; and any new economic growth is likely to see even steeper increases in demand, some of which will be met by new, and larger, but not necessarily faster, aircraft. There is also likely to be a substantial demand for smaller jets to operate feeder services between regional airports, and from them to the hubs. Soviet civilian aircraft of the past have suffered from low-quality avionics, have needed more maintenance than western jets, and have burnt twice as much fuel; but the USSR has led the world in the design and construction of the heaviest freighters. Russia may, therefore, be well placed to meet any increased demand for air freight; and it has already indicated that it will compete in the market for passenger jets, with planes powered by western engines or using other western components, and built to western standards of airworthiness. New jumbo jets will probably be available from Airbus, but also from Boeing and Macdonald, after the mid-1990s, which will be capable of flying non-stop from Europe to Australia, carrying 650 people each; and it is likely that these companies will win most of the replacement orders for those which are now in service, as well as supplying those which will be required to meet further increases in the demand for air travel. Meanwhile, consortia, such as Airbus, or others involving the Italian and Dutch firms, Alenia and Fokker, may supply some of the market for smaller jets, though, here again, the Americans will continue to be major suppliers.

The manufacture of these large and complex vehicles will continue to be characterised by advanced technology, close interaction between research and production, and very large start-up costs. It is highly unlikely that any new manufacturer will enter the industry in either eastern or western Europe, and no new centres of production are likely to be established. There will, however, be very great reluctance on the part of any of the countries which currently build large jets to lose the industry in any pan-European rationalisation following the end of the Cold War or closer integration of the continent; and there may be greater scope for joint ventures than in the past. Producers in Russia, the Ukraine, and other former republics of the Soviet Union will necessarily be obliged to cooperate if they are to continue the work which they were doing within it; and they and such other east European countries as have appropriate expertise may also be increasingly involved in collaboration with the industry in western Europe. Cooperative ventures of this type are less efficient than the centralised production of, say, Boeing aircraft; but political constraints are likely to prevent the spatial rationalisation of production (Klepper 1991b).

Textiles

The development of the textile industry in Europe up to 2020 will depend crucially upon the degree to which international trade is allowed. Eastern European markets were completely closed to foreign competition in the recent past; the Multi-Fibre Agreement has protected western European producers [illegible]

those of cheaper goods. [illegible] such a demand, with flexible, computer-based design and manufacture well established, and major chemical companies, such as Akzo of the Netherlands, Courtaulds in Britain and Lenzing of Austria, investing heavily in research. Meanwhile, the suitability of computer-based forms of production to small-scale enterprises offers the countries of eastern Europe an opportunity to replace their state-owned, mass-market industries with privately-owned workshops, in much the same way that the Italians have done since the 1950s. Such a development might quickly lead to the establishment of an integrated market in Europe for the highest-priced products, in which items with Parisian and Italian labels, but also others from Prague or St. Petersburg, might enjoy a certain *cachet.*

Markets for cheaper fabrics, however, are likely to be subject to strong competition. Almost all the output of the industry in eastern Europe in recent times has come from huge factories which lack the most advanced machinery and have large workforces, and has been of low- and medium-quality goods for the domestic market. Some have also been sold in western Europe, and imports from eastern Europe could undercut much of the remaining mass-market industry in the west. However, a much greater threat would be posed by Asian imports; and a widespread rundown of the sort which affected northwest Europe during the fourth Long Wave would probably occur in all the countries of eastern and southern Europe, if protection were to end. It is likely that there will be continuing international pressure to reduce the barriers to such trade, and that Europe, and especially western countries, will be obliged to give up market share.

Television sets

Something similar could happen in the manufacture of consumer electronics. Almost all households in Europe in the early 1990s possessed a television set; output from the industry was growing only slowly; and employment in it was falling. The level of demand for televisions and related products in future is likely to be closely connected with technological advance, and large increases are only likely to occur if new and improved forms of transmission and presentation of television signals are introduced. High-definition, three-dimensional, stereo, liquid-crystal and split-screen television all exist; but they await development by companies and the judgement of the market (Dunnett 1990, pp. 16–17). The introduction of high-definition television, for instance, would involve a change from analog to digital technology, which would probably require the replacement of the entire stock of Europe's television receivers (Bowen 1991).

Most of the larger countries in Europe manufacture television sets and peripheral equipment, though several producers in western Europe do so on licence from Japanese companies, and are concerned with the assembly of sets, rather than with product development. Britain became a net exporter of sets again in the early 1990s, thanks to such Japanese investment. But the industry has lost its technical lead, and European producers may be increasingly unable to influence decisions about which standards, such as the number of lines for high-definition television, are adopted. It also faces strong competition. The establishment of a single market in the Community, together with technical improvements which remove the major incompatibilities between the PAL and SECAM systems, will increase competition between producers in western Europe. Meanwhile, Asian producers have been poised for many years to invade any European market for existing television technology into which they are allowed entry; and the establishment of the industry in several of the less-developed countries there, and in Brazil and Turkey, will make it increasingly difficult for western Europe to hide behind voluntary import restraints and other protective devices (Cawson and Holmes 1991). Any free-trade area, which linked eastern with western Europe, might encourage manufacturers of televisions in the west to move eastward to cheap-labour locations, perhaps taking over and upgrading existing factories there; but it is likely that Asian and other producers would also invest in the region. In either event, the quality of production in eastern Europe is likely to rise sharply, and a large industry may be maintained. In western Europe, in contrast, the future looks bleak.

Conclusion

All of the industries mentioned above were well established by the late 1980s, and the demand for their products is likely to continue until 2020. None will die worldwide during a fifth Kondratiev; but their scale and location within Europe may change drastically as they modify their present products and methods of production, and as the institutional framework within which trade within the continent, and between it and the rest of the world, is altered. They may also be joined by new industries, manufacturing new products. If it is the case that these developments will be associated predominantly with advanced forms of technology – such as the microbic reduction of iron ore, the use of [illegible]

are likely to be the locations of the new forms of manufacturing. Most of these lie in northwest Europe; but Klodt (1991) foresees that Czechoslovakia, Hungary and Poland, which have well-developed educational systems, will also be able to attract technology-intensive multinational enterprises, thus allowing them to increase their production in the 'mobile Schumpeterian industries'. Moreover, they may not be the only countries to benefit, for any closer integration of the continent may also bring those regions in Russia which have been concerned with research and development into more direct competition with those of northwest Europe.

Services

It has been suggested above that, while the composition of the primary and secondary sectors of the economies of Europe may change in the period to 2020, it is unlikely that their role will grow. Rather, it may decline. The tertiary sector, in contrast, is more likely to expand, though growth will very probably be greater in eastern Europe, where it employed less than half the population in the late 1980s, than in the west. Indeed, the scope for change in western Europe, arising out of the mutual recognition of the service industries in the different states within the Community – leading to strong competition by, say, British insurers for Spanish custom or Dutch road hauliers for German traffic – is more likely to be bound up with increased labour productivity, and perhaps falls in employment, than growth of the sort which occurred during the fourth Long Wave. There is great scope in eastern Europe, in contrast, for the development of personal and professional services of many types; but that is not to say that it will occur in the places which will be shedding jobs in the primary and secondary sectors. We shall briefly review the prospects for the two service industries which were considered in Section III, namely, banking and tourism; and we shall also consider some of the changes which may occur in transport and communications.

Banking

The banking industry in Europe in the early 1990s was, like the curate's egg, only 'good in parts'. Deregulation in Britain and elsewhere had led to unsustainable growth in both the wholesale and retail markets for several of its products; protection of outdated and expensive operations in some Community countries was about to be removed by the establishment of the Single Market (Cecchini 1988, pp. 37–42); and eastern Europe needed to replace what had passed for financial services with those appropriate to the running of a free market. We shall examine the likely development of the two aspects of the industry which were considered in Section III, namely, international financial centres and the provision of local services.

If a European central bank, which has been proposed by the Community, is set up, it will inevitably strengthen the economy of whatever city it is placed in, attracting the European headquarters of American and Japanese financial institutions, and becoming the location of the principal market for the European currency. Its establishment will also weaken the role of central banks in the capital cities of the countries which participate in a monetary union. Such a bank will probably be sited in the Frankfurt–Amsterdam–London–Paris–Zurich region, thus increasing its financial and political importance still further, and could be crucial to the result of the competition which exists between these financial centres. Indeed, so important is the choice of location that the governments of the Community may not choose any of the existing centres, but some other city, such as Bonn or Lyons. But, whatever the choice, it is not certain that all of the major financial centres will be able to maintain their positions as the markets for currency, futures, securities and other products become truly worldwide. Nor is it likely that minor centres, such as Copenhagen and Dublin, which were attempting to make themselves more attractive to international transactions, will be able to emulate the recent success of Luxembourg in this regard. Gardener and Molyneux (1990, pp. 163–4) suggest that future success in the wholesale banking market will depend upon 'a liberal attitude towards regulation, a stable political environment, and the ability to react to change'; that economies of scale are likely to mean that London will retain its dominant role in the near future; and that there may be an enhanced role for tax havens outwith the Community, such as Liechtenstein. The smaller centres in northwest Europe may, however, decline. Nor is it probable that, even if the currencies of eastern Europe become convertible, their stock markets established, and their trading links with the rest of the world firmly based upon a market footing, those countries will attract international banking business on a scale to rival any of the established west European centres. Rather, they are likely to be customers of those centres; and the development of their economies will be conditioned in part by the decisions which are made in them.

Gardener and Molyneux believe that any future growth in banking activity [illegible] largely with the provision of [illegible]

[illegible] able to extend their activities into those countries in which banking is relatively inefficient – Greece, Italy, Portugal and Spain (Cecchini 1988, p. 42, Molyneux 1989). However, given the large number of banking institutions and their outlets in western Europe, it is unlikely that banks in one country will find it worthwhile to establish widespread branch networks in other countries; and such an integration of western Europe's banking industry is not likely to be accompanied by any major increases in employment. Rather, it is likely to reveal a problem of overcapacity, as improvements in communications, including telephone banking and the international use of cash dispensers, allow yet more transactions to be conducted without the help of bank clerks. The problem has already become acute in Britain, where the chief executive of one major clearer estimated in the early 1990s that the 20,000 bank and building society branches would eventually be halved (Rodgers 1992). Meanwhile, the spread of retailers' cards, which offer deposit, cash withdrawal, credit, and securities purchase facilities, will offer an increasing challenge to the role of banks as providers of deposit and payment systems; and insurance companies, which, like banks, face problems of overcapacity, are also likely to attempt to break into the traditional areas of banking activity (Gardener and Molyneux 1990, p. 99).

The greatest potential for growth in the provision of local banking services up to 2020 may, however, be in eastern Europe. Some of the products which are increasingly being provided by banks in western Europe, such as insurance, mortgages, personal pensions, and portfolio management, hardly existed there in the early 1990s; and it is possible that much of the initial advice over their introduction may be supplied by west European firms. Provision thereafter may also be undertaken by branches of western companies, though it will inevitably be carried out largely by local employees. Much of that employment will be in the capital cities, where new stock and wholesale financial markets were being established in the early 1990s, and the headquarters of new and reformed financial institutions located, and in other centres of population; but there is also scope for the establishment of branches in smaller settlements, to rival those of the officially-designated savings bank in each country, and for the introduction of automatic and remote-access retail banking facilities, based upon computer networks (Dobosiewicz 1992, pp. 76–9).

Developments in Poland offer an insight into the way in which the industry may develop. The first stage seems to have been the dismantling of the monobank system, in which the National Bank of Poland was not only the central bank and source of notes, but also the chief source of credit, was in state ownership, and controlled all other financial institutions in the country. Several new, though still publicly-owned, banks were established in 1989, each of which was given the power to set its own interest rates and other conditions of business; and, shortly after, the privatisation of some of these was begun. New, independent banks were also licensed; and it was made clear that not only would western capital be welcome in connection with the privatisation programme, but that Poland was anxious to attract foreign banks in the expectation that they would help to build up the country's international economic links, facilitate the inflow of foreign capital, and raise the level of expertise and competition within its banking industry (Lindsay 1992, pp. 138–9). Thus, by the early 1990s, Poland had a central bank, several commercial banks, some of which specialised in foreign trade, and a large number of local cooperative and savings institutions. Several foreign banks had also opened branches, chiefly in Warsaw. But there was little effective competition, for, although the head offices of most of the commercial banks were located in Warsaw, and several banks operated limited branch networks, many of the smaller towns and villages were served by only a single branch, and many types of transaction could only be conducted through one bank (World Bank 1990, pp. 232–48). The full development of universal banking, and rival branch networks, has yet to occur. Nor has the industry done more than begin to adopt the electronic equipment which is essential if it is to become part of an integrated European financial market.

Tourism

Tourism is also likely to grow, especially in eastern Europe, during any Fifth Kondratiev. Expenditure on travel generally increases faster than incomes; and the closer integration of the continent is likely to encourage tourists to visit those parts which hitherto were closed to them or did not offer the standards of accommodation and other services which they require. Thus, following the establishment of western hotel chains and tour companies, it is likely that all those types of western European resort which benefited from the growth of the industry between the 1950s and 1980s will be replicated in eastern Europe by the year 2020. Very considerable investments could be attracted to the Black Sea coast, the Carpathian and Caucasus Mountains, and the most-historic cities of the region; and employment in these areas could increase sharply, but only where potential visitors perceive them to be politically stable (Dobosiewicz 1992, pp. 87–90).

Tourism is also expected to grow in western Europe, not least because, as the [illegible] visited by tourists, but are close to established resorts and transport facilities. There will also be a continuing demand for high-quality conference facilities in attractive locations, close to major airports.

Transport and communications

Previous experience suggests that the demand for transport and communication, like that for tourism, will also grow faster than that of the economy as a whole in any new period of long-term expansion. We shall consider each of the major forms and transport and communication in turn.

Air traffic is likely to increase at more than the rate of economic growth; and price competition, following deregulation, is likely to lead to even faster growth (Klepper 1991a). The British Airports Authority has suggested that the demand for passenger services may treble between the late 1980s and 2020, and is planning to maintain the primacy of Heathrow as the busiest airport in Europe by raising its capacity from 46 to 80 million by 2016. Failure to do so may allow Amsterdam and Paris to capture more of the interchange traffic. Conversely, if national airlines cease to be subsidised, following the application of the Community's Competition Policy and economic reform in eastern Europe, and as some of the smaller ones are forced into mergers with other carriers, some of the smaller capital cities may become relatively less well connected. However, the efficient allocation of traffic among competing airports is unlikely in the absence of the regular auctioning of the available landing slots amongst both national flag carriers and other airlines, and of the widespread adoption of 'fifth freedom' rights under the Chicago Convention of 1944, which allow carriers from a third country to transport passengers within and between others. While the Community's Council of Ministers has recommended that airlines in the Community should charge what fares they like, no reforms had been proposed with regard to landing slots by the early 1990s; and it is likely that progress in these areas, even within the Community, will be slow. If, however, slots were to be allocated in such a way, many regional airports might be able to support direct international services, gaining custom from those hub airports in capital cities through which passengers are presently obliged to transit. There would also seem to be much scope for a further substitution of air transport for rail in Russia and the Ukraine, for, despite the Soviet policy of favouring long-distance passenger transport by air rather than rail, the average non-commuter rail passenger in the Soviet Union travelled no less than 600 kilometres in the 1980s, and rarely at more than eighty kilometres per hour (Symons 1990, p. 235). Air freight is also likely to continue to grow strongly; and any increase in the trade of high-value goods between, say, Russia and the Ukraine, at one extreme of the continent, and Britain and France, at the other, will enlarge the scope for such services.

There will also be much investment in rail services in the future. The high-speed rail network, which will link the centres of Amsterdam, Brussels, Cologne, London and Paris, using the Channel Tunnel, will be complete in the mid-1990s; and related projects elsewhere in western Europe will extend the service to a limited number of large cities before 2020. Some of these will be in

Spain and Portugal, which are to adopt the standard gauge for their new lines. Button and Swann (1991) suggest that these services may prove to be strong competitors for the airlines over distances of up to 1,500 kilometres, but will themselves be subject to competition from motorways for journeys of a thousand kilometres or less. Services elsewhere, however, will probably show little improvement. Railways in the former Soviet Union will still be operating on the wide gauge; and the costs of integrating the various electrical and other systems will be such that it will be unlikely that a fully-integrated rail system will be created even within the Community by that date (Mayes 1991).

However, it may be the growth of road traffic which will prove to be strongest over the next twenty to thirty years, for it is anticipated that car ownership will continue to rise well into next the century throughout the continent, and that the rate will be four times faster in eastern, than in western, Europe. It is inevitable that this will lead to demands for more investment in the road network; but major extensions to it are likely to be controversial in western Europe, though less so in the poorer countries of the east. The chief arguments against such development are likely to be on grounds of atmospheric pollution, congestion, and the use of farmland, though the land requirements for this and other transport developments will be small in comparison with the area which is likely to become surplus to agricultural requirements over the next thirty years. Some new developments may be delayed or prevented; and this will damage the economic prospects of the areas which they would otherwise have served, and deflect economic growth to those with spare capacity. Alternatively, governments may charge transport users more directly than at present for the costs which they incur, through the use of road licensing. Such an approach would be more in line with the spirit of the late twentieth century, that is, of deregulation and the internalisation of external diseconomies – the principle that the polluter should pay – but it is doubtful whether it would reduce the rate of increase in road traffic very greatly. Road capacity may also be increased

motorways and jet aeroplanes did in their eras.

The construction of the necessary broadband, fibre-optic networks will be very expensive; and it is likely that such networks will be installed first in the areas of greatest potential demand, namely the major commercial centres of western Europe, and only subsequently elsewhere. Privatisation is likely to increase this divergence, unless governments intervene to ensure parity of service (Masser *et al.*, 1992, pp. 161–176). Core regions needing, and being able to afford, to build up their links with each other, will do so, in part through the construction of private networks, while peripheral regions will not be able to generate sufficient traffic to provide matching levels of service, or only at high costs to users. Eastern Europe is also likely to remain relatively backward, though a large investment programme was launched there by the G-24 group of the richest western nations in 1990. Indeed, the backwardness of eastern Europe offers the opportunity for the countries there to avoid the problems which have plagued western Europe during the period of rapid telecommunications innovation since the 1940s (Nguyen 1991), and to move directly from early twentieth-century, manual technology to cellular, satellite and optical fibre systems, digital switching and telematics – from the 'knitting needle' to the videophone (Dobosiewicz 1992, pp. 84–7). Improvements in communications will allow office workers and others to avoid some high-cost, low-amenity journeys – by working, and perhaps shopping, more from home. Thus, it will hold down the costs of agglomeration in the major cities; but it will not have replaced the need for face-to-face contact in Europe by 2020 (O'Brien 1992, p. 76). One simple, but major change, which should come about as a result of the Community's Single Market, will be the disappearance of the differences between the prices of telecommunication which are internal to each country, and those between member states.

All parts of the continent are likely to be affected in one way or another by the improvements in transport and communication which have been mentioned above, and the demand for transport services is likely to rise everywhere within the space economy. Some of the greatest changes, however, are likely to occur in eastern Europe, where economic reform will encourage the industry to catch up with the levels of service which are already available in the west, as well as to adopt further innovations. The effect of such changes on the form of the space economy could be substantial. Now that the Stalinist model of development, which stimulated the demand for transport in many ways, but allocated it only minimal levels of investment, is about to be replaced by a more market-based approach, demands for freight transport may fall, while those for passenger transport and communications are likely to undergo a modal shift from public to private transport, and to grow strongly. North (1991) suggests, that, if the former Soviet Union develops a level of external trade commensurate with its size, ports and the transport links to them will need to be expanded, but that the resources which have hitherto been put into subsidising some of the links with the sparsely-populated north and east of Russia may not be available in the future. As the true costs of logging, mining and other activities in such areas become apparent, the quality and frequency of transport services to them may deteriorate; some of their activities may be abandoned; and the space economy may contract.

The European space economy to 2020

We are now in a position to make some assessment of the likely pattern of the European space economy during the expansionary phase of a fifth Long Wave. We shall not, however, adopt the approach which was used in Chapter 7 to describe developments during the Fourth Kondratiev, in which only the effects of technical change and of integration were treated, and that separately. Rather, we shall attempt to summarise the conclusions which have been reached concerning these influences and also that of the map of economic rents, and to do so more concisely, indicating which countries and regions are likely to prosper, and which not.

The review of institutional change at the beginning of this section concluded that the economies of the continent will not be fully integrated by 2020: that there will be no common European home. Nevertheless, some further coming together is probable; and the space economy will also be affected by the growth of some industries, the decline of others, and the interplay between all these changes and the map of resources and opportunities which the various regions of Europe offer.

Substantial areas of the European space economy will probably manage only slow economic growth over the next twenty to thirty years, and some may decline. Investment in them will be only slightly above replacement levels, employment may fall, and the intensity of land use may be little changed. More people may leave such places than move to them, and some land may be abandoned. Slow growth will occur, either because the areas are being used by activities which are themselves ceasing to be as important as before, or because their research and development efforts are small, or because they lack the attributes which would make them attractive to productive activities of one sort or another. Despite the fact that labour in such areas may be cheap, the price of credit will be forced up in some by the high levels of government expenditure, balance of payments deficits, inflation and social upheaval which will be

development, or few decisions of commercial significance are made;

- with harsh climates, or which are not well connected with the transport and communication infrastructure, or which are far from large cities, or which suffer from severe environmental degradation or civil unrest;
- whose economic activities enjoy no comparative advantage, but have been protected in the past.

BOX 6

The Ukraine

Three of the most important countries of Europe have recently re-emerged after periods in which they have been either divided or submerged in larger states. Each is likely to play a major role in the development of the European space economy in future.

The Ukraine is the largest country in Europe, other than the Russian Federation, being somewhat larger than France or Spain. It is also one of the more populous countries. It has been ruled from Moscow for almost all of the last three hundred years, and the boundaries between the Ukraine and other parts of the Soviet Union have been of little more than nominal value over that period. Large numbers of Russians live in the industrial areas of the Donbas and elsewhere in the country, and account for about one-sixth of the population. The Crimean peninsula, which had not previously been a part of the country, and was inhabited largely by Russians, was transferred to it in 1954 at the whim, or so it appeared, of the Soviet government. The economic activities of the country have been developed since the nineteenth century as part of the Russian space economy. In particular, western and central Ukraine have been major sources of foodstuffs, the Donbas one of the chief centres of coal mining and the heavy industries, the Black Sea coast has provided warm-water ports, and the Crimea an important tourist facility, for that economy. These links were considerably disrupted by the secession of the Ukraine from the Soviet Union in 1991.

The country's space economy is articulated around the industrial towns of the Donbas, the capital city of Kiev, the agricultural heartland of southwestern Ukraine, and the port of Odessa. Population thins out in the Polesian marshes to the northwest and on the Black Sea and Crimean steppes to the southeast; but almost all of the country is low-lying and capable of being used for agriculture or settlement. Economic reform and greater integration with the rest of Europe are likely to affect the economy considerably. Coal mining and heavy industry may decline; agriculture probably has the potential to regain its traditional markets in western Europe, but only if those markets are opened to it; and the growth of service industries will maintain, and may enhance, the role of the cities as the foci of its space economy. The metropolitan role of Kiev, which has been emasculated under Russian rule, can now be resumed. Environmental degradation, however, effects much of the country, from soil erosion in many agricultural areas to atmospheric pollution in the industrial cities, shortages of clean water in the eastern half of the country, and a polluted coastline.

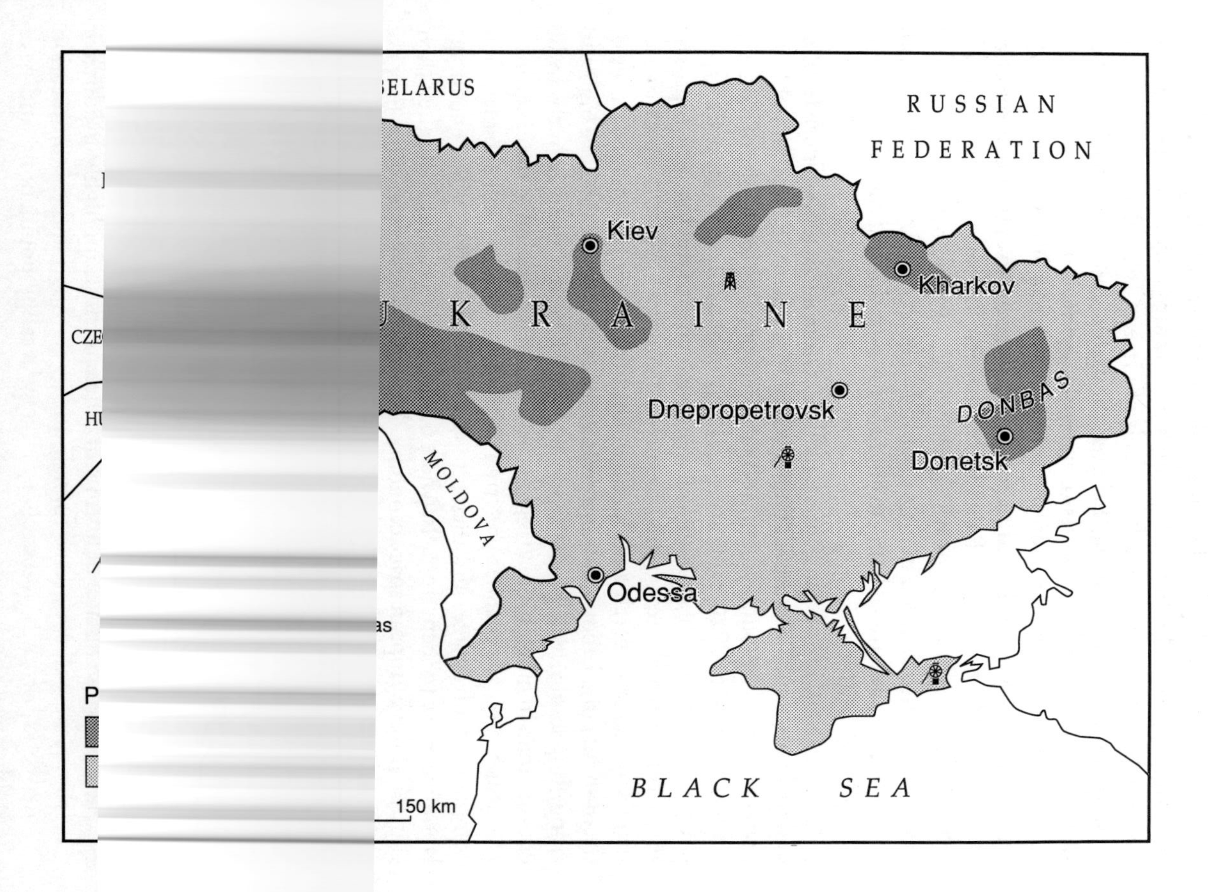
RUSSIAN FEDERATION
UKRAINE
Kiev
Kharkov
Dnepropetrovsk
DONBAS
Donetsk
MOLDOVA
Odessa
BLACK SEA
150 km

It may be that a return to rapid and sustained economic growth in the expansion phase of a fifth Long Wave will allow such areas to benefit, as many peripheral areas did in the Long Boom, from opportunities for their workers to migrate to regions of labour shortage, and from the receipt of regional aid, social security benefits and remittances. However, the areas which would appear to be vulnerable are large, including much of Greece, Ireland and Portugal, in western Europe, and Albania, Belarus, the Baltic and Caucasian republics, Moldova, Slovakia and the successor states of Yugoslavia, further east. There are also regions within other countries which are characterised by some of the weaknesses listed above, including much of Europe north of sixty degrees, rural areas remote from cities in Poland, the Russian Federation, Spain and the Ukraine, and agglomerations whose economies are dominated by heavy and polluting industries. It is extremely doubtful whether even another Long Boom can raise the standards of living in all these towards those of the more wealthy areas of the continent.

Other parts of Europe, in contrast, will offer substantial rents of both fertility and location, which will attract high levels of investment and lead to stable or, perhaps, increasing employment, and sustained or rising intensities of land use. Over the period to 2020, rents are most likely to be available in areas which are already the locations of economic activities which are growing, which possess the attributes which are required by such activities, which are the locations of firms with large research and development budgets, or important centres of decision making. Labour and land costs in many of these areas will be high and rising, but so also will productivity; and credit within them is likely to be cheaper than in more troubled regions. Any closer integration of the economies of Europe, after the manner preferred by the Community, will enhance their comparative advantage, and therefore the rents which they offer, encourage labour to move to them from elsewhere on the continent, and strengthen their control of the European space economy. Moreover, to the extent that they are also areas in which levels of income and personal wealth are relatively high, the rents which they generate are likely to be reinvested within them or paid to their inhabitants in the form of dividends, endowment insurance and personal pensions.

More particularly, areas which are likely to prosper will include many of those which:

— are the centres of research and development or decision making or other specialised services;
— have pleasant climates or historic or other amenities, or highly-productive labour, are well connected to high-quality transport and communication networks, or easily accessible to large or wealthy populations, and have stable social conditions;
— and those with such attributes which become more closely integrated with others.

These characteristics suggest that it will be select regions, rather than countries as a whole, which will be the foci of future growth. Nor should it be assumed that regions which have experienced growth during the Fourth Kondratiev will continue to do so during a fifth Long Wave. Just as the torch of development passed from Nordrhein-Westfalen in the Third Kondratiev to Baden-Württemburg in the Fourth, and from areas lying north and west of the Tees-Exe line in Britain to those of the south and east, so it may move to other areas in the future. Nevertheless, it would seem to indicate that, while the Moscow area, Kiev and some of the Black Sea coasts may eventually become areas of rapid and sustained economic growth, as may the Czech lands and Hungary, it will be Germany, France, and the Low Countries, together with Austria, Switzerland, northern Italy, lowland Britain and southern Scandinavia which, in a fifth Long Wave, beginning in the 1990s, will resume the role which they have traditionally played, but which has been interrupted by the twentieth century division of the continent, in the game of economic geography – that of the core of the European space economy.

Further reading

Books about the future pattern of the European space economy vary from the general, wide-ranging and ambitious to the very specific and cautious. *The Geography of Europe's Futures* (Masser *et al.* 1992) gives a broad view of the way in which three alternative aspirations – for economic growth, equity or environmental protection – may react with economic, technical and social changes to mould the lifestyle of western Europe by the year 2020. Camagni *et al.* (1991) and Vickerman (1992) give shorter assessments of the likely effects of the establishment of the Single Market, concentrating on the likely form of an emerging western Europe hierarchy

1992. Dobosiewicz (1992) describes *Foreign Investment in Eastern Europe*, but not in what was the Soviet Union, up to 1991.

European Agriculture: Policy Issues and Options to 2000 (Alexandratos 1990) examines agriculture in great detail, though necessarily before the full implication of the events of 1989–91 could be considered; and Hall and Preston (1988) discuss the likely advances in telecommunications, and their impact upon the economic geography of western Europe, during a fifth Kondratiev in *The carrier wave: New information technology and the geography of innovation, 1846–2003.* Gowland (1992) provides accounts of the early stages of reform in the banking industry in east Germany, Hungary and Poland in *Finance in Eastern Europe.*

Maillat (1990) indicates some possible developments in some of the border regions of western Europe arising from the introduction of the Single Market, and Schwok (1991) assesses the future for *Switzerland and the European Common Market.*

REFERENCES

Ahnström, L. (1990), *Economic growth, stagnation and the working population in western Europe*, Belhaven, London.

Alexandratos, N. (1990), *European agriculture: Policy issues and options to 2000*, Belhaven, London.

Aydalot, P. and Keeble, D. (1988), *High technology industry and innovative environments: The European experience*, Routledge, London.

Bade, F. and Kunzmann, K.R. (1991), 'Deindustrialization and regional development in the Federal Republic of Germany', in *Industrial change and regional economic transformation: The experience of western Europe*, ed. L. Rodwin and H. Sazanami, HarperCollins, London, 70–104.

Balassa, B. (1961), *The Theory of Economic Integration*, George Allen & Unwin, London.

Baldwin, R. (1989), 'The growth effects of 1992', *Economic Policy*, 9, 247–81.

Barr, B.M. (1991), 'Environmental degradation in the Soviet forest', in *The Soviet Union: A new regional geography?* ed. M.J. Bradshaw, Belhaven, London, 119–42.

Bater, J.H. (1989), *The Soviet scene: a geographical perspective*, Edward Arnold, London.

Beckouche, P. (1991), 'French high-tech and space: a double cleavage', in *Industrial change and regional development: the transformation of new industrial spaces*, ed. G. Benko and M. Dunford, Belhaven, London, 205–25.

Blanchard, W.O. and Visher, S.S. (1931), *Economic geography of Europe*, McGraw-Hill, New York.

[illegible]

Camagni, R., Cheshire, P., de Gaudemar, J.P., Hall, P., Rodwin, L. and [illegible] 'Europe's regional-urban futures: conclusions, inferences and surmises', in *Industrial change and regional economic transition: The experience of western Europe*, ed. L. Rodwin and H. Sazanami, HarperCollins, London, 301–15.

Cantwell, J. (1992), 'The effects of integration on the structure of multinational corporation activity in the EC', in *Multinationals in the New Europe and global trade*, ed. M.W. Klein and P.J.J. Welfens, Springer-Verlag, Berlin, 193–233.

REFERENCES

Carter, F. W. (1985), 'Pollution problems in post-war Czechoslovakia', *Transactions*, Institute of British Geographers, 10, 17–44.

Cawson, A. and Holmes, P. (1991), 'The new consumer electronics', in *Technology and the future of Europe: Global competition and the environment in the 1990s*, ed. C. Freeman, M. Sharp and W. Walker, Pinter, London, 169–82.

Cecchini, P. (1988), *The European challenge 1992: The Benefits of a single market*, Wildwood House, Aldershot.

Charles, D.(1990), 'The changing structure of the subscriber equipment industry', in *The single European market and the information and communication technologies*, ed. G. Locksley, Belhaven, London, 147–61.

Chisholm, G.G. (1889), *Handbook of commercial geography*, Longman, London.

Chisholm, M. (1966), *Geography and economics*, Bell, London.

Christaller, W. (1966), *Central Places in Southern Germany*, Prentice Hall, Englewood Cliffs (English translation by C. Baskin of original, published in 1933).

Clough, P. (1992), 'Economists see long and troubled road to CIS reform', *The Independent*, 27 January

— (1991), 'German investors make their mark on Central Europe', *The Independent*, 31 December.

Clout, H.D. (1975) (ed.), *Regional development in western Europe*, Wiley, London.

Cole, J.P. (1984), *Geography of the Soviet Union*, Butterworth, London.

Commission of the European Communities (1987a), *Third periodic report from the Commission on the social and economic situation and development of the regions of the Community*, Brussels.

— (1987b), *The Agricultural Situation in the Community*, 1986 Report, Brussels 1987.

— (1988), *The Future of Rural Society*, Brussels.

— (1991), *The Agricultural Situation in the Community*, 1990 Report, Brussels 1991.

Cook, E.C. (1992), 'Agriculture's role in the Soviet economic crisis', in *The disintegration of the Soviet economic system*, ed. M. Ellman and V. Kontorovich, Routledge, London, 193–216.

Court, W.H.B. (1954), *A concise economic history of Britain*, Cambridge University Press, Cambridge.

Dawson, A.H. (1987a) (ed.), *Planning in eastern Europe*, Croom Helm, London.

— (1987b), 'Yugoslavia', in *Planning in eastern Europe*, ed. A.H. Dawson, Croom Helm, London, 275-91

Dewdney, J. (1990), 'Population changes in the Soviet Union', *Geography*, 75, 273–77.

Dicken, P. (1986), *Global shift: Industrial change in a turbulent world*, Harper & Row, London.

Dobosiewicz, Z. (1992), *Foreign investment in Eastern Europe*, Routledge, London.

Dunford, M. and Benko, G. (1991), 'Neo-Fordism or post-Fordism? Some conclusions and further remarks', in *Industrial change and regional development: the transformation of new industrial spaces*, ed. G. Benko and M. Dunford, Belhaven, London, 286–305.

Dunnett, P.J.S. (1990), *The world television industry: An economic analysis*, Routledge, London.

Dunning, J.H. (1972), 'The Location of International Firms in an Enlarged EEC: An Exploratory Paper', *Manchester Statistical Society*, 1–45.

East, G. (1935), *An historical geography of Europe*, Methuen, London.

Ellman, M. and Kontorovich, V. (1992a), *The disintegration of the Soviet economic system*, Routledge, London.

— (1992b), 'Overview', in *The disintegration of the Soviet economic system*, ed. M. Ellman and V. Kontorovich, Routledge, London, 1–39.

FAO (1989a), *FAO yearbook, production, 1988*, Rome.

— (1989b), *The state of food and agriculture, 1989*, Rome.

Federal Republic of Germany, *Statistiche Jahrbücher*, Statistiches Bundesamt, Wiesbaden.

Forrester, J.W. (1976), 'Business structure, economic cycles and national policy', *Futures*, 8, 195–214.

Forsyth, W. (1992), 'The socialist financial system: the case of the DDR', in *Finance in eastern Europe*, ed. D.H. Gowland, Dartmouth, Aldershot, 16–45.

Freeman, C. (1983), *Long waves in the world economy*, Butterworth, London.

Freeman, C., Clarke, J. and Soete, J. (1982), *Unemployment and technical innovation: A study of long waves and economic development*, Pinter, London.

French, R.A. (1989), 'Introduction', in *The development of Siberia*, ed. A. Wood and R. A. French, Macmillan, London, 1–10.

Friedman, J. (1972), 'A general theory of polarized development', in *Growth centers in regional economic development*, ed.N.M. Hansen, The Free Press, New York.

Gardener, E.P.M. and Molyneux, P. (1990), *Changes in western European banking*, Unwin Hyman, London.

de Gaudemar, J. and Prud'homme, R. (1991), 'Spatial impacts of deindustrializtion in France', in *Industrial change and regional economic transition: The experience of western Europe*, ed. L.Rodwin and H. Sazanami, HarperCollins, London, 105–36.

GATT (1990), *International Trade 1989–90*, Geneva.

Giersch, H. (1949), 'Economic Union between Nations and the Location of Industry', *Review of Economic Studies*, 17, 87–97.

Gillespie, A. (1987), 'Telecommunications and the development of Europe's less-favoured regions', *Built Environment*, 8, 229–36.

Giroux, A. (1989), 'Sibérie 89: atouts et constraints', *Le courrier de pays de l'est*, 342, 3–29.

Gittelman, M. and Dunning, J.H. (1992), 'Japanese multinationals in Europe and the United States: Some comparisons and contrasts', in *Multinationals in the new Europe and global trade*, ed. M. Klein and P.J.J. Welfens, Springer-Verlag, Berlin, 237–68.

Gomulka, S. (1986), *Growth, Innovation and Reform in Eastern Europe*, Wheatsheaf Books, Brighton.

Gowland, D.H. (1992) (ed.), *Finance in eastern Europe*, Dartmouth, Aldershot.

Grenon, M. and Batisse, M. (eds) (1989), *Futures for the Mediterranean Basin: The Blue Plan*, Oxford University Press, Oxford.

Hall, D.R. (ed.) (1991), *Tourism and economic development in Eastern Europe and the Soviet Union*, Belhaven, London.

Hall, P. (ed.) (1977), *Europe 2000*, Duckworth, London.

— and Preston, P. (1988), *The carrier wave: New information technology and the geography of innovation, 1846–2003*, Unwin Hyman, London.

Hardill, I. (1987), *The regional implications of restructuring in the wool textile industry*, Gower, Aldershot.

Harrison, R.J. (1985), *The Spanish economy in the twentieth century*, Croom Helm, London.

Heater, D. (1992), *The idea of European unity*, Leicester University Press, Leicester.

[illegible]

Analysis of Albania, Bulgaria, Greece, Romania and Yugoslavia, Praeger, New York.

Holland, S. (1980), *Uncommon Market: Capital, Class and Power in the European Community*, Macmillan, London.

Houseman, S.N. (1991), *Industrial restructuring with job security: The case of European steel*, Harvard University Press, Cambridge, Mass.

Howells, J. (1988), *Economic, technological and locational trends in European services*, Avebury, Aldershot.

— (1990), 'Market integration, economic location and the development of European information services', in *The single European market and the information and communication technologies*, ed. G. Locksley, Belhaven, London, 202–13.
Hungary (1987), *Statisztikai Evkönyv 1986*, Budapest.
Illeris, S. (1989), *Services and regions in Europe*, Avebury, Aldershot.
Inotai, A. (1991), 'Foreign direct investment in reforming CMEA countries: Facts, lessons and perspectives', in *Multinationals in the new Europe and global trade*, ed. M. Klein and P.J.J. Welfens, Springer-Verlag, Berlin, 129–52.
International Energy Agency (1985), *Coal Information*, OECD, Paris.
Isard, W. (1956), *Location and Space-Economy: A General Theory Relating to Industrial Location, Market Areas, Land Use, Trade, and Urban Structure*, The M.I.T. Press, Cambridge, Massachusetts.
John, B. (1984), *Scandinavia: A new geography*, Longman, London.
Jones, P.N. (1990), 'Recent ethnic German migration from Eastern Europe to the Federal Republic', *Geography*, 249–52.
Keesing, D. B. and Wolf, M. (1980), *Textile quotas against developing countries*, Trade Policy Research Centre, London.
Klein, M.W. and Welfens, P.J.J. (eds) (1992), *Multinationals in the new Europe and global trade*, Springer-Verlag, Berlin.
Klepper, G. (1991a), 'Airlines', in *The European challenge: Industry's responses to the 1992 programme*, ed. D.G. Mayes, Harvester, New York, 162–83.
— (1991b), 'The aerospace industry', in *The European challenge: Industry's responses to the 1992 programme*, ed. D.G. Mayes, Harvester, New York, 184–208.
Klodt, H. (1992), 'Technology-based trade and multinationals' investment in Europe: Structural change and competition in Schumpeterian goods', in *Multinationals in the new Europe and global trade*, ed. M. Klein and P.J.J. Welfens, Springer-Verlag, Berlin, 107–26.
Komarov, B. (1980), *The destruction of nature in the Soviet Union*, M.E. Sharpe, New York (English translation by M. Vale and J. Hollander of original, published in 1978).
Kontorovich, V. (1992), 'Technological progress and research and development', in *The disintegration of the Soviet economic system*, ed. M. Ellman and V. Kontorovich, Routledge, London, 217–38.
Kornai, J. (1980), *Economics of shortage*, North Holland, Amsterdam.
Kramer, J.M. (1987), 'The environmental crisis in Poland', in *Environmental problems in the Soviet Union and eastern Europe*, ed. F. Singleton, Lynne Rienner, Boulder, 149–67.
League of Nations (1933), *Statistical yearbook of the League of Nations 1932/3*, Geneva.
Liebowitz, R.D. (1991), 'Spatial inequality under Gorbachev', in *The Soviet Union: A new regional geography?*, ed. M.J. Bradshaw, Belhaven, London, 15–37.
Lindsay, M. (1992), *Developing capital markets in eastern Europe: A business reference*, Pinter, London.
Locksley, G. (ed.) (1990), *The single European market and the information and communication technologies*, Belhaven, London.
McAuley, A. (1991), 'Economic constraints on devolution: the Lithuanian case', in *Soviet Federalism: Nationalism and economic decentralisation*, ed. A. McAuley, Leicester University Press, Leicester, 178–95.
McFarlane, J. (1914), *Economic geography*, Pitman, London.
McKee, D.L. (1991), *Schumpeter and the political economy of change*, Praeger, New York.
Mackowsky, M. (1968), 'European carboniferous coalfields', in *Coal and coal-bearing strata*, ed. D. Murchison and T.S. Westoll, Oliver & Boyd, Edinburgh, 325–45.
Maillat, D. (1990), 'Transborder regions between members of the EC and non-member countries', *Built Environment*, 16, 38–51.
Mansell, R.E. (1990), 'Telecommunication tariff policies: an uncertain consensus', in *The single European market and the information and communication technologies*, ed. G. Locksley, Belhaven, London, 73–88.

Mansfield, E., Romeo, A., Schwartz, M., Teece, D. and Wagner, S. (1982), *Technology transfer, productivity, and economic policy*, Norton, New York.

Marples, D.R. (1991), *Ukraine under Perestroika: Ecology, economics and the workers' revolt*, Macmillan, London.

Marshall, A. (1992), 'Finland to apply for EC membership', *The Independent*, 26 February.

Marshall, M. (1987), *Long waves in regional development*, Macmillan, London.

Martinelli, F. and Schoenberger, E. (1991), 'Oligopoly is alive and well: notes for a broader discussion of flexible accumulation', in *Industrial change and regional development: the transformation of new industrial spaces*, ed. G. Benko and M. Dunford, Belhaven, London, 116–31.

Masser, I., Svidén, O. and Wegener, M. (1992), *The Geography of Europe's Futures*, Belhaven, London.

Mayes, D.G. (ed.) (1991), *The European challenge: Industry's responses to the 1992 programme*, Harvester, New York.

— (1991), 'The railway industry', in *The European challenge: Industry's responses to the 1992 programme*, ed. D.G. Mayes, Harvester, New York, 130–61.

Mellor, R.E.H. (1975), *Eastern Europe: A Geography of the Comecon Countries*, Macmillan, London.

— (1987), 'Comecon', in *Planning in Eastern Europe*, ed. A.H. Dawson, Croom Helm, London, 293–323.

— and Smith, E.A. (1979), *Europe: A geographical survey of the continent*, Macmillan, London.

Mensch, G. (1979), *Stalemate in technology: Innovations overcome the depression*, Ballinger, New York.

Merritt, L. (1991), *Eastern Europe and the USSR: The challenge of freedom*, Kogan Page, London.

Minshull, G.N. (1979), *The new Europe: an economic geography of the EEC*, Hodder & Stoughton, London.

Molle, W. (1990), *The Economics of European Integration: Theory, Practice, Policy*, Dartmouth, Aldershot.

— and Cappellin, R. (1988) (eds), *Regional impact of Community policies in Europe*, Avebury, Aldershot.

— and van Mourik, A. (1988), 'International movements of labour under conditions of economic integration: the case of Western Europe', *Journal of Common Market Studies*, 26, 317–42.

— and van Mourik, A. (1989), *Wage Differentials in the European Community: Convergence or Divergence?*, Avebury, Aldershot.

[illegible]

Nalivkin, D.V. (1973), *Geology of the USSR*, Oliver & Boyd, Edinburgh.

Nello, S.S. (1991), *The New Europe: Changing economic relations between east and west*, Harvester Wheatsheaf, New York.

Newbigin, M.I. (1932), *Southern Europe. A regional and economic geography of the Meditteranean lands*, Methuen, London.

Nguyen, G.D. (1985), 'Telecommunications: a challenge to the old order', in *Europe and the New Technologies: Six Studies in Innovation and Adjustment*, ed. M. Sharp, Pinter, London.

Nicoll, W. and Salmon, T.C. (1990), *Understanding the European Communities*, Philip Allan, London.
North, R.N. (1991), 'Perestroyka and the Soviet transportation system', in *The Soviet Union: A new regional geography?*, ed. M.J. Bradshaw, Belhaven, London, 143–64.
O'Brien, R. (1992), *Global financial integration: The end of Geography*, Pinter, London.
OECD (1985), *Tourism policy and international tourism in OECD countries*, OECD, Paris.
Ozawa, T. (1992), 'Comments on: Japanese multinationals in Europe and the United States: Some comparisons and contrasts', in *Multinationals in the new Europe and global trade*, ed. M. Klein and P.J.J. Welfens, Springer-Verlag, Berlin, 269–75.
Pallot, J. (1991), 'The countryside under Gorbachev', in *The Soviet Union: A new regional geography?*, ed. M. Bradshaw, Belhaven, London, 83–100.
Panic, M. and Schioppa, C. (1989), 'Europe's Long-term Capital Flows since 1971', in *European Factor Mobility: Trends and Consequences*, ed. I. Gordon and A.P. Thirlwall, Macmillan, London.
Parker, G. (1969), *The logic of unity: A geography of the European Economic Community*, Longman, London.
Parker, W.H. (1969), *An historical geography of Russia*, University of London Press, London.
Patel, P. and Pavitt, K. (1991), 'Europe's technological performance', in *Technology and the future of Europe: Global competition and the environment in the 1990s*, ed. C. Freeman, M. Sharp and W. Walker, Pinter, London, 37–58.
Pinder, D. (1983), *Regional Economic Development and Policy: Theory and Practice in the European Community*, George Allen & Unwin, London.
Pinder, J. (1990) (ed.), *Western Europe: Challenge and change*, Belhaven, London.
Piore, M.J. and Sabel, C.F. (1984), *The second industrial divide: possibilities for prosperity*, Basic Books, New York.
Poland (1939), *Maly rocznik statystyczny 1939*, Glowny Urzad Statystyczny, Warszawa.
— (1987), *Rocznik statystyczny 1987*, Glowny Urzad Statystyczny, Warszawa.
Pollard, S. (1981), *The Integration of the European Economy since 1815*, George Allen & Unwin, London.
Pounds, N.J.G. (1969), *Eastern Europe*, Longman, London.
— (1974), *An historical geography of Europe, 450 BC–AD 1300*, Cambridge University Press, Cambridge.
— (1979), *An historical geography of Europe, 1500–1840*, Cambridge University Press, Cambridge.
— (1990), *An historical geography of Europe*, Cambridge University Press, Cambridge.
Ritter, C. (1804–7), *Europa, ein Geographisch-Historisch-Statisches Gemälde*, Frankfurt.
Robson, P. (1987), *The Economics of International Integration*, 3rd. edn, Allen & Unwin, London.
Rodgers, P. (1992), 'Banks "need to close half their branches"', *The Independent*, 28 February.
Rodwin, L. and Sazanami, H. (eds) (1991), *Industrial change and regional economic transformation: The experience of Western Europe*, HarperCollins, London.
Roesler, J. (1991), 'Mass unemployment in eastern Germany', *Journal of European Social Policy*, 1, 129–50.
Ronge, V. (1991), 'Social change in Eastern Europe: Implications for the western poverty agenda', *Journal of European Social Policy*, 1, 49–56.
Rostow, W.W. and Kennedy, M. (1979), 'A simple model of the Kondratiev cycle', *Research in Economic History*, 4, 1–36.
Samoteikin, E. (1987), 'The goals of Vladivostok', in *The Soviet Union as an Asian Pacific Power*, ed. R. Thakur and C. Thayer, Westview, Boulder, 11–18.
Savchenko, V.K. (1991), 'The Chernobyl catastrophe and the biosphere', *Nature & Resources*, 27, 37–46.
Schamp, E. (1991), 'Towards a spatial reorganisation of the German car industry? The implications of new production concepts', in *Industrial change and regional development: the*

transformation of new industrial spaces, ed. G. Benko and M. Dunford, Belhaven, London, 159–70.

Schumpeter, J.A. (1939), *Business Cycles, I and II: A theoretical, historical and statistical analysis of the capitalist process*, McGraw-Hill, New York.

Schwok, R. (1991), *Switzerland and the European common market*, Praeger, New York.

Seers, D. (1980), 'Theoretical Aspects of Unequal Development at Different Spatial Levels', in *Integration and Unequal Development*, ed. D. Seers and C. Vaitsos, Macmillan, London.

—, Schaffer, B. and Kiljunen, M. (1979), *Underdeveloped Europe: Studies in Core-Periphery Relations*, The Harvester Press, Hassocks.

— and Vaitsos, C. (1980), *Integration and Unequal Development: The Experience of the EEC*, Macmillan, London.

Shabad, T. (1986), 'Geographic aspects of the new Soviet five-year plan, 1986–90', *Soviet Geography*, 27, 1–16.

Sharp, M. (1991), 'The single market and European technology', in *Technology and the future of Europe: Global competition and the environment in the 1990s*, ed. C. Freeman, M. Sharp and W. Walker, Pinter, London, 59–76.

Shepherd, G. (1981), *Textile-industry adjustment in developed countries*, Trade Policy Research Centre, London.

Siebert, H. (1991), *The new economic landscape in Europe*, Blackwell, Oxford.

Singleton, F. (1987) (ed.), *Environmental problems in the Soviet Union and eastern Europe*, Lynne Rienner, Boulder.

Smith, C.T. (1967), *An historical geography of western Europe before 1800*, Longman, London.

Smith, D.H. (1925), *An economic geography of Europe*, Longman, London.

Smith, G. (1990) (ed.), *The Nationalities Question in the Soviet Union*, Longman, London.

Solomou, S. (1987), *Phases of Economic Growth, 1850–1973: Kondratiev Waves and Kuznets Swings*, Cambridge University Press, Cambridge.

Stebelsky, I. (1987), 'Agricultural development and soil degradation in the Soviet Union: Policies, patterns and trends', in *Environmental problems in the Soviet Union and eastern Europe*, ed. F. Singleton, Lynne Rienner, Boulder, 71–96.

Straubhaar, T. (1988), 'International labour migration within a common market: Some aspects of EC experience', *Journal of Common Market Studies*, 27, 45–62.

Surrey, J. (1991), 'The EC in the global energy context', in *Technology and the future of Europe: Global competition and the environment in the 1990s*, ed. C. Freeman, M. Sharp and W. Walker, Pinter, London, 284–99.

Sweden (1990), *The Agricultural Reform in Sweden*, Ministry of Agriculture, Stockholm.

London.

Tsoukalis, L. (1991), *The New European Economy: The politics and economics of integration*, Oxford University Press, Oxford.

Turnock, D. (1978), *Eastern Europe*, Dawson, Folkestone.

— (1989), *Eastern Europe: An economic and political geography*, Routledge, London.

Tylecote, A. (1992), *The long wave in the world economy*, Routledge, London.

United Nations (1991), *1989 Energy statistics yearbook*, New York.

— (1990), *1988 international trade statistics yearbook*, New York.
USSR, *Narodnoe Khozyaistvo SSSR*, Moscow.
Vaitsos, C. (1979), 'Transnational Corporations (TNCs) and Europe', in *Underdeveloped Europe: Studies in Core-Periphery Relations*, ed. D. Seers, B. Schaffer and M. Kiljunen, The Harvester Press, Hassocks.
Veltz, P. (1991), 'New models of production organisation and trends in spatial development', in *Industrial change and regional development: the transformation of new industrial spaces*, ed. G. Benko and M. Dunford, Belhaven, London, 193–204.
Vernon, R. (1966), 'International investment and international trade in the product cycle', *Quarterly Journal of Economics*, 80, 190–207.
Vickerman, R.W. (1992), *The Single European Market: Prospects for economic integration*, Harvester Wheatsheaf, New York.
Warriner, D. (1964), *Economics of peasant farming*, 2nd edn, Frank Cass, London.
Welfens, P.J.J. (1992), 'Internationalization of production, investment and European integration: Free trade in goods, technology and assets?' in *Multinationals in the new Europe and global trade*, ed. M. Klein and P.J.J. Welfens, Springer-Verlag, Berlin, 9–63.
Wilkinson, T. (1992), 'Italy to sell 45% of state firms', *The Independent*, 13 July.
Williams, A.M. (1987), *The western European economy: A geography of post-war development*, Hutchinson, London.
— (1991), *The European Community: The contradictions of integration*, Blackwell, Oxford.
— and Shaw, (1991) (eds), *Tourism and Economic Development: Western European Experiences*, Belhaven, London.
Wilson, J.S.G. (1986), *Banking policy and structure: A comparative analysis*, Croom Helm, London.
World Bank (1990), *An agricultural strategy for Poland*, Washington.
— (1992), *World development report 1992*, Oxford University Press, Oxford.
Youngson, A.J. (1967), *Britain's economic growth 1920–1966*, Allen & Unwin, London.

SUBJECT INDEX

accessibility – *see* transport
accumulation 9, 10, 19, 75
Adriatic Sea 159
aerospace – *see* aircraft
agglomerations 28, 30, 33, 63, 124, 132, 136, 139–40, 142–3, 160, 176, 188, 195, 202, 204, 206
agriculture 8, 27–8, 43, 46, 49, 68, 72–4, 78, 80–92, 103, 122, 140–41, 147–51, 157–9, 163–4, 181–2, 201, 203–4, 207
aircraft 32, 45, 54, 77, 105, 110–3, 116, 118, 127, 137, 192–3, 195, 201
air transport 50, 163–4, 166–7, 200–201
airports 117, 192, 199, 200
Albania 9, 41, 62, 86, 88, 101, 108, 162, 167, 171, 206
Alps 127–30, 150, 156, 158, 187
Amsterdam 125, 166, 197, 200
Arctic Ocean 13, 153, 155, 169
Armenia 40–41, 162
Asia, central 13, 97, 99, 155, 162, 169, 181, 188
association agreements 16, 40, 60, 185, 193
ausseidler – *see* migration

Belarus 41, 157–8, 179, 206
Belgium 39, 41, 51, 57, 59, 93, 95, 97, 101, 104, 106–7, 109–10, 114, 116, 123, 145
Benelux 39
Berlin 13, 38, 136, 140, 142, 162, 169, 176, 181
Black Earth region 140–41, 148, 188
Black Sea 155–6, 159, 169, 191, 199, 204, 207
Bohemia – *see* Czech lands
borders – *see* frontiers
Bosnia 40–41, 143, 162
Bretton Woods 39–40, 56, 70
Britain – *see* United Kingdom
brown coal – *see* lignite
Brussels 125–6, 133–4, 200
Budapest 136, 140–41
Bulgaria 9, 41, 46, 82, 86, 101, 104, 120, 128, 130, 145, 156, 167, 178–9

cabotage 50
capital 2–3, 9–10, 13–14, 16, 18–19, 21, 23–4, 26–35, 38–40, 44–6, 51, 56–8, 60, 62–3, 68, 72–3, 76–8, 80, 86, 88, 90, 94, 113, 124, 126–7, 133, 136, 138, 140, 143, 147, 158, 167, 169, 175–82, 184, 187, 190–91, 194–5, 198, 201–3, 206–7
Carpathians 148, 151, 153, 156, 158, 199
Caucasus 98, 143, 171, 188, 199, 206
Chernobyl 55, 93, 157–8, 172, 186
climate 2, 5–9, 18, 28, 88, 98, 127, 129, 148, 150, 156–7, 203, 206
coal 8, 10, 72, 92, 94–9, 102, 106–8, 113–4, 116,

Competition Policy 45, 191, 200
convergence 28, 30, 33, 35–6, 59, 62–3, 141–2, 144–5, 174
COCOM – *see* Coordinating Committee for Multilateral Export Controls
Coordinating Committee for Multilateral Export Controls 55, 167
core 2, 9, 11, 14, 29, 31–3, 35–6, 57, 62–4, 202, 207

SUBJECT INDEX

Council for Mutual Economic Assistance 9, 22, 39–40, 48, 53, 58, 60, 78, 92, 109, 123, 132, 134, 136, 173–4, 179, 185
counterurbanisation 141–2
Crimea 128–9, 156, 169, 171, 204
Croatia 40–41, 143, 162
customs union 35
Czech lands 82, 151, 178, 181, 207
Czechoslovakia 1, 10, 16, 40–41, 47, 60, 86, 93, 95–7, 101, 104, 106–7, 112, 114, 120, 144–5, 158, 167, 172, 174, 176, 178–9, 185, 190–91, 193, 195

Danube 7, 150, 176
decision-making 132–6, 143, 203, 206
deepening 1, 24, 34–6, 63, 178
defence 14, 45, 75, 78, 105, 111, 113, 120, 137–8, 148, 167, 190, 192, 203
deindustrialisation 104
demographic transition 162
Denmark 39, 41, 59, 2, 80, 82–3, 85, 88, 90, 101, 145, 151, 163, 178
deregulation 124–5, 200–201
divergence 24, 29–34, 36, 62–3, 77, 132, 141–6, 201
Donbas 94–6, 106–9, 139, 158, 160, 186, 188, 204

economic and monetary union 16, 29, 35–6, 38–9, 44, 62–3, 173–4, 178, 181, 197
economic rent 2–3, 19, 28, 133, 147–72, 174, 203, 206
EEC – *see* European Community
EFTA – *see* European Free Trade Association
Eire – *see* Ireland
Ekibastuz 96, 186
electricity 73, 92–4, 96–7, 114, 159, 185, 187, 191
emigration – *see* migration
energy 45–6, 49, 54, 57, 71, 77, 80, 92–103, 151–5, 160, 181, 185–7, 195
England – *see* United Kingdom
environment, degradation of 156–60, 172, 180, 203–4
Estonia 40–41, 144–5, 171, 179
ethnic minorities 169–71, 174, 179
Euratom 39
eurocurrency 56, 124–6
European Coal and Steel Community 39, 109, 121
European Community 1, 9–10, 16–17, 21, 29, 40, 42–54, 57–60, 62–4, 77–8, 85–6, 88, 90–92, 102, 104, 114, 120, 123–4, 126, 132, 134–6, 140, 142, 144, 146, 164, 166–7, 173–5, 178, 180–81, 183–5, 190–91, 193, 195–7, 200–203, 206
    budget 43–4, 59, 134
European Economic Space 40, 60
European Free Trade Association 16, 39–40, 42, 46–9, 57, 59–60, 63–4, 78, 88, 90–92, 132, 134, 144, 167, 173–4, 178, 181, 184, 197
euromarkets – *see* eurocurrency
Europe of regions 136
European Monetary System 56, 56–9
European Payments Union – *see* payments union
Eurosclerosis 40, 178
Exchange Rate Mechanism – *see* European Monetary System
expertise 38, 44, 53–5, 187, 190, 193, 198

farms, collective 81–3, 86, 92–7, 140, 176, 182
finance – *see* banking
Finland 14, 41, 104, 118, 144–5, 184, 186
forestry – *see* forests
forests 13, 19, 28, 81, 148, 151, 157–60, 184, 202
France 7, 38–41, 45, 47–9, 51–2, 56, 58–9, 62, 70, 81, 83, 88, 94–5, 97–9, 101–2, 104, 106–7, 109–14, 116–8, 122, 124, 126–9, 136, 138, 140–45,148, 150, 160, 176, 186, 200, 204, 207
Frankfurt 124–5, 133–4, 142, 166, 176, 197
free market 3, 21–2, 29–31, 33, 37, 43–4, 46, 62, 65, 78, 124, 173–4, 178–80, 182–3, 188, 191, 196, 202
free trade 35, 38–9, 44, 48–50, 52, 60, 63, 129, 181, 195
frontiers 25–6, 30, 43, 63, 143, 163, 169, 208
fuel – *see* coal, energy, lignite, natural gas, oil

gastarbeiter 51–2, 163
GATT – *see* General Agreement on Tariffs and Trade
GDP – *see* gross national product
General Agreement on Tariffs and Trade 39, 49, 180
geology 2, 7, 9
Georgia 41, 113, 156, 179
Germany 3, 7, 10, 25, 40–41, 45, 47–9, 51–3, 56–9, 62, 64, 70, 73, 80–83, 86, 88, 93–9, 101, 104–14, 117–8, 120, 122, 124–6, 129–30, 136, 138, 140–43, 145, 148, 150, 160, 163, 166–7, 171, 173, 175–8, 181, 183, 185–7, 190, 196–7, 207–8
GNP – *see* gross national product
goods 2, 4, 17–18, 23–5, 30–31, 34–5, 38, 40, 44–50, 54, 56–7, 60, 70–72, 74–5, 77, 82, 105, 123–4, 163–4, 180–81, 190
Great Depression 18, 70, 73, 75–6, 80, 99, 106, 175
Greece 9, 41, 50–53, 57, 59, 62–3, 85, 88, 90, 101, 104, 114, 128–9, 134, 138, 145, 151, 166–7, 181, 190, 197, 206
grid, electricity 93, 186
gross national product 41, 45, 48–50, 57, 59–63, 104, 120, 122, 129, 134, 144, 176, 180

SUBJECT INDEX

Hamburg 113, 136, 176
harmonisation 29, 35, 40, 44–6
Heathrow – *see* London
Hellweg 176
Holland – *see* Netherlands
Hungary 16, 25, 40–41, 46, 55, 60, 82, 86, 88, 93, 101, 104, 108, 120, 130, 144–5, 167, 171, 178–9, 181, 185, 190–91, 193, 195, 207–8

Iberia 157, 166
Ile de France – *see* Paris
immigration – *see* migration
industrial regions – *see* agglomerations
innovation 3, 5, 17–18, 20, 28, 32, 34, 72–5, 77–9, 82, 102, 105, 111, 120, 123, 133, 136–7, 174, 190, 195, 202–3, 207
investment – *see* capital
Ireland 40, 51, 59, 62–3, 83, 86, 101, 138–9, 145, 151, 166–7, 171, 178, 190, 206
Iron Curtain 10, 111, 169, 173
Italy 31, 39–41, 45, 48–9, 51–2, 58–9, 62, 81–3, 85–6, 88, 94, 98–9, 101, 104, 106–10, 112, 114, 117, 120, 122, 128–9, 134, 138, 143, 145, 157, 160, 162, 164, 166–7, 176, 191, 194, 197, 207

Japan 44, 49, 54–5, 57, 62, 104–5, 117–8, 124, 138, 194, 196
joint projects 53–5, 58, 112, 186, 193

Karaganda 96, 186
Kazakhstan 14, 53, 83, 96, 157–9, 179, 185–7
Kiev 113, 140, 204, 207
Kondratiev cycle 3, 18, 67–146, 151, 153, 155, 158–9, 163–4, 174, 178, 180, 182, 185, 187, 190–92, 194–6, 199, 203, 206–8
Kosovo 143, 171
Krakow 96, 108–9, 156, 160
Krivoi Rog 106, 108–9

90, 92, 97, 133, 139–40, 150–51, 160, 162–3, 169, 171, 182–4, 201, 203, 206
land use – *see* land
Latvia 40–41, 144–5, 171, 179
least-favoured regions – *see* lagging regions
Liechtenstein 197
lignite 97, 99, 153, 158, 187
Lithuania 40–41, 179
Lodz 114, 139
Lombardy 114, 138
London 6, 124, 128, 133–4, 138, 166, 197, 200
Long Boom 22, 51, 63, 70, 73, 78, 106, 120, 130, 141–2, 174, 178, 185, 206
Long wave – *see* Kondratiev cycle
Lorraine 109, 139, 142
Low countries 62, 82, 85, 104, 109, 134, 148, 160, 176, 207
Luxembourg 39, 57, 106, 110, 125, 134

Maastricht Treaty 62
Macedonia 40–41
manufacturing 26, 28, 30, 32, 43, 48–9, 52, 55, 57, 69, 73, 75–8, 81, 85, 104–23, 136, 139–42, 146, 158–9, 163, 176, 178–80, 190–96
Marshall Plan 57
Massif Central 140, 148, 151, 153
Mediterranean Sea 169, 199
Mediterranean states 51, 90, 116, 127–9, 139, 148, 150, 155, 157, 162
Mezzogiorno 39, 52, 108, 138, 166
migration 9, 12–13, 20, 23–4, 30–31, 43, 53, 70, 81, 97, 133, 140, 174, 206–7
minerals 5, 8, 13, 19, 23, 30, 147, 151, 156, 160, 162–3, 180–81
mining 8, 14, 19, 43, 49, 68, 72, 74, 78, 81, 94–7, 106, 122, 139, 140–42, 146, 153, 157, 159, 163, 185, 202–3
Moldova 41, 53, 143, 156, 171, 183, 206
monetary union – *see* economic and monetary union
Montenegro 41
Moscow 95, 97–8, 109, 113–14, 133, 136–7, 143, 188, 204, 207
motorways – *see* roads
multinational companies 21, 32, 34, 50, 54, 62, 116, 139, 179

North Atlantic Treaty Organisation 112, 125, [illegible]
North Sea 94, 98–9, 108, 187, 191
Norway 14, 41, 50, 90, 97–9, 101, 145, 155
nuclear power 54–5, 93–4, 97, 99, 102, 158, 160, 186–7

oil 40, 53, 56, 70, 73, 75, 92–4, 97, 99, 102, 106, 117, 151, 153–5, 159, 172, 179, 186–90, 205

SUBJECT INDEX

Paris 113, 124, 128, 133–4, 138, 142, 166, 194, 197, 199–200
payments union 39, 180
Perestroika 78
periphery 3, 9, 11, 14, 16, 21, 29–36, 57, 62, 140, 143, 148, 150, 167, 169, 176, 183–5, 202–3, 206
pipelines 53, 93, 98–9, 164, 186–7
planning, central 3, 10, 18–19, 22, 29, 46, 48, 50, 58, 65, 71, 78–9, 88, 102, 120, 123, 126, 134, 136, 143–4, 174–5, 180, 183
Poland 16, 40–41, 53, 55, 60, 81–3, 85–6, 88, 92, 94–7, 99, 101–3, 106–8, 114, 120, 122, 130, 141, 144–5, 151, 153, 156, 162, 166–7, 169, 172, 176, 178–9, 181, 183, 185–6, 188–9, 191, 193, 195, 198, 206, 208
pollution 14, 19, 22–3, 77, 93, 97, 137, 139, 147, 158–60, 185, 187, 191, 199, 201, 204, 206
population 2, 13–14, 19, 23, 26, 31, 41, 43, 68, 74, 78, 80, 82–3, 88, 90, 116, 140–41, 158–64, 166, 172, 176–7, 179, 181–2, 187–8, 196, 198, 204–5
ports 14, 108, 164, 169, 202, 204
Portugal 39, 41, 51–3, 57, 59, 62–3, 85–6, 88, 101, 114, 128–9, 145, 167, 179, 181, 190, 197, 201, 206
Prague 136, 156, 194
privatisation 19, 46, 55, 175–6, 179, 182, 191, 198
product life cycle 32, 75, 122
public ownership 3, 40, 45–6, 50, 54–5, 86, 111–12, 134, 182, 190, 193, 198

railways 13, 17, 50, 92–3, 106, 108–9, 111, 116, 163–4, 166–7, 186, 190–91, 200–201
refugees – *see* migration
Regional and Social Funds 43–5, 58–9
regional policy 35, 62–3, 85, 133, 140, 206
rent – *see* economic rent
research and development 28, 32, 45, 75, 105, 111, 113, 136–40, 176, 193, 196, 203, 206
Rhine 7, 176
roads 13, 50, 127, 163–7, 190, 201
Romania 9, 41, 46, 53, 81, 86, 90, 92, 101, 104, 106–7, 109, 112, 120, 122, 130, 145, 153, 156, 158, 162, 167, 178
Ruhr 96, 106, 109, 139, 142, 153, 176
rural areas 28, 43, 82, 132, 140–41
Russia 5, 7–8, 13–14, 17, 40–41, 53, 82, 113–4, 118, 140–41, 148, 153, 157, 159, 162, 169–71, 176–7, 179, 181, 183, 186–9, 191–3, 196, 200, 202–3, 206
Russian Federation – *see* Russia

Saar 142, 176
St. Petersburg 140, 143, 156, 188, 194
Saxony 114, 139, 158, 176
Scandinavia 10, 14, 16, 62, 163, 197, 207
security – *see* defence
Serbia 41, 179
services 2, 17, 23–6, 30, 38, 40, 44–5, 49–52, 56–8, 60, 68–9, 81, 85, 117, 122–31, 140–42, 146, 163, 176, 180–81, 185, 196–202, 204
Siberia 13–14, 53, 83, 92, 97–9, 137, 148, 150–51, 153, 155, 157, 159, 185–8
single market 16, 43, 45–6, 50, 52, 54, 60, 62, 77, 102, 120, 173, 180, 185, 195–7, 202, 207–8
Slovakia 108, 171, 181, 206
Slovenia 40–41, 143
soil 2, 5, 8, 19, 23, 28, 88, 148, 150, 152, 157, 182–3, 204
soil erosion 19, 148, 150, 157
Soviet Union – *see* USSR
Spain 31, 41, 49, 51–3, 57, 62–3, 81–3, 85–6, 88, 92, 94, 99, 101, 104, 107, 109, 112, 114, 116, 128–30, 136, 138, 145, 164, 166–7, 171, 185, 190, 196–7, 201, 204, 206
steel 49, 105–10, 113, 118, 139, 142, 159–60, 176, 190–92, 195, 205
Stuttgart 136, 138, 142
Sweden 14, 41, 49, 56, 83, 88, 101, 104, 112, 120, 126, 134, 138, 145, 184, 188
Switzerland 7, 10, 39, 41, 47, 49, 51–2, 56, 62, 101, 110, 125–6, 129, 134, 138, 145, 150, 166–7

technology 14, 34, 44, 48, 54–5, 69, 73, 75, 79–80, 82–3, 92, 105, 110–11, 126–7, 132, 138–9, 146–7, 169, 171, 186–7, 190, 193–5
telecommunications 45–6, 50, 55, 105, 138, 163, 166–8, 172, 195, 201–2, 207
television 49, 105, 116–9, 137, 194–5, 201
textiles 7, 17, 49, 72–3, 76, 105, 113–6, 118, 120, 142, 193–4
Tokyo – *see* Japan
tourism 19, 43, 50, 122–3, 127–131, 147, 155–6, 158, 196, 199–200, 204
trade 3–8, 12–13, 17, 21, 23–4, 27–8, 33–5, 38–9, 43–4, 47–51, 54–6, 58, 60, 64, 70, 73, 77, 79–80, 88, 91–2, 102, 105, 120, 123, 127, 129, 134, 146, 151, 174, 176, 178–80, 185, 188, 191, 195, 197–8, 202, 207
transport 2–3, 5–6, 8, 14, 23, 26–8, 40, 45–6, 50, 54, 68, 77, 80, 82, 93, 108, 110–113, 122–3, 127, 129, 134, 140–41, 147, 156, 163–7, 169, 183, 186–8, 196, 199–203, 206
Treaty of Rome 39, 50, 54, 62
Turkey 51–2, 116, 181, 195
Tyumen 98–9

SUBJECT INDEX

Ukraine 40–41, 46, 53, 94–5, 98, 107, 113, 118, 140, 148, 150, 157–9, 162, 171, 176, 179, 181, 183, 185–6, 188, 191, 193, 200, 204–6
United Kingdom 6, 9, 38–41, 45, 47–9, 52, 56–7, 59, 62, 70, 73, 77, 80–83, 88, 93–9, 101, 104–14, 116–8, 121–2, 126, 128–9, 136, 138–9, 144–6, 148, 153, 155, 157, 160, 162–4, 167, 178–9, 193–4, 196–8, 200, 207
United States of America 44, 50, 54, 56–7, 62, 70, 73, 77, 82, 86, 91, 93, 104–5, 112, 124, 137, 193, 196
Upper Saxony – *see* Saxony
Upper Silesia 95–6, 106, 109, 139, 153, 158, 176
Urals 3, 7–8, 14, 96, 98, 107–9, 137, 139, 143, 153, 155, 158–9, 188
USSR 3, 9–14, 18, 38–40, 46–8, 53, 55–6, 58, 60, 70, 72, 80–81, 83, 86, 88, 90–92, 94–9, 101–2, 104–9, 112–4, 117–8, 120, 122, 126, 128–30, 137, 139, 141, 143–5, 151, 153, 157–9, 162, 164, 167, 172, 174, 176, 178–9, 181–2, 185–6, 188, 192–3, 200–202, 204

Virgin Lands 83, 157
Volga 98, 143, 148, 150, 153, 157–8, 171, 186, 188

war 8, 10, 12, 17, 21, 34, 38–9, 47, 51, 53, 55–6, 60, 70, 73, 81, 86, 93, 95, 97–8, 104, 110, 112–3, 126–7, 130, 134, 139, 141, 143, 155, 162, 167, 169–70, 174, 176, 203
Warsaw 136, 140, 199
Warsaw Pact 55, 123
water 139, 148, 157–60, 172, 187, 199, 204
widening 1, 24, 34–6, 63, 178

Yorkshire 6, 96, 114
Yugoslavia 1, 3, 9, 40–41, 51, 82–3, 85–6, 88, 90, 97, 101, 104, 108, 122, 130, 143, 145, 162–3, 167, 174, 183, 206

Zollverein 39
Zurich 166, 197

AUTHOR INDEX

Ahnström, L. 172
Alderman, N. – *see* Thwaites
Alexandratos, N. 103, 182, 207
Aydalot, P. 120

Bade, F. 138, 142
Balassa, B. 24, 37
Baldwin, R. 180
Barr, B.M. 159
Bater, J.H. 143
Batisse, M. – *see* Grenon
Bechouche, P. 113
Blanchard, W.O. 8, 14, 20
Bond, A.R. 14
Bowen, H.P. 194
Bradshaw, M. 9, 11, 18, 20
Breburda, J. 157, 183
Button, K. 50, 201

Camagni, R. 77, 207
Cantwell, J. 138
Cappellin, R. – *see* Molle
Carter, F.W. 172
Cawson, A. 117, 195

[illegible]

Cook, E.C. 88
Court, W.H.B. 72

Dawson, A.H. 65, 143
Dewdney, J. 14
Dicken, P. 118
Dobosiewicz, Z. 178, 198–9, 202, 207
Dunnett, P.J.S. 116–7, 194

Dunning, J.H. 24, 57

East, G. 17
Ellman, M. 78

FAO 84, 87, 89–90
Federal Republic of Germany 51
Forrester, J.W. 74–5
Forsyth, W. 175
Freeman, C. 73, 79
French, R.A. 14
Friedman, J. 32

Gardener, E.P.M. 125–6, 131, 197–8
de Gaudemar, J. 142
GATT 49
Giersch, H. 30, 32
Gillespie, A. 166
Giroux, A. 14
Gittelman, M. 57
Gomulka, S. 79
Gowland, D.H. 127, 131, 208
Grenon, M. 11, 157, 199

[illegible]

Holland, S. 17, 40, 62, 64
Holmes, P. – *see* Cawson
Houseman, S.N. 120
Howells, J. 122, 131, 166–7
Hungary 88

Illeris, S. 131
Inotai, A. 175, 178

AUTHOR INDEX

International Energy Agency 93–4
Isard, W. 27–8, 36

John, B. 14, 16
Jones, P.N. 163

Keeble, D. – *see* Aydalot
Keesing, D.B. 121
Kennedy, M. – *see* Rostow
Klein, M.W. 54, 79, 146
Klepper, G. 45, 111, 193, 200
Klodt, H. 32, 195
Komarov, B. 157, 159, 172
Kontorovich, V. 18 – *see also* Ellman
Kornai, J. 11
Kramer, J.M. 172
Kunzmann, K.R. – *see* Bade

League of Nations 95, 107
Liebowitz, R.D. 143
Lindsay, M. 198

McAuley, A. 179
McFarlane, J. 6–7, 12
McKee, D.L. 79
Mackowsky, M. 153
Maillat, D. 208
Mansfield, E. 55
Mansell, R.E. 167
Marples, D.R. 159, 172, 185
Marshall, A. 184
Marshall, M. 146
Martinelli, F. 75
Masser, I. 11, 199, 201, 207
Mayes, D.G. 45, 201
Mellor, R.E.H. 9, 58, 60
Mensch, G. 74
Merritt, L. 179, 207
Minshull, G.N. 9, 16
Molle, W. 32, 35, 51–2, 146
Molyneux, P. 197 – *see also* Gardener
Monkhouse, F.J. 8
Morawitz, R. 109
van Mourik, A. – *see* Molle
Murrell, P. 34
Mutton, A.F.A. 8, 10
Myrdal, G. 17, 30–31, 33, 36–7, 143

Nalivkin, D.V. 153
Nello, S.S. 55, 65, 183, 187, 207
Newbigin, M.I. 8
Nguyen, G.D. 45, 202
Nicolaides, P. – *see* Thomsen
North, R.N. 202

O'Brien, R. 56, 126, 202
OECD 128–9
Ozawa, T. 57

Pallot, J. 88, 141
Panic, M. 57
Parker, G. 9
Parker, W.H. 17
Patel, P. 138
Pavitt, K. – *see* Patel
Pinder, D. 63
Pinder, J. 9
Piore, M.J. 75, 114, 117
Poland 55, 130, 164
Pollard, S. 36
Pounds, N.J.G. 8, 17, 20
Preston, P. – *see* Hall, P.
Prud'homme, R. – *see* de Gaudemar

Ritter, C. 4
Robson, P. 37, 58
Rodgers, P. 198
Rodwin, L. 146
Roesler, J. 53
Ronge, V. 53
Rostow, W.W. 74–5

Sabel, C.F. – *see* Piore
Samoteikin, E. 169
Savchenko, V.K. 158
Sazanami, H. – *see* Rodwin
Schamp, E. 75
Schioppa, C. – *see* Panic
Schoenberger, E. – *see* Martinelli
Schumpeter, J.A. 3, 18, 32, 48, 72–5, 78–9, 195
Schwok, R. 59, 208
Seers, D. 33, 146
Shabad, T. 14
Sharp, M. 54
Shaw, D.J.B. – *see* Williams
Shepherd, G. 121
Siebert, H. 28–9, 35, 78, 175, 178, 180, 207
Simpson, J. – *see* Todd
Singleton, F. 172
Smith, C.T. 17
Smith, D.H. 7–8
Smith, E.A. – *see* Mellor
Soete, J. – *see* Freeman
Solomou, S. 73, 77, 79
Stebelsky, I. 153
Strabhaar, T. 52
Surrey, J. 185
Svidén, O. – *see* Masser
Swann, D. – *see* Button
Sweden 184
Symons, L. 11, 96, 113, 120, 148, 200

Thomsen, S. 57–8
Thwaites, A.T. 138
Tiratsoo, E.N. 143–5, 172
Todd, D. 121

AUTHOR INDEX

Tracy, M. 80, 103
Tsoukalis, L. 28, 52–3, 57, 59, 63–4, 178
Turnock, D. 9, 103, 120
Tylecote, A. 72–3, 75–7, 79

United Nations 91, 94–5, 97–8, 107, 115, 119
USSR 83

Vaitsos, C. 34
Vernon, R. 31
Vickerman, R.W. 64, 207
Visher, S.S. – *see* Blanchard

Warriner, D. 81
Wegener, M. – *see* Masser
Welfens, P.J.J. 48, 54, 57, 138
Wilkinson, T. 45
Williams, A.M. 9, 16, 18, 20, 45, 54, 85, 103–4, 120, 131, 138, 160
Wilson, J.S.G. 126
World Bank 41, 62, 81, 86, 103, 127, 162, 183–4, 199
Wolf, M. – *see* Keesing

Youngson, A.J. 73